COWBOY SONGS AND OTHER FRONTIER BALLADS

COWBOY SONGS

AND OTHER FRONTIER BALLADS

Revised and Enlarged

COLLECTED BY

JOHN A. LOMAX

AND

ALAN LOMAX

THE MACMILLAN COMPANY, NEW YORK

Collier-Macmillan Limited, London

What keeps the herd from running,
    Stampeding far and wide?
The cowboy's long, low whistle,
    And singing by their side.

* * * * *

Oh, it was a long and tiresome go,
Our herd rolled on to Mexico;
With music sweet of the cowboy song
For New Mexico we rolled along.

* * * * *

I've roamed the Texas prairies,
I've followed the cattle trail;
I've rid a pitchin' pony
Till the hair come off his tail.

* * * * *

I've been where the lightning, the lightning
Tangled in my eyes;
The cattle I could scarcely hold;
I think I heard my boss-man say,
"I want all brave-hearted men
Who ain't afraid to die
To whoop the cattle from morning till night
Way up on the Kansas line."

Cheyenne
Aug 28th 1910

Dear Mr. Lomax,

You have done
a work emphatically worth doing
and one which should appeal
to the people of all our country, but
particularly to the people of the
west and southwest. Your subject
is not only exceedingly interesting to
the student of literature, but also to
the student of the general history of
the west. There is something very curious
in the reproduction here on this new
continent of essentially the conditions
of ballad-growth which obtained in
mediæval England; including, by the way,
sympathy for the outlaw, Jesse James
taking the place of Robin Hood. Under
modern conditions however, the native ballad is
speedily killed by competition with the music
hall songs; the cowboys becoming ashamed to
sing the crude homespun ballads in view of
which Owen Wister calls the "ill-smelling saloon

cleverness of the far less interesting compositions of the music-hall singers. It is therefore a work of real importance to preserve permanently this unwritten ballad literature of the back country and the frontier.

With all good wishes, I am

very truly yours

Theodore Roosevelt

PREFACE

THE first edition of "Cowboy Songs and Other Frontier Ballads" appeared in 1910. The music for that early volume, consisting of a small number of melodies with piano accompaniment, was prepared by Professor Henry Leberman, long connected with the Texas State Institute for the Blind. For the present edition, a different musical policy has been adopted—that of printing the airs of many songs and deleting all accompaniments. This procedure has two distinct advantages. It provides space for more music, and it leaves the tunes free from arbitrary harmonizations.

The melodies in this book have come from several sources, some of which are now drawn upon for the first time. The music printed in the 1910 edition has been revised and, when necessary, corrected. Not a few of the songs were taken from manuscripts furnished by both professional and amateur singers. In preparing them for publication, I have insisted on as little alteration as possible. Some of the papers submitted and accepted had been written by people whose musical knowledge was not sufficient to guarantee absolute clearness, although the unquestionable validity of these contributions demanded their inclusion. In such cases, the two chief requirements were to make the melody fit the words and to leave no doubt concerning the musical orthography. Any liberties taken with these songs, then, were justified by the necessity of making them singable, a prime consideration in a book of this type. Some of the tunes have come from various collections of cowboy lore. In making these selections, of course, great care was taken to choose only the most representative. Another important source of music is the recent phonograph recording done by Mr. Lomax and his son Alan for the Archive of American Folk-Song in the Library of Congress. Here was a rich supply of virgin material, ready to be transcribed, as accurately as possible, in the manner in which it was performed.

The cowboy, like all folk-singers, proceeding from one stanza to another, adds or subtracts as many notes as the text requires. This element of variation arises from the fact that the number of syllables in a stanza is by no means constant, the vocal quantity changing according to poetic and dramatic necessity. A reader with little experience in such a practice is nothing less than bewildered when he notices that the syllabic content often varies for a recurring phrase of melody. In spite of this inner decrease and increase of notes, however, the tune remains essentially the same, just as recognizable sung to the eighth stanza of a song as to the first or second.

In the interest of practicability, some solution had to be offered. Many of the songs are printed with two stanzas underlying the music, and thus the reader is afforded hints as to the manner of this type of variation. Whenever possible, the notes for the first appear with the stems pointed upward, for the second with the stems downward. It is easy to see, by this plan, when a quarter note applies to one syllable in one stanza, and when two eighth notes apply to two syllables in the next. Occasionally, it is awkward to place two melodic variants over the text. The comparatively simple change from one quarter to two eighth notes is not as vexing as a change from two eighths to an eighth-note triplet, or to a dotted eighth followed by a sixteenth. At times, auxiliary notes were indispensable to the clarity of some transcripts, and there were instances of text changes so extreme that another complete version of the entire melody seemed the only solution. This was the case with "The Buffalo Skinners," one of the finest songs in the book.

A transcription for an eight-stanza ballad, therefore, might require eight separate melodic versions; but lack of space prohibits such a detailed procedure. Even the uninitiated reader, however, will be able to see the difficulties involved; and, aided by the two-stanza presentation, he will be prepared to make similar adaptations accordingly.

These songs are instantaneous in their appeal to listeners and singers. Their general atmosphere is immediately apparent in the words, which are, for the most part, paired with melodies of kindred spirit. Indications for performance can be found in the texts themselves, which are notable for clarity and directness. The "expression marks" consist of single words or short phrases which suggest sympathetic interpretations. Varied as these songs are, revealing many shades of human feeling, they remain absolutely secure from any charge of insincerity or artificiality. Like the men who sing them, they are stamped with straightforwardness, spontaneity, and integrity of purpose, characteristics which are permanently associated with the hardy plainsmen and mountaineers to whom the West owes its development and prestige.

EDWARD N. WATERS

Division of Music
Library of Congress
July 28, 1937

THE EDITOR AGAIN

FROM 1870 to 1890 one million mustang ponies and twelve million head of longhorn cattle were driven up the trail from Texas to markets in Kansas, Wyoming, Montana, and other Western states. The herds numbered usually from one thousand to three thousand, though at times as many as five thousand cattle made up a single trail herd. Behind and around and ahead of each bunch of cattle rode a group of men, mostly very young, bold, youthful vikings of the seas of sage grass through which they pushed their way. They came to be known as cowboys—the boys who take care of the cows. They rode with a song on their lips, voicing youth, the freedom and the wildness of the plains. Hence come cowboy songs.

"The trail boss would never pick on [employ] a fellow that couldn't sing and whistle, and we boys would consider it a dull day's drive if we didn't add at least one verse. And bad, dark nights the cowboy that could keep up the most racket was the pet of the bunch. We called him the bellwether, and he always brought up his side of the herd." J. M. Grigsby of Fort Worth, Texas, thus pays tribute to the cowboy who could sing or make a "racket," as the circumstances demanded, in pushing up the trail from Texas.

Professor J. Frank Dobie, in Volume VI of the Publications of the Texas Folk-Lore Society, gives other evidence of the singing cowboy who

> Galloped and sang
> The long days through,
> Shortened the trail
> By the songs he knew.

[xv]

R. L. Smith of Killeen, Texas, writes to Mr. Dobie: "I once punched cattle on the T-Bar Ranch, and as we followed a long string of white-faces across the bed of an old alkali lake reflecting the moon's light, while the wind swept across the plains and the coyotes howled from the head of Laguna Rica, I wanted to answer the forces of nature, and did answer them, in wild half-maniac-like compositions of my own. At such times as this ballads are born."

Billie Fox, "an old-time buffalo hunter and then range rider of the Cherokee strip, now living near Marshall, Oklahoma," adds: "There was once a peeler in my outfit who used to sing just a line or two of 'Oh, listen to the crickets,' and how beautiful his soothing voice and the words sounded away across the herd in the still night! Singing was company to us just as it was to the cattle. One time when I was line-riding, I met a peeler from another range. We stopped down under some shade trees next to a spring and exchanged songs. Each taught the other the tunes, and then each wrote down the words for the other to learn. Of course we learned a verse or two of each song while we were learning the tune. Lots of the boys couldn't sing but just sorter hummed, putting in words now and then."

R. S. Scott, "who was familiar with the big cow outfits on the Little Missouri River twenty-five or thirty years ago, recalls how 'just singing' played an important part in the social life of the cowboys." He writes: "Nearly every well established ranch had for its own individual song a set of verses of its own making. Some 'smart' cowboy would lead off composing these verses, which the outfit would take up, chorusing in whenever the song was sung. When a puncher from another outfit drifted into camp, he was expected to sing any new song he might know or new stanzas to an old song, and to teach them to the camp he was visiting. In exchange he took the novelties his hosts knew. Thus songs like 'The Old Chisholm Trail' became of interminable length. . . . In the singing about camp, a cowboy would often cut loose with a song too vile to repeat; great cheers and hurrays would usually follow and there would be calls for more. After the climax in this class of songs had been reached, some puncher would strike up an old-time religious hymn, and that also would be cheered to the echo."

Miss Ruth Dodson, of Mathis, Texas, suggests finally: "My mother said that during her life in Nueces County, from 1868 to 1929, no song was ever as popular in the seventies among the cowboys as 'When You and I Were Young, Maggie.' She said that the Americans sang it and the Mexicans whistled it. The melody is ideal to *ride by*. I wonder that a 'cowboy' song hasn't been set to this tune. Is it too late to do it now? Perhaps the reason this has not been done is that the words of such a song, like the original, must be capable of taking on shades of feeling from the very sad to the almost gay, depending on the mood of the singer or the gait of horse."

The songs in this book afford testimony that the cowboy sang at his work. The evidence printed in the quotations comes from persons who actually heard him sing, and they tell us why he sang. Some of these songs the cowboy "made up"; but he had his favorites among the popular airs of his time. In addition to "When You and I Were Young, Maggie," he was fond of singing, and the cattle were soothed to sleep by, such songs as "Darling, I Am Growing Old" and "Lorena":

> Our heads will soon lie low, Lorena,
> Life's tide is ebbing out so fast.

The stars to which the lovelorn cowboy also sang seemed only a little less distant than the girl he had left behind him in Mississippi, Alabama, or Tennessee. Often he sang more truly than he knew. His work was hard and dangerous. His pony might step into a prairie-dog hole in the dark, he and his horse might get caught in a whirlpool of cattle while swimming a river—in either case his head might lie low almost before the echo of "Lorena" had died. Then he wore a pistol. He could shoot. Dodge City and the end of the trail, after months of privation and hardships, invited with saloons which never closed, with the red lights of the demimonde. Youth and recklessness, pockets stuffed with money in a frontier town. "We had twenty-two men in our outfit," said one trail boss. "Twenty-one of them had killed their man."

These boys in their twenties, who could ride and rope and shoot and sing, came mainly from the Southern states. They brought the gallantry, the grace, and the song heritage of their English ancestors. Their own rough songs often took the form and manner of English ballads. Irish tunes were widely popular in America during the eighteenth and nineteenth centuries, and many of these songs were patterned after the Irish "Come All Ye." We cannot trace all the influences, but we do know that the aftermath of the Civil War sent to Texas many a young Virginia aristocrat; many sons of Alabama, Mississippi, and Georgia planters; many a coon hunter from Kentucky; roving and restless young blades from all over the South (and from everywhere else). From such a group, given a taste for killing in the Civil War, in which Southern feeling and sentiments predominated, came the Texas cowboy and the cowboy songs.

To tell the stories back of finding all these songs, some of which have become widely popular, would fill a book. Tom Hight of Mangum, Oklahoma, the person who furnished the largest number of tunes, sang for me throughout two happy, bibulous days. If ever printed, many of Tom's songs could only be circulated by express shipment and then not without danger. Tom in former years had represented his Texas ranch in singing marathons, where each ranch put forward its champion. The contests, held when work was slack, might go on for several nights. "I could always sing my man down," declared Tom. Singing turn and turn about, the man who won the accolade was the man who sang the last song. The best singer knew "by heart" the greatest number of songs.

Some one told me that in San Antonio, Texas, lived a Negro singer and cook, who had first plied the latter art in the rear of a chuck wagon which followed many a herd of long-horned cattle up the trail from Texas to Fort Dodge, Kansas. I found him in 1908 leaning against a stunted mulberry tree at the rear of his place of business, a low drinking dive.

"I'se too drunk to sing today. Come back tomorrow," he muttered.

On the following morning among other songs he gave me the words and tune of "Home on the Range." Both the words and the tune sung today were first printed in the 1911 edition of "Cowboy Songs," and attracted no attention for nearly twenty years. Then two sheet-music arrangements—one pirated—helped the tune to a radio audience. Lawrence Tibbett and other singers included it among their concert numbers. A group of newspaper reporters is said to have sung it on the doorstep of Governor Franklin D. Roosevelt the night he was elected to the Presidency. It has since become a White House favorite, and it is said that the President sometimes leads the chorus. Admiral Richard Byrd found the tune a comfort during his lonely South Pole vigil: "I played my record of 'Home on the Range' until my little phonograph froze and after that I sang it myself. This is the one South Pole adventure that my friends, who know my ability as a singer, have found it hard to believe." Finally, two Arizona claimants to its authorship lost a suit against the National Broadcasting Company and others for $500,000. The humble and modest cowboy song has at last rippled the sea of American music.

The radio is chiefly responsible for the active interest in folk music. But the electric sound machine has helped. The new "Cowboy Songs" contains a number of cowboy tunes which I have happened on during a quarter-of-a-million-mile search for every type of folk song during the past five years. Among them is "The Lonesome Trail," with the lovely refrain,

> It's rain or shine, sleet or snow,
> Me and my Doney Gal are bound to go.

Alex Moore, a Texan who followed the border country until the border slopped over into the Rio Grande, furnishes half a dozen new ones properly branded by a long usage; and the song about "Diamond

Joe"—the man who buttoned his buckskin jacket with diamond soli-
taires—should cause him to rival Diamond Jim Brady in his romantic
niche in history.

The cowboys, as they punched along the drags behind the trail herd
(the drags were the baby calves that were forced to eat grass before
they could digest it easily and, therefore, carried overgrown paunches
on their spindly legs), would say, "You got nothing in your guts but
dough." They called them "dough-guts." The next step, a linguist
might agree, would be "dogies." So the late Captain George W.
Saunders, who was head of the San Antonio stock yards for many
years, once explained the word to me. "Cowboy Songs" popularized
the word "dogies" and first printed the expression "Git along, little
dogies," most familiar from its use in "The Last Round-Up." N.
Howard Thorp of New Mexico holds to the opinion that "dogie"
came from the Spanish word *dogal,* which refers to the short tie rope
that keeps the young calf away from its mother while she is being
milked. Popular usage transferred the word *dogal* to the calf itself.
Hence "dogie." Perhaps, *quién sabe?*

The East has met the West in cowboy song literature, and has
sucked up its treasures, except for a vagrant melody here and there,
and now and then a fresh couplet to such a song as "The Old Chisholm
Trail." Only a few million-acre ranches yet survive. The trail drives
ended with the discovery of barbwire and the coming of a sea of nesters
who plowed up the plains. Broadway now produces cowboy songs,
attempting to interpret this life. The West, few if any. But as long
as red blood runs, the rough words and the plaintive lonely notes
found in some of the tunes will move the heart of man.

The songs in the 1910 edition were set out in somewhat the same
haphazard order in which they were found. The present volume
groups them under specific headings. The round-up naturally precedes the trail drive, but since the trail songs seem more vital and
more highly charged with reality, I place that chapter first. To those
whose aid I acknowledged in 1910, I must now add the names of

Mrs. Minta Morgan, Bells, Texas; Mrs. Lucile Henson, San Antonio, Texas; J. B. Dillingham, Austin, Texas; the Gant family, Austin, Texas; Henry Zweiful and Sterling Brown of the Zweiful Ranch; Red King, San Antonio, Texas; John Selman ("Scandalous John"), Stamford, Texas; and Miss Elizabeth Prior, Division of Music, Library of Congress, Washington, D.C., who transcribed from discs twenty of the tunes used in this book.

J. A. L.

INTRODUCTION

It is now four or five years since my attention was called to the collection of native American ballads from the Southwest, already begun by Professor Lomax. At that time, he seemed hardly to appreciate their full value and importance. To my colleague, Professor G. L. Kittredge, probably the most eminent authority on folk-song in America, this value and importance appeared as indubitable as it appeared to me. We heartily joined in encouraging the work, as a real contribution both to literature and to learning. The present volume is the first published result of these efforts.

The value and importance of the work seems to me double. One phase of it is perhaps too highly special ever to be popular. Whoever has begun the inexhaustibly fascinating study of popular song and literature—of the nameless poetry which vigorously lives through the centuries—must be perplexed by the necessarily conjectural opinions concerning its origin and development held by various and disputing scholars. When songs were made in times and terms which for centuries have not been living facts but facts of remote history or tradition, it is impossible to be sure quite how they began, and by quite what means they sifted through the centuries into the forms at last securely theirs, in the final rigidity of print. In this collection of American ballads, almost if not quite uniquely, it is possible to trace the precise manner in which songs and cycles of song—obviously analogous to those surviving from older and antique times—have come into being. The facts which are still available concerning the ballads of our own Southwest are such as should go far to prove, or to disprove, many of the theories advanced concerning the laws of literature as evinced in the ballads of the old world.

Such learned matter as this, however, is not so surely within my province, who have made no technical study of literary origins, as is the other consideration which made me feel, from my first knowledge of these ballads, that they are beyond dispute valuable and important. In the ballads of the old world, it is not historical or philological considerations which most readers care for. It is the wonderful, robust vividness of their artless yet supremely true utterance; it is the natural vigor of their surgent, unsophisticated human rhythm. It is the sense, derived one can hardly explain how, that here is the expression straight from the heart of humanity; that here is something like the sturdy root from which the finer, though not always more lovely, flowers of polite literature have sprung. At times when we yearn for polite grace, ballads may seem rude; at times when polite grace seems tedious, sophisticated, corrupt, or mendacious, their very rudeness refreshes us with a new sense of brimming life. To compare the songs collected by Professor Lomax with the immortalities of olden time is doubtless like comparing the literature of America with that of all Europe together. Neither he nor any of us would pretend these verses to be of supreme power and beauty. None the less, they seem to me, and to many who have had a glimpse of them, sufficiently powerful, and near enough beauty, to give us some such wholesome and enduring pleasure as comes from work of this kind proved and acknowledged to be masterly.

What I mean may best be implied, perhaps, by a brief statement of fact. Four or five years ago, Professor Lomax, at my request, read some of these ballads to one of my classes at Harvard, then engaged in studying the literary history of America. From that hour to the present, the men who heard these verses, during the cheerless progress of a course of study, have constantly spoken of them and written of them, as of something sure to linger happily in memory. As such I commend them to all who care for the native poetry of America.

BARRETT WENDELL

Nahant, Massachusetts
    July 11, 1910

[xxiv]

COLLECTOR'S NOTE

OUT IN the wild, far-away places of the big and still unpeopled West—in the cañons along the Rocky Mountains, among the mining camps of Nevada and Montana, and on the remote cattle ranches of Texas, New Mexico, and Arizona—yet survives the Anglo-Saxon ballad spirit that was active in secluded districts in England and Scotland even after the coming of Tennyson and Browning. This spirit is manifested both in the preservation of the English ballad and in the creation of local songs. Illiterate people, and people cut off from newspapers and books, isolated and lonely folk—thrown back on primal resources for entertainment and for the expression of emotion —express themselves through somewhat the same character of songs as did their forefathers of perhaps a thousand years ago. In some such way have been made and preserved the cowboy songs and other frontier ballads contained in this volume. The songs represent the operation of instinct and tradition. They are chiefly interesting to the present generation, however, because of the light they throw on the conditions of pioneer life, and more particularly because of the information they contain concerning that unique and romantic figure in modern civilization, the American cowboy.

The profession of cow-punching, not yet a lost art in a group of big Western states, reached its greatest prominence during the first two decades succeeding the Civil War. In Texas, for example, immense tracts of open range, covered with luxuriant grass, encouraged the raising of cattle. One person in many instances owned thousands. To care for the cattle during the winter season, to round them up in the spring and mark and brand the yearlings, and later to drive from Texas to Fort Dodge, Kansas, those ready for market, required large forces of men. The drive from Texas to Kansas came to be

[xxv]

known as "going up the trail," for the cattle really made permanent, deep-cut trails across the otherwise trackless hills and plains of the long way. It also became the custom to take large herds of young steers from Texas as far north as Montana, where grass at certain seasons was more nutritious than in the South. Texas was the best breeding ground, while the climate and grass of Montana developed young cattle for the market.

A trip up the trail made a distinct break in the monotonous life of the big ranches, often situated hundreds of miles from places where the conventions of society were observed. The ranch community consisted usually of the boss, the straw-boss, the cowboys proper, the horse wrangler, and the cook—often a Negro. These men lived on terms of practical equality. Except in the case of the boss, there was little difference in the amount paid each for his services. Society, then, was here reduced to its lowest terms. The work of the men, their daily experiences, their thoughts, their interests, were all in common. Such a community had necessarily to turn to itself for entertainment. It was natural for the men to seek diversion in song, and when they had sung all the songs that they could recall the cowboys began to make up songs. Whatever the most gifted man could produce must bear the criticism of the entire camp, and agree with the ideas of a group of men. In this sense, therefore, any song that came from such a group would be the joint product of a number of them, telling perhaps the story of some stampede they had all fought to turn, some crime in which they had all shared equally, some comrade's tragic death which they had all witnessed. The song-making did not cease as the men went up the trail. Indeed the songs were here utilized for very practical ends. Not only were sharp, rhythmic yells—sometimes beaten into verse—employed to stir up lagging cattle, but also during the long watches the night-guards, as they rode round and round the herd, improvised cattle lullabies which quieted the animals and soothed them to sleep. So long as the cattle could hear a familiar voice crooning some cattle lullaby they had no fear of the howl of the wolf, the scream of a Mexican lion, or any of the sudden noises of the night. Some of the best of the so-called "dogie songs" seem to have been created for the purpose of preventing cattle stampedes—such songs coming straight from the heart of the cowboy, speaking familiarly to his herd in the stillness of the night.

The long drives up the trail occupied months, and called for sleepless vigilance and tireless activity both day and night. When at last a shipping point was reached, the cattle marketed or loaded on the cars, the cowboys were paid off. It is not surprising that the consequent relaxation led to reckless deeds. The music, the dancing, the click of the roulette ball in the saloons, invited; the lure of crimson lights was irresistible. Drunken orgies, reactions from months of toil, deprivation, and loneliness on the ranch and on the trail, brought to death many a temporarily crazed buckaroo. To match this daredeviltry, a saloon man in one frontier town, as a sign for his business, with psychological ingenuity painted across the broad front of his building in big black letters this challenge to God, man, and the devil: *The Road to Ruin*. Down this road, with swift and eager footsteps, strode many a pioneer viking of the West. Quickness to resent an insult real or fancied, exaggerated by unaccustomed drink, the ready pistol always at his side, the tricks of the professional gambler violating his sense of fair play, and finally his own wild recklessness urging him on—one or another of these forces sometimes brought a cowboy into tragic conflict with a spirit equally heedless and daring. Not nearly so often, however, as one might suppose, did he die with his boots on. Many of the most wealthy and respected citizens now living in the border states rode the ranges as cowboys before settling down to quiet domesticity.

A cow-camp in the seventies generally contained several types of men. It was not unusual to find a Negro who, because of his ability to handle wild horses or because of his skill with a lasso, had been promoted from the chuck-wagon to a place in the ranks of the cowboys. Another familiar figure was the adventurous younger son of some British family, through whom perhaps became current the English ballads found in the West. Furthermore, so considerable was the number of men who had fled from the states because of grave imprudence or crime, it was bad form to inquire too closely about a person's real name or where he came from. "My name is nothing extry, so that I will not tell," runs a cowboy song. Most cowboys, however, were bold young spirits who emigrated to the West for the same reason that their ancestors had come across the seas. They loved roving; they loved freedom; they were pioneers by instinct; an impulse set their faces from the East, put the itch for roaming in their veins, and sent them ever, ever westward.

That the cowboy was brave has come to be axiomatic. If his life of isolation made him taciturn, it at the same time created a spirit of hospitality, primitive and hearty as that found in the mead-halls of Beowulf. He faced the wind and the rain, the snow of winter, the fearful dust-storms of alkali desert wastes, with the same uncomplaining quiet. Not all his work was on the ranch and the trail. To the cowboy, more than to the gold-seekers, more than to Uncle Sam's soldiers, is due the final conquest of the West. Along his early winding cattle trails the Forty-niners found their way to California. The cowboy fought back the Indians from the time ranching became a business and as long as Indians remained to be fought. He played his part in winning the great slice of territory that the United States took away from Mexico. He has always been on the skirmish line of civilization. Restless, fearless, chivalric, elemental, he lived hard, shot quick and true, and died with his face to the foe. Still much misunderstood, he is often slandered, nearly always caricatured, both by the press and by the stage. Perhaps these songs, coming direct from the cowboy's experience, giving vent to his careless and his tender emotions, will afford future generations a truer conception of what he really was than is now possessed by those who know him only through highly colored romances.

The big ranches of the West are now being cut up into small farms.

The nester has come, and come to stay. Gone are the buffalo, the Indian warwhoop, the free grass of the open plain—even the stinging lizard, the tarantula, the horned frog, the centipede, the prairie dog, the rattlesnake, the Gila monster, the vinegarroon, are fast disappearing. Save in some of the secluded valleys of southern New Mexico, the old-time round-up is no more; the trails to Kansas and to Montana have become grass-grown or lost in fields of waving grain; the maverick steer, the regal longhorn, has been supplanted by his unpoetic but more beefy and profitable Polled Angus, Durham, and Hereford cousins from across the sea. The changing and romantic West of the early days lives mainly in story and in song. The last figure to vanish is the cowboy, the animating spirit of the vanishing era. He sits his horse easily as he rides through a wide valley, enclosed by mountains, clad in the hazy purple of coming night—with his face turned steadily down the long, long road, "the road that the sun goes down." Dauntless, reckless, without the unearthly purity of Sir Galahad though as gentle to a pure woman as King Arthur, he is truly a knight of the twentieth century. A vagrant puff of wind shakes a corner of the crimson handkerchief knotted loosely at his throat; the thud of his pony's feet, mingling with the jingle of his spurs, is borne back; and as the careless, gracious, lovable figure disappears over the divide, the breeze brings to the ears, faint and far yet cheery still, the refrain of a cowboy song:

> Whoopee ti yi yo, git along, little dogies;
>   It's your misfortune and none of my own.
> Whoopee ti yi yo, git along, little dogies;
>   For you know Wyoming will be your new home.

As for the songs of this collection, I have violated the ethics of ballad gatherers, in a few instances, by selecting and putting together what seemed to be the best lines from different versions, all telling the same story. Frankly, the volume is meant to be popular. The songs have been arranged in some such haphazard way as they were collected —jotted down on a table in the rear of a saloon, scrawled on an envelope while squatting about a campfire, caught behind the scenes of a bronco-busting outfit. Later, it is hoped that enough interest will be aroused to justify printing all the variants of these songs, accompanied by the music and such explanatory notes as may be useful; the Negro folk-songs, the songs of the lumberjacks, the songs of the mountaineers, and the songs of the sea, already partially collected, being included in the final publication. The songs of this collection, never before in print, as a rule have been taken down from singing or recitation. In only a few instances have I been able to discover the authorship of any song. They seem to have sprung up as quietly and mysteriously as does the grass on the plains. All have been popular with the range riders, several being current all the way from Texas to Montana, and quite as long as the old Chisholm Trail stretching between these states. Some of the songs the cowboy certainly composed; all of them he sang. Obviously, a number of the most characteristic cannot be printed for general circulation. To paraphrase slightly what Sidney Lanier said of Walt Whitman's poetry—they are raw collops slashed from the rump of Nature, and never mind the gristle. Likewise some of the strong adjectives and nouns have been softened— Jonahed, as George Meredith would have said. There is, however, a Homeric quality about the cowboy's profanity and vulgarity that pleases rather than repulses. The broad sky under which he slept, the limitless plains over which he rode, the big, open, free life he lived near to Nature's breast, taught him simplicity, calm, directness. He spoke out plainly the impulses of his heart. But as yet so-called polite society is not quite willing to hear.

It is entirely impossible to acknowledge the assistance that I have received from many persons. To Professors Barrett Wendell and George Lyman Kittredge, of Harvard, I must gratefully acknowledge constant and generous encouragement. Even dear Dean Briggs of the Sheldon Awards Committee always smiled indulgently at the most lurid cowboy songs. Professor H. M. Belden, of the University of Missouri, sent me several songs and offered many wise suggestions.

Messrs. Jeff Hanna, of Meridian, Texas; John B. Jones, Los Angeles; H. Knight, Sterling City, Texas; John Lang Sinclair, New York; A. H. Belo & Co., Dallas; Tom Hight of Oklahoma; Roy Bedichek, of the University of Texas; Benjamin Wyche; Mrs. M. B. Wight, of Fort Thomas, Arizona; Professors L. W. Payne, Jr., and J. Frank Dobie of the University of Texas; Harry Stephens, Denison, Texas; Elwood Adams, St. Louis; J. E. McCauley, of Seymour, Texas; John M. Grigsby, of Comanche, Texas; the San Antonio *Express;* and my brother, R. C. Lomax—these have rendered me especially helpful service in furnishing material, for which I also render grateful thanks.

Among the Negroes, rivermen, miners, soldiers, seamen, lumbermen, railroad men, and ranchmen of the United States and Canada there are many indigenous folk-songs not included in this volume. Of some of them I have traces, and I shall surely run them down. I beg the coöperation of all who are interested in this vital, however humble, expression of American literature.

J. A. L.

Bedichek's Ranch
Deming, New Mexico
August 8, 1910

CONTENTS

[xxxiii]

Contents

Contents

Contents

Contents

Contents

I

UP THE TRAIL

He an' I was the only ones in an outfit of twenty-two that had not killed a man.

—*Old Trail Drivers' Records.*

The gay jolly cowboy is up with the sun,
And quick to the saddle is he,
He swings his quirt and jingles his spurs,
And a dashing vaquero is he;
 Hoop-la, set 'em on fire,
 Shouts the rider free;
 Give 'em the spurs and burn the earth,
 A cowboy's life for me.

* * * * *

I'm ridin' tonight round the dam bed-ground,
Ridin' on a sore-backed hoss;
And I don't care a cuss what happens to the cows,
For I'm gittin' forty dollars and found;
Forty a month and chuck-wagon food,
Forty a month and found;
Oh, think of the joys of a cowboy's life,
While you're ridin' on the old bed-ground.

* * * * *

When relieved by nightherders a group of three cowboys would catch some sleep quickly by lying down so as to form a triangle, each cowboy using the ankles of his partner for a pillow.

I rode in Montana and old Idaho,
I rode trips down in New Mexico;
I rode mountain lions and grizzly bears,
And used cronish cactus for combing my hair.

I rode the dry deserts no water between;
I rode through Death Valley without a canteen;
In riding dry deserts I'm hard to outdo,
I'm a high-lopin' cowboy and a wild buckaroo.

* * * * *

Oh, I would be a cowboy and with the cowboys stand,
With leather chaps upon me and a six-gun in my hand;
I'd ride a full-stamped saddle and a silver-mounted bit,
With the conchos big as dollars and silver spurs to fit;
And out upon the round-up I'd ride the bucking horse,
And spur him in the shoulder, with my silver spurs, of course.

* * * * *

Down in the land of the center-fire saddle,
Down where the cayuse is pesky to straddle,
There's where the cowboy is bound to skedaddle
Back to the sand and the sun,
Where the coffee grows on live-oak trees,
And the rivers flow with brandy.
Then it's fare you well, my own true love,
For we're bound for the Rio Grandy.

COWBOY'S GETTIN'–UP HOLLER

A common call in Far West camp life.

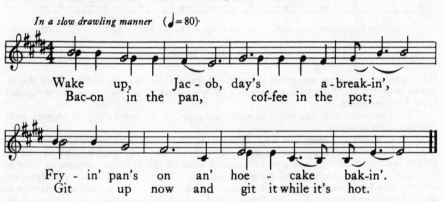

In a slow drawling manner (♩ = 80)

Wake up, Jac - ob, day's a - break-in',
Bac-on in the pan, cof-fee in the pot;

Fry - in' pan's on an' hoe - cake bak-in'.
Git up now and git it while it's hot.

Wake up, Jacob, day's a-breakin';
Fryin' pan's on an' hoecake bakin'.

Bacon in the pan, coffee in the pot;
Git up now and git it while it's hot.

[3]

WHOOPEE TI YI YO, GIT ALONG, LITTLE DOGIES*

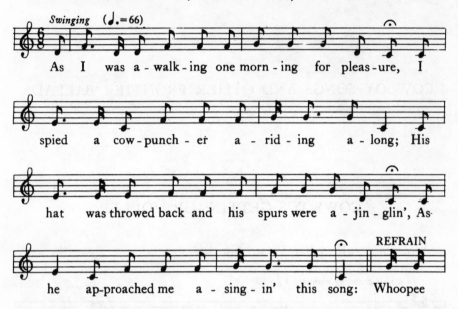

Swinging (♩.=66)

As I was a-walk-ing one morn-ing for pleas-ure, I

spied a cow-punch-er a-rid-ing a-long; His

hat was throwed back and his spurs were a-jin-glin', As

he ap-proached me a-sing-in' this song: Whoopee **REFRAIN**

---

* The tune of this song was given me at the Texas Cattlemen's Convention, Fort Worth, Texas, 1910, by Mrs. Trantham, a wandering gypsy minstrel. The words were woven together from five fragments.

The controversy that has raged around the origin of the word "dogie" resolves itself into two main opinions:

(1) N. Howard Thorp, old-time cowman and cowboy poet, at present adviser to the W.P.A. Writers' Project of New Mexico, suggests that the word is of Spanish derivation. *Dogal*, meaning "halter," was used in a special sense by the Mexican cowboys to refer to the halter by means of which a suckling calf was restrained from its mother. The American cowboys may have misunderstood and assumed that the Mexicans were applying this term to the calf itself, and not simply to the halter. Or the Mexicans may actually have come to call the calf by this term as an abbreviation. However that may be, the Americans, as the theory goes, not having a very good ear for Spanish, corrupted the word to "dogie." This explanation appears feasible when you consider that the greater part of our western terms applying to cattle, ranching, horses, etc., have been borrowed from the Spanish.

(2) The ranchmen of the Southwest are usually of the opinion that the "dogie" is a stunted calf that, "since its mammy is dead and its pappy ran off with another cow," has had to fend for itself and subsist at too tender an age on grass and so has grown pot-bellied. "Dough-bellied" is the cowboy's vivid expression. "There's nothing in their guts but dough, them little dough-guts." Thus "dough-guts" was shortened to "doughgies" and was misspelled as "dogies" by collectors of cowboy song. At this point we leave the controversy to the philologists. The word is not, as most radio singers pronounce it, "doggies."

[4]

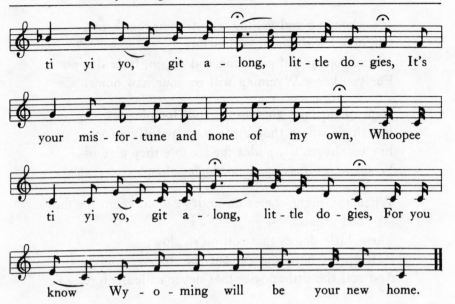

ti yi yo, git a - long, lit - tle do - gies, It's

your mis - for - tune and none of my own, Whoopee

ti yi yo, git a - long, lit - tle do - gies, For you

know Wy - o - ming will be your new home.

As I was a-walking one morning for pleasure,
I spied a cow-puncher a-riding along;
His hat was throwed back and his spurs were a-jinglin',
As he approached me a-singin' this song:

> Whoopee ti yi yo, git along, little dogies,*
> It's your misfortune and none of my own;
> Whoopee ti yi yo, git along, little dogies,
> For you know Wyoming will be your new home.

Early in the springtime we'll round up the dogies,
Slap on their brands, and bob off their tails;
Round up our horses, load up the chuck wagon,
Then throw those dogies upon the trail.

* The refrain is sometimes sung, according to Owen Wister:
> Hi-o, git along, you damned little dogies,
> Wyoming shall be your new home;
> And 'twas swearing and cursing and damning the dogies
> To our misfortune and none of their own.

[5]

It's whooping and yelling and driving the dogies,
Oh, how I wish you would go on;
It's whooping and punching and go on, little dogies,
For you know Wyoming will be your new home.

Some of the boys goes up the trail for pleasure,
But that's where they git it most awfully wrong;
For you haven't any idea the trouble they give us
When we go driving them dogies along.

When the night comes on and we hold them on the
    bed-ground,
These little dogies that roll on so slow;
Roll up the herd and cut out the strays,
And roll the little dogies that never rolled before.

Your mother she was raised way down in Texas,
Where the jimson weed and sand-burrs grow;
Now we'll fill you up on prickly pear and cholla
Till you are ready for the trail to Idaho.

Oh, you'll be soup for Uncle Sam's Injuns;
"It's beef, heap beef," I hear them cry.
Git along, git along, git along, little dogies
You're going to be beef steers by and by.

Owen Wister's Version

Gently swinging ($\downarrow$. = 60)

As I walked out one morn-ing for pleas-ure, I

met a cow-punch-er a - jog - ging a - long. His

hat was thrown back and his spurs they was jin-gling, And

REFRAIN

as he ad-vanced he was sing-ing this song, Sing-ing

Whoop-ti-o, git a-long, my lit-tle do-gies, For Wy-

o-ming shall be your new home, And its

driv-ing and damn-ing and curs-ing those do-gies to

our mis-for-tune but none of their own.

THE COLORADO TRAIL*

Slowly ($\quad$ = 66)

Eyes like the morn-ing star, Cheek like a rose,

* From Carl Sandburg's *The American Songbag* (New York: Harcourt, Brace & Co.). Sung by a horsewrangler from a hospital bed in Duluth, Minn.

[7]

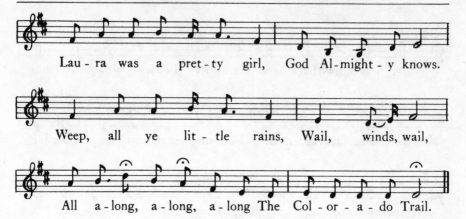

Lau - ra was a pret - ty girl, God Al - might - y knows.

Weep, all ye lit - tle rains, Wail, winds, wail,

All a - long, a - long, a - long The Col - or - a - do Trail.

Eyes like the morning star,
 Cheek like a rose,
Laura was a pretty girl,
 God Almighty knows.

Weep, all ye little rains,
 Wail, winds, wail,
All along, along, along
 The Colorado Trail.

DONEY GAL

From the singing of Mrs. Louise Henson, San Antonio, Texas, who learned the song from her uncle in Oklahoma.

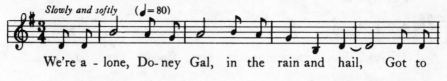

Slowly and softly (♩ = 80)

We're a - lone, Do - ney Gal, in the rain and hail, Got to

NOTE.—The first eight measures of this melancholy song serve only as a fitting introduction; they are not to be repeated except arbitrarily to vary the attractive monotony of the identical stanzas and refrain.

[8]

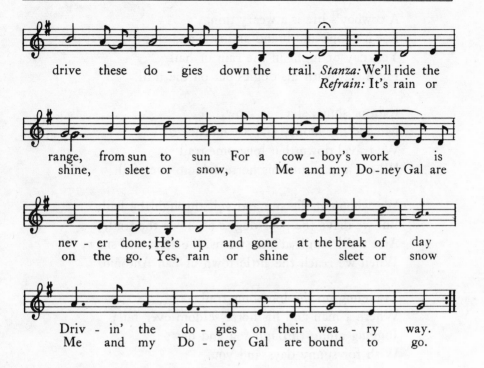

drive these do - gies down the trail. *Stanza:* We'll ride the
Refrain: It's rain or

range, from sun to sun For a cow - boy's work is
shine, sleet or snow, Me and my Do - ney Gal are

nev - er done; He's up and gone at the break of day
on the go. Yes, rain or shine sleet or snow

Driv - in' the do - gies on their wea - ry way.
Me and my Do - ney Gal are bound to go.

We're alone, Doney Gal, in the rain and hail,
Got to drive these dogies down the trail.

We'll ride the range from sun to sun,
For a cowboy's work is never done;
He's up and gone at the break of day,
Drivin' the dogies on their weary way.

Refrain:

It's rain or shine, sleet or snow,
Me and my Doney Gal are on the go.
Yes, rain or shine, sleet or snow,
Me and my Doney Gal are bound to go.

[9]

A cowboy's life is a weary thing,
For it's rope and brand and ride and sing;
Yes, day or night in the rain or hail,
He'll stay with his dogies out on the trail.

Rain or shine, sleet or snow,
Me and my Doney Gal are on the go;
We travel down that lonesome trail
Where a man and his horse seldom ever fail.

We whoop at the sun and yell through the hail,
But we drive the poor dogies on down the trail,
And we'll laugh at the storms, the sleet and snow,
When we reach the little town of San Antonio.

Traveling up the lonesome trail
Where a man and his horse seldom ever fail;
Jogging along through fog and dew,
Wish for sunny days and you.

Over the prairies lean and brown,
On through the wastes where there ain't no town;
Swimming the rivers across our way,
We fight on forward day-end on day.

Trailing the herd through mountains green,
We pen the cattle in Abilene.
Round the camp-fire's flickering glow,
We sing the songs of long ago.

Refrain:

    It's rain or shine, sleet or snow,
    Me and my Doney Gal are on the go;

Yes, rain or shine, sleet or snow,
Me and my Doney Gal are bound to go.

We're alone, Doney Gal, in the rain and hail,
Got to drive these dogies down the trail:
Get along, little dogie, on your way.

ME AN' MY DONEY–GAL*

It started into raining
  An' followed with a sleet an' snow;
It makes no difference how cold it gets,
  Me an' my Doney-Gal has to go.

A thousand head of cattle,
  Caught in the snow,
Were frozen while a-millin',
  A-tryin' to keep on the go.

Poor Joe with the millin' herd
  Was found a-layin' low;
He struck a drift and froze
  A-hard 'n the snow.

That blizzard kept a-comin'
  Over that frozen shelf of snow;
An' sent the cattle huntin' shelter
  From the wind that was moanin' low.

The snowflakes keep a-fallin',
  Till my Doney-Gal is covered with snow;

* Sent by Gene Anna Bell Coe of Oklahoma, to the *Wild West Weekly*.

But rain, shine, sleet or snow,
Me and my Doney-Gal must go.

In the dark cold night,
Through the fallin' snow,
I keep my Doney-Gal a-moving
To the herd in the frozen snow.

I froze myself aplenty
While keepin' on the go,
A-lookin' for my herder—
An' found him frozen in the snow.

Soon spring will be comin'
With plenty of hay to mow—
An' no cattle to eat it,
For he left them in the snow.

GOOD–BY, OLD PAINT

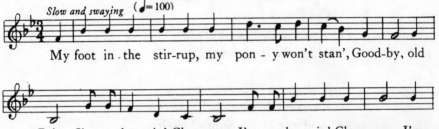

My foot in the stir-rup, my pon - y won't stan', Good-by, old

Paint, I'm a - leav-in' Chey-enne. I'm a - leav-in' Chey-enne, I'm

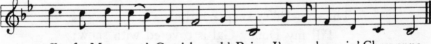

off for Mon - tan', Good-by, old Paint, I'm a leav-in' Chey-enne.

My foot in the stirrup, my pony won't stan',
Good-by, old Paint, I'm a-leavin' Cheyenne.
I'm a-leavin' Cheyenne, I'm off for Montan';
Good-by, old Paint, I'm a-leavin' Cheyenne.*

I'm a-ridin' old Paint, I'm a-leadin' old Fan;
Good-by, old Paint, I'm a-leavin' Cheyenne.
With my feet in the stirrups, my bridle in my hand;
Good-by, old Paint, I'm a-leavin' Cheyenne.

Old Paint's a good pony, he paces when he can;
Good-by, little Annie, I'm off for Cheyenne.
Oh, hitch up your horses and feed 'em some hay,
And seat yourself by me as long as you stay.

My hosses ain't hungry, they won't eat your hay;
My wagon is loaded and rollin' away.
I'm a-ridin' old Paint, I'm a-leadin' old Dan,†
I'm a-goin' to Montan' to throw the hoolihan.

They feed in the coulees, they water in the draw,
Their tails are all matted, their backs are all raw.
Old Bill Jones had two daughters and a song;
One went to Denver, the other went wrong.

His wife died in a pool-room fight,
And still he sings from morning till night.
I'm a rambler and a gambler and far from my home,
And those that don't like me can leave me alone.

Oh, whiskey and beer, they are nothing to me,
They killed my old Dad, now they can try me.

* The final line of each stanza can be repeated *ad libitum* as a refrain.
† Or, with a pack on old Baldy and riding old Dan.

I'll tell you the truth, not lyin' or jokin',
I'd rather be in jail than to be heart-broken.

Oh, when I die take my saddle from the wall,
Put it on my pony, lead him from the stall,
Tie my bones to his back, turn our faces to the west,
And we'll ride the prairie that we love the best.

THE SKEW-BALL BLACK*

It was down to Red River I came,
Prepared to play a damned tough game—
Whoa! skew, till I saddle you, whoa!

I crossed the river to the ranch where I intended to work,
With a big six-shooter and a derned good dirk—
Whoa! skew, till I saddle you, whoa!

They roped me out a skew-ball black,
With a double set-fast on his back—
Whoa! skew, till I saddle you, whoa!

And when I was mounted on his back,
The boys all yelled, "Just give him slack—"
Whoa! skew, till I saddle you, whoa!

They rolled and tumbled and yelled, by God,
For he threw me a-whirling all over the sod—
Whoa! skew, till I saddle you, whoa!

* The Negroes sing a stirring work-song about Stewball. See *American Ballads and Folk-songs*, p. 68 (New York: Macmillan, 1934).

I went to the boss and I told him I'd resign,
The fool tumbled over, and I thought he was dyin'—
Whoa! skew, till I saddle you, whoa!

And it's to Arkansaw I'll go back,
To hell with Texas and the skew-ball black—
Whoa! skew, till I saddle you, whoa!

THE KANSAS LINE

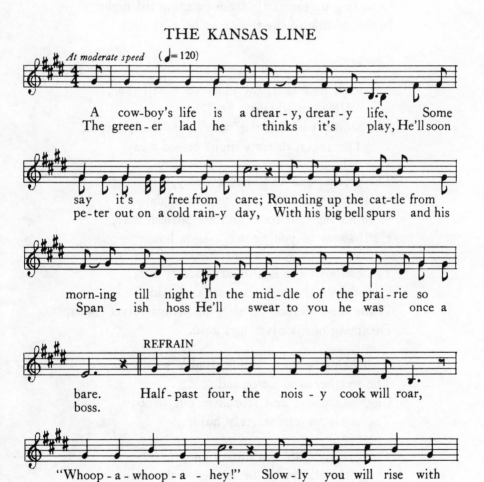

At moderate speed (♩ = 120)

A cow-boy's life is a drear-y, drear-y life, Some
The green-er lad he thinks it's play, He'll soon

say it's free from care; Rounding up the cat-tle from
pe-ter out on a cold rain-y day, With his big bell spurs and his

morn-ing till night In the mid-dle of the prai-rie so
Span-ish hoss He'll swear to you he was once a

REFRAIN

bare. Half-past four, the nois-y cook will roar,
boss.

"Whoop-a-whoop-a-hey!" Slow-ly you will rise with

sleep-y feel-ing eyes, The sweet dream-y night passed a - way.

A cowboy's life is a dreary, dreary life,
Some say it's free from care;
Rounding up the cattle from morning till night
In the middle of the prairie so bare.

Chorus:

Half-past four, the noisy cook will roar,
"Whoop-a-whoop-a-hey!"
Slowly you will rise with sleepy-feeling eyes,
The sweet, dreamy night passed away.

The greener lad he thinks it's play,
He'll soon peter out on a cold rainy day,
With his big bell spurs and his Spanish hoss,
He'll swear to you he was once a boss.

The cowboy's life is a dreary, dreary life,
He's driven through the heat and cold;
While the rich man's a-sleeping on his velvet couch,
Dreaming of his silver and gold.

Spring-time sets in, double trouble will begin,
The weather is so fierce and cold;
Clothes are wet and frozen to our necks,
The cattle we can scarcely hold.

The cowboy's life is a dreary one,
He works all day to the setting of the sun;

[16]

And then his day's work is not done,
For there's his night herd to go on.

The wolves and owls with their terrifying howls
Will disturb us in our midnight dream,
As we lie on our slickers on a cold, rainy night
Way over on the Pecos stream.

You are speaking of your farms, you are speaking of
        your charms,
You are speaking of your silver and gold;
But a cowboy's life is a dreary, dreary life,
He's driven through the heat and cold.

Some folks say that we are free from care,
Free from all other harm;
But we round up the cattle from morning till night
Way over on the prairie so dry.

I used to run about, now I stay at home,
Take care of my wife and child;
Nevermore to roam, always stay at home,
Take care of my wife and child.

Chorus:

Half-past four the noisy cook will roar,
"Hurrah, boys! She's breaking day!"
Slowly we will rise and wipe our sleepy eyes,
The sweet, dreamy night passed away.

[17]

GEORGE BRITTON*

In ballad style (♩.=66)

I want to tell you of a trip I did take Up the
Lone Star Trail and a-cross Plain's Stake; And
talk-in' 'bout hard times, we act-ually had one. The
dog-ies stam-ped-ed, law, how they did run.

I want to tell you of a trip I did take
Up the Lone Star Trail and across Plain's — — Stake;
And talkin' 'bout hard times, we actually had one.
The dogies stampeded, law, how they did run!

George Britton was there, a gay jolly kid;
Done the danger'est riding that a cowboy ever did;
He rid in the lead of 'em, over hills he did go
But he never ceased singing to 'em, "Ho, dogies, ho."

We started from Brady one dark stormy night
When the cattle stampeded and of course taken flight
And into the drag George Britton he flew
And broke his leg, he broke it in two.

* From Alex Moore, Austin, Texas.

[18]

And Tip he cried out like a man that was slain,
His leg being broken of course give him pain,
But nevertheless he set on his horse
And he stayed with the dogies that Britton had lost.

I saw the Comanches, I had them to fight;
But I never rode out in a more darker night;
The lightning flashed, the hail it did fall,
The cattle stampeded, law, how they did bawl!

They broke up and scattered and all taken flight,
Some dangerous ol' riding was done that night;
The boys sung to them, sung "Ho, dogies, ho,"
But the more they sung to them the faster they'd go.

Come all you young cowboys, take warning by this,
Don't never go riding in the wild open West.
There's nothing in it but trouble and woe
You're bound to have a hard time wherever you go.

THE LONE STAR TRAIL

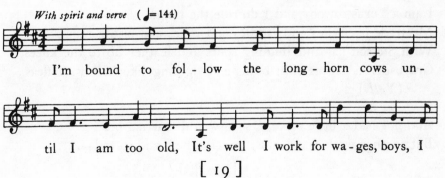

With spirit and verve (♩ = 144)

I'm bound to fol-low the long-horn cows un-

til I am too old, It's well I work for wa-ges, boys, I

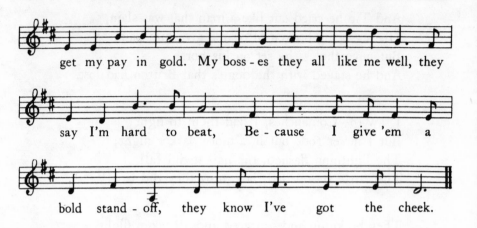

get my pay in gold. My boss-es they all like me well, they
say I'm hard to beat, Be-cause I give 'em a
bold stand-off, they know I've got the cheek.

I'm bound to follow the longhorn cows until I am too old,
It's well I work for wages, boys, I get my pay in gold;
My bosses they all like me well, they say I'm hard to beat—
Because I give 'em a bold stand-off, they know I've got the cheek.

Yell:

Ki-yi-yipi-yipi-yea.

I'm a rowdy cowboy just off the stormy plains,
My trade is girting saddles and pulling bridle reins.
Oh, I can tip the lasso, it is with graceful ease;
I rope a streak of lightning, and ride it where I please. (*Yell.*)

I am a Texas cowboy and I do ride the range;
My trade is cinches and saddles and ropes and bridle reins;
With Stetson hat and jingling spurs and leather up to the knees,
Graybacks as big as chili beans and fighting like hell with fleas.
(*Yell.*)

And if I had a little stake, I soon would married be,
But another week and I must go—the boss said so today.

[20]

My girl must cheer up courage and choose some other one,
For I am bound to follow the Lone Star Trail until my race is run.
  (*Yell.*)

It almost breaks my heart for to have to go away,
And leave my own little darling, my sweetheart so far away.
But when I'm out on the Lone Star Trail often I'll think of thee,
Of my own dear girl, the darling one, the one I would like to see.
  (*Yell.*)

And when I get to a shipping point, I'll get on a little spree
To drive away the sorrow for the girl that once loved me.
And though red licker stirs us up we're bound to have our fun,
And I intend to follow the Lone Star Trail until my race is run.
  (*Yell.*)

It's when we are on the trail where the dust and bellows fly,
It's fifty miles from water and the grass is scorching-dry;
The boss is mad and ringy* as you can plainly see,
And I want to leave the trail and one honest farmer be. (*Yell.*)

And then there comes a rain, boys, one of the gentle kind;
The lakes git full of water, and the grass is waving fine.
The boss will shed his frown, and a pleasant smile you'll see,
And I want to leave my happy home and a roving cowboy be. (*Yell.*)

Well, it's when we git them bedded, boys, we think it's for the
    night,
Some horse will shake a saddle and give the herd a fright;
They'll rise to their feet, boys, and madly dash away;
And "It's moving time, to the lead, boys," you'll hear some cowboy
    say. (*Yell.*)

* Mad, like a horse that (w)rings its tail.

And when we git around them and quieted down again,
A dark cloud will rise in the west, and a fire will play in their
    horns;
The boss will ride around and say, "Stay with 'em, boys, and your
    pay will be gold";
I'm bound to follow the longhorn steer until I am too old. (*Yell.*)

I went up the Lone Star Trail in Eighteen Eighty-three;
I fell in love with a pretty miss and she in love with me.
"When you get to Kansas write and let me know;
And if you get in trouble, your bail I'll come and go." (*Yell.*)

When I got up in Kansas, I had a pleasant dream;
I dreamed I was down on Trinity, down on that pleasant stream;
I dreamt my true love right beside me, she come to go my bail;
I woke up broken-hearted with a yearling by the tail. (*Yell.*)

THE TEXAS COWBOY*

(*Tune same as "The Jolly Cowboy, page 275*)

Oh, I am a Texas cowboy, far away from home.
If ever I get back to Texas I nevermore will roam.
Montana is too cold for me and the winters are too long;
Before the round-ups do begin our money is all gone.

Take this old hen-skin bedding, too thin to keep me warm—
I nearly freeze to death, my boys, whenever there's a storm.
And take this old tarpoleon,† too thin to shield my frame—
I got it down in Nebraska a-dealin' a monte game.

---

* "This song was composed by a cowboy who was going up the trail from Texas to Montana.
The Mussel Shell is a lake in west Texas. The Circle and D. T. are brands of big outfits
that ranch near this like."—A. B. EDSALL.
† Waterproof bedding, usually shortened to "tarp" (corrupt form of "tarpaulin").

[22]

Now to win these fancy leggins I'll have enough to do;
They cost me twenty dollars the day that they were new.
I have an outfit on the Mussel Shell, but that I'll never see,
Unless I get sent to represent the Circle or D. T.

I've worked down in Nebraska where the grass grows ten feet
    high,
And the cattle are such rustlers that they seldom ever die;
I've worked up in the sand hills and down upon the Platte,
Where the cowboys are good fellows and the cattle always fat;

I've traveled lots of country—Nebraska's hills of sand,
Down through the Indian Nation, and up the Rio Grande;
But the Bad Lands of Montana are the worst I ever seen,
The cowboys are all tenderfeet and the dogies are too lean.

If you want to see some bad lands, go over on the Dry;
You will bog down in the coulees where the mountains reach the
    sky.
A tenderfoot to lead you who never knows the way,
You are playing in the best of luck if you eat more than once a
    day.

Your grub is bread and bacon and coffee black as ink;
The water is so full of alkali it is hardly fit to drink.
They will wake you in the morning before the break of day,
And send you on a circle a hundred miles away.

All along the Yellowstone 'tis cold the year around;
You will surely get consumption by sleeping on the ground.
Work in Montana is six months in the year;
When all your bills are settled there is nothing left for beer.

Work down in Texas is all the year around;
You will never get consumption by sleeping on the ground.
Come all you Texas cowboys and warning take from me,
And do not go to Montana to spend your money free.
But stay at home in Texas where work lasts the year round,
And you will never catch consumption by sleeping on the ground.

ON THE TRAIL TO IDAHO

Sent to me by J. M. Grigsby of Comanche, Texas, who writes (March 26, 1912): "There is some cowboys that don't like to talk about the old times. I guess they are a shame of their cowboy life. I am not. I tell you the truth when I tell you I never stole a yearling or defaced a brand in my life and I never had a boss to ask me to. They had quit when I went on."

I met the boss; he wanted me to go
Help drive his herd to Idaho.
I told the boss it was out of my range,
But if he had the price, I was about to change.

We started out the first of May;
Everything looked good, everything was gay.
We rolled along just like a ball
Until one night we had a squall.

The cattle stampeded all over the ground;
We couldn't get them all to lay down.
We drove for days and sometimes weeks,
We couldn't see nothing but the mountain peaks.

[24]

The sand did roll and fill my eyes,
And I thought of home and almost cry.
We crossed three rivers we didn't know,
Out on the trail to Idaho.

It was a long and lonesome go
Out on the trail to Idaho.
We saw some Indians; they were on the run;
They were kinder jubus* of our needle guns.

They divided up in twos and fours,
They didn't like old forty-fours.
When I got home I told the boys
Out on that run they'd see no joys.

Long stretches we drove was very dry,
All the water we drank was alkali.
I made up my mind when back on the range
Not to scamper off after the little extra change.
　　　　　Go 'long, Blue Dog.

JOHN GARNER'S TRAIL HERD

Come all you old-timers and listen to my song;
I'll make it short as possible and I'll not keep you long;
I'll relate to you about the time you all remember well
When we, with old John Garner, drove a beef herd up the trail.

When we left the ranch it was early in the spring,
We had as good a corporal as ever rope did swing;
Good hands and good horses, good outfit through and through—
We went well equipped, we were a jolly crew.

* Dubious.

We had no little herd—two thousand head or more—
And some as wild a brush beeves as you ever saw before.
We swung to them all the way and sometimes by the tail—
Oh, you know we had a circus as we all went up the trail.

All things went on well till we reached the open ground,
And then them cattle turned in and they gave us merry hell.
They stampeded every night that came and did it without fail—
Oh, you know we had a circus as we all went up the trail.

We would round them up at morning and the boss would make a count,
And say: "Look here, old punchers, we are out quite an amount;
You must make all losses good and do it without fail
Or you will never get another job of driving up the trail."

When we reached Red River we gave the Inspector the dodge.
He swore by God Almighty, in jail old John should lodge.
We told him if he'd taken our boss and had him locked in jail,
We would shore get his scalp as we all came down the trail.

When we reached the Reservation, how squirmish we did feel,
Although we had tried old Garner and knew him true as steel.
And if we would follow him and do as he said do,
That old bald-headed cow-thief would surely take us through.

When we reached Dodge City we drew our four months' pay.
Times were better then, boys, that was a better day.
The way we drank and gambled and threw the girls around—
"Say, a crowd of Texas cowboys has come to take our town."

The cowboy sees many hardships although he takes them well;
The fun we had upon that trip, no human tongue can tell.
The cowboy's life is a dreary life, though his mind it is no load,
And he always spends his money like he found it in the road.

If ever you meet old Garner, you must meet him on the square,
For he is the biggest cow-thief that ever tramped out there.
But if you want to hear him roar and spin a lively tale,
Just ask him about the time we all went up the trail.

THE CROOKED TRAIL TO HOLBROOK*

Come all you jolly cowboys that follow the bronco steer,
I'll sing to you a verse or two your spirits for to cheer;
It's all about a trip, a trip that I did undergo
On that crooked trail to Holbrook, in Arizona oh.

It's on the seventeenth of February, our herd it started out,
It would have made your hearts shudder to hear them bawl and shout;
As wild as any buffalo that ever rode the Platte
Those dogies we were driving, and every one was fat.

We crossed the Mescal Mountains on the way to Gilson Flats,
And when we got to Gilson Flats, Lord, how the wind did blow;
It blew so hard, it blew so fierce, we knew not where to go,
But our spirits never failed us as onward we did go—
On that crooked trail to Holbrook, in Arizona oh.

That night we had a stampede; Christ, how the cattle run!
We made it to our horses; I tell you, we had no fun;
Over the prickly pear and catclaw brush we quickly made our way;
We thought of our long journey and the girls we'd left one day.

* From Mrs. M. B. Wight, Fort Thomas, Ariz.

[27]

It's long by Sombserva we slowly punched along,
While each and every puncher would sing a hearty song
To cheer up his comrade as onward we did go,
On that crooked trail to Holbrook, in Arizona oh.

We crossed the Muggyone Mountains where the tall pines do grow,
Grass grows in abundance, and rippling streams do flow;
Our packs were always turning, of course our gait was slow,
On that crooked trail to Holbrook, in Arizona oh.

At last we got to Holbrook, a little gale did blow;
It blew up sand and pebble stones and it didn't blow them slow.
We had to drink the water from that muddy little stream
And swallowed a peck of dirt when we tried to eat a bean.

But the cattle now are shipped and homeward we are bound
With a lot of as tired horses as ever could be found;
Across the reservation no danger did we fear,
But thought of wives and sweethearts and the ones we love so dear.
Now we are back in Globe City, our friendship there to share;
Here's luck to every puncher that follows the bronco steer.

THE OLD CHISHOLM TRAIL

The name is pronounced *Chizzum*. This song in its entirety would give all the possible experiences of a group of cowboys driving a herd of cattle from Texas to Dodge City, Kansas. Many stanzas are not mailable. Thus far no one has shown that it is not a product of the plains—a genuine cowboy song, both words and music. Of all songs, the most universally sung by the cowboys.

Lustily (♩=104)

Come a-long, boys, and lis-ten to my tale, I'll

tell you of my troub-les on the old Chis-holm trail. Com-a

ti yi you-py you-py yea, you-py yea, Com-a

ti yi you-py you-py yea.

Come along, boys, and listen to my tale,
I'll tell you of my troubles on the old Chisholm trail.

    Coma ti yi youpy, youpy yea, youpy yea,
    Coma ti yi youpy, youpy yea.

I started up the trail October twenty-third,
I started up the trail with the 2-U herd.

Oh, a ten-dollar hoss and a forty-dollar saddle,
And I'm goin' to punchin' Texas cattle.

I woke up one morning on the old Chisholm trail,
Rope in my hand and a cow by the tail.

I'm up in the mornin' afore daylight
And afore I sleep the moon shines bright.

[29]

Old Ben Bolt was a blamed good boss,
But he'd go to see the girls on a sore-backed hoss.

Old Ben Bolt was a fine old man
And you'd know there was whisky wherever he'd land.

My hoss throwed me off at the creek called Mud,
My hoss throwed me off round the 2-U herd.

Last time I saw him he was going 'cross the level
A-kicking up his heels and a-running like the devil.

It's cloudy in the west, a-looking like rain,
And my damned old slicker's in the wagon again.

No chaps and no slicker, and it's pouring down rain,
And I swear, by God, that I'll never night-herd again.

Crippled my hoss, I don't know how,
Ropin' at the horns of a 2-U cow.

We hit Caldwell and we hit her on the fly,
We bedded down the cattle on the hill close by.

No chaps, no slicker, and it's pouring down rain,
And I swear, by God, I'll never night-herd again.

Feet in the stirrups and seat in the saddle,
I hung and rattled them longhorn cattle.

Last night I was on guard and the leader broke the ranks,
I hit my horse down the shoulders and I spurred him in the flanks.

The wind commenced to blow, and the rain began to fall,
Hit looked, by grab, like we was goin' to lose 'em all.

My slicker's in the wagon and I'm gittin' mighty cold,
And these longhorn sons-o'-guns are gittin' hard to hold.

Saddle up, boys, and saddle up well,
For I think these cattle have scattered to hell.

I jumped in the saddle and grabbed holt the horn,*
Best blamed cow-puncher ever was born.

I hit my pony and he gave a little rack,
And damned big luck if we ever git back.

With my blanket and my gun and my rawhide rope,
I'm a-slidin' down the trail in a long, keen lope.

I popped my foot in the stirrup and gave a little yell,
The tail cattle broke and the leaders went to hell.

I don't give a damn if they never do stop;
I'll ride as long as an eight-day clock.

Foot in the stirrup and hand on the horn,
Best damned cowboy ever was born.

I herded and I hollered and I done very well,
Till the boss said, "Boys, just let 'em go to hell."

I and old Blue Dog arrived on the spot
And we put them to milling like the boiling of a pot.

Stray in the herd and the boss said kill it,
So I shot him in the rump with the handle of the skillet.

We rounded 'em up and put 'em on the cars,
And that was the last of the old Two Bars.

Oh, it's bacon and beans most every day—
I'd as soon be a-eatin' prairie hay.

* "One stampede I remember the boss got so scared he run up a tree and tried to pull his pony up with him."

I'm on my best horse and I'm goin' at a run,
I'm the quickest-shootin' cowboy that ever pulled a gun.

I went to the wagon to get my roll,
To come back to Texas, dad-burn my soul.

Well, I met a little gal and I offered her a quarter,
She says, "Young man, I'm a gentleman's daughter."

I went to the boss to draw my roll,
He had it figgered out I was nine dollars in the hole.

I'll sell my outfit just as soon as I can,
I won't punch cattle for no damned man.

I'll sell my horse and I'll sell my saddle;
You can go to hell with your longhorn cattle.

Goin' back to town to draw my money,
Goin' back to town to see my honey.

With my knees in the saddle and my seat in the sky,
I'll quit punching cows in the sweet by-and-by.

Fare you well, old trail-boss, I don't wish you any harm,
I'm quittin' this business to go on the farm.

No more cow-puncher to sleep at my ease,
'Mid the crawlin' of the lice and the bitin' of the fleas.

　　Coma ti yi youpy, youpy yea, youpy yea,
　　Coma ti yi youpy, youpy yea.

*　*　*　*　*

It's round up your cavvy, and it's rope out your pack,*
And strap your old kak well fast on his back;

Your foot in the stirrup and your hand on the horn,
You're the best durned cowboy that ever was born;

You land in the saddle and give a loud yell,
For the longhorn cattle have got to take the hill.

You round up a bunch of dogies and take down the trail,
But the first thing you know you land in jail.

But the sheriff's an old puncher and he fixes your bail,
It's a durned poor country with a cowboy in jail.

So round up your foreman and hit him for your roll,
You're goin' to town and act a little bold.

You strap on your chaps, your spurs and your gun,
For you're going to town to have a little fun.

You ride a big bronc' that will buck and prance,
And you pull out your gun and make the tenderfoot dance.

You go into the gamblin' house looking kinda funny
For you got every pocket just chuck-full o' money.

You play cards with a gambler who's got a marked pack;
You walk back to the ranch with your saddle on your back.

Now I've punched cattle from Texas to Maine,
And I've known some cowboys by their right name.

No matter though whatever they claim,
You'll find every dirty cuss exactly the same.

* These stanzas sent in to "Fiddlin' Joe's Song Corral" in *Wild West Weekly* by a Mr. Long of the Canal Zone, who entitled them "Eleven Slash Eleven."

So, dig in your spurs and peel your eyes to heaven,
And never overlook a calf with Eleven Slash Eleven.

Chorus:

    Singing hi yi yippi, hi yippi yea,
    Singing hi yi yippi, yippi yea yea.

*   *   *   *   *

I went to the bar and called for a drink,*
The bartender said I was a gink.

Chorus:

    Tum-a-ti-yi-yippi-yippi-ya-ya,
    Tum-a-ti-yippi-yippi-ya.

He knew these words would likely cause a fight,
An' he went for his hip like a streak of light.

I beat him to the draw and hit him on the ear,
And down he went like an old beef steer.

Oh, the peckerwood's a-peckin' an' the children are a-cryin',
The old folks a-fightin' an' the hogs are a-dyin'.

I met her in the road but she wouldn't tell her name;
I thought, by gosh, what a fine-lookin' dame!

I'm a-goin' to the boss an' git my roll,
I'm a-goin' downtown an' take a little stroll.

I went up to the boss and we had a little chat,
I slapped him in the face with my big slouch hat.

* These stanzas sent in to "Fiddlin' Joe's Song Corral" in *Wild West Weekly* by F. B. Swank of Oklahoma, who entitled them "Ti-ya-yippi-yippi-ya."

[34]

Oh, the boss says to me, "I'll fire you,
Not only you, but the whole damn crew."

Oh, my roll's on my saddle an' my head's in the sky,
An' it's all day long on the old XY.

*   *   *   *   *

After we got through, we put them on the cars,*
And that was the last of the old Two Bars.

I hit the first train, it was the Cannon Ball,
I went rockin' home right early in the fall.

I hadn't been home but two days or three,
Till I put off my gal for to see.

"If you've made up your mind to quit the cowboy life,
I have fully decided to be your little wife."

Farewell, old Blue Dog, I wish you no harm,
I have quit the business to go on the farm.

Good-by, old Blue Dog, on you I could rely,
I shall always love you until the day I die.

Good-by, old Blue Dog, you've been a good friend,
Around the night herds on you I could depend.

With lightning in his eye and thunder in his heels,
He went spinning 'round like a hoop on a reel.

I'll sell my saddle and I'll buy me a plow,
And I'll swear, begod, I'll never rope another cow.

* These stanzas received from J. M. Grisby of Comanche, Texas.

[*Version 2*]

[*Version 3*]

NOTE.—This version was taken from the singing of John A. Lomax. It is in direct contrast, as regards expression and tempo, with the melodies usually sung to these words. Mr. Lomax knows of no other instance where this version has been reproduced.—E. N. W.

ti   yi   you - py   com - a   ti   yi   yea.

[*Version* 4]

Moderately, but with spirit   (♩=88)

Well, come a - long, boys, and lis - ten to my tale; I'll

tell you of my troub - les on the old Chis - holm trail.

REFRAIN

Com - a ti yi youp - y youp - y yea, youp - y yea! Com - a

ti   yi   youp - y   youp - y   yea!

CLEAR ROCK'S CHISHOLM TRAIL*

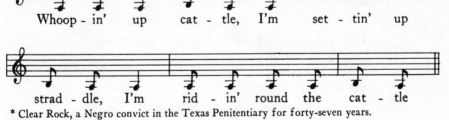

Briskly   (♩=96)

Whoop - in' up   cat - tle, I'm   set - tin' up

strad - dle, I'm rid - in' round the cat - tle

* Clear Rock, a Negro convict in the Texas Penitentiary for forty-seven years.

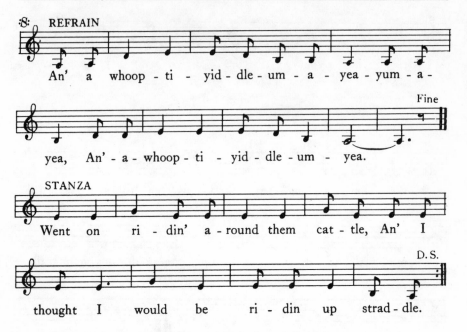

REFRAIN

An' a whoop - ti - yid - dle - um - a - yea - yum - a -

Fine

yea, An' - a - whoop - ti - yid - dle - um - yea.

STANZA

Went on ri - din' a - round them cat - tle, An' I

D. S.

thought I would be ri - din up strad - dle.

Whoopin' up cattle, I'm settin' up straddle,
I'm ridin' round the cattle,
    An'-a-whoop-ti-yiddle-um-a-yea-yum-a-yea,
    An'-a-whoop-ti-yiddle-um-yea.

Went on ridin' around them cattle,
An' I thought I would be ridin' up straddle,
    An'-a-whoop-ti-yiddle-um-a-yea-yum-a-yea,
    An'-a-whoop-ti-yiddle-um-yea.

Went out ridin' an' I got astraddle,
An' the mule throwed me right back up on the saddle.
    An'-a-whoop-ti-yiddle-um-a-yea-yum-a-yea,
    An'-a-whoop-ti-yiddle-um-yea.

Let me tell you about that Sill,
They throwed me right on the foot of the hill.

[38]

An'-a-whoop-ti-yiddle-um-a-yea-yum-a-yea,
An'-a-whoop-ti-yiddle-um-yea.

Hoss throwed me on a limb, I lay there a-poppin';
Come a little wind, an' down I come a-droppin'.
    An'-a-whoop-ti-yiddle-um-a-yea-yum-a-yea,
    An'-a-whoop-ti-yiddle-um-yea.

LEADBELLY'S CHISHOLM TRAIL*

When I was a cow-boy way out on de west-ern plains,
When I was a cow-boy way out on de west-ern plains, I
made a half a mil-lion, but it al-ways got a-way. Com-a
ti yi yip-py, ti yi yip-py, yip-py yea.

When I was a cowboy way out on de western plains,
When I was a cowboy way out on de western plains,
I made a half a million, but it always got away.
    Coma ti yi yippy, ti yi yippy, yippy yea.

* From *Negro Folksongs As Sung by Leadbelly* (New York: Macmillan Company, 1936).

[39]

When I was a cowboy, I could throw a lasso true,
When I was a cowboy, I could throw a lasso true,
I could rope a streak of lightnin' and ride upon it, too.
    Coma ti yi yippy, ti yi yippy, yippy yea.

When I was a cowboy way out on de western plains,
When I was a cowboy way out on de western plains,
I made a half a million, pullin' on de bridle reins.
    Coma ti yi yippy, ti yi yippy, yippy yea.

Come all you cowboys, don't you want to go?
Come all you cowboys, don't you want to go?
To see the rangers in the range of the buffalo?
    Coma ti yi yippy, ti yi yippy, yippy yea.

Feets in my stirrups, settin' deep down in my saddle,
Feets in my stirrups, settin' deep down in my saddle,
I'm the best cowboy that ever herded cattle.
    Coma ti yi yippy, ti yi yippy, yippy yea.

Went to my girl's house, she was settin' there alone;
Went to my girl's house, she was settin' there alone;
"I'm a po' western cowboy, great long ways from home."
    Coma ti yi yippy, ti yi yippy, yippy yea.

When he lef' his girl's house, she was rockin' in a rockin' cheer;
When he lef' his girl's house, she was rockin' in a rockin' cheer;
"A po' western cowboy—please doncha leave me here."
    Coma ti yi yippy, ti yi yippy, yippy yea.

Wo, de hardes' battle was ever on Bunker's Hill,
Wo, de hardes' battle was ever on Bunker's Hill,
When me an' a bunch o' cowboys run into Buffalo Bill.
    Coma ti yi yippy, ti yi yippy, yippy yea.

Wo, de hardes' battle was ever on de western plains,
Wo, de hardes' battle was ever on de western plains,
When me an' a bunch o' cowboys run into Jesse James.
　　Coma ti yi yippy, ti yi yippy, yippy yea.

If yo' house catch afire, an' dey ain' no water roun',
If yo' house catch afire, an' dey ain' no water roun',
Throw yo' jelly out de window, let de doggone shack burn down.
　　Coma ti yi yippy, ti yi yippy, yippy yea.

BOGGY CREEK

A cowboy version of "The Buffalo Skinners." From H. Knight,
Sterling City, Texas.

Come all you old-time cowboys and listen to my song,
But do not grow weary, I will not detain you long;
It is concerning some cowboys who did agree to go
To spend one summer so pleasantly on the trail to Mexico.

I found myself in Griffin* in the spring of '83.
A noted cow drover one morning came to me,
Saying, "How do you do, young fellow, how would you like to go
And spend one summer pleasantly out in New Mexico?"

I being out of employment, to the drover I did say:
"A-going out to New Mexico depends upon the pay;
If you'll pay me good wages and transportation to and fro,
I believe I will go with you out in New Mexico."

"Of course I'll pay good wages and transportation, too,
Provided you agree to stay with me the season through,

* Formerly a frontier army post near Albany, Texas.

But if you do grow homesick and back to Griffin go
I will not furnish you a horse to ride from the hills of Mexico."

With all of his flattering talk he enlisted quite a train—
Some ten or twelve in number, strong, able-bodied men;
Our trip it was a pleasant one, o'er the road we had to go
Until we crossed old Boggy Creek out in New Mexico.

And there our pleasures ended and troubles they began.
The first hard storm we had on us, oh, how the cattle ran!
While running through thorns and stickers we had but little show,
And the Indians watched to pick us off in the hills of New Mexico.

The summer season ended, the drover would not pay,
"The crowd was so extravagant and he was in debt that day."
But bankrupt law among cowboys, I tell you will not go,
So we left that drover's bones to bleach out in New Mexico.

And now we are crossed old Boggy Creek and homeward we are bound.
No more in that cursed country will we ever be found.
Go home to wives and sweethearts, tell others not to go
To the God-forsaken country they call New Mexico.

THE RAILROAD CORRAL

Smoothly, with quiet enthusiasm (♩. = 60)

Oh, we're up in the morn-ing ere break-ing of day, The
Oh, come take up your cin-ches, come shake out your reins; Come

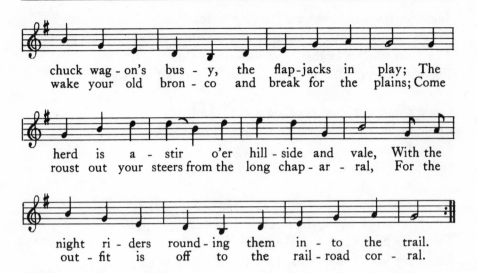

chuck wag - on's bus - y, the flap-jacks in play; The
wake your old bron - co and break for the plains; Come

herd is a - stir o'er hill - side and vale, With the
roust out your steers from the long chap - ar - ral, For the

night ri - ders round - ing them in - to the trail.
out - fit is off to the rail - road cor - ral.

Oh, we're up in the morning ere breaking of day,
The chuck wagon's busy, the flapjacks in play;
The herd is astir o'er hillside and vale,
With the night riders rounding them into the trail.

Oh, come take up your cinches, come shake out your reins;
Come wake your old bronco and break for the plains;
Come roust out your steers from the long chaparral,
For the outfit is off to the railroad corral.

The sun circles upward; the steers as they plod
Are pounding to powder the hot prairie sod;
And it seems as the dust makes you dizzy and sick
That we'll never reach noon and the cool, shady creek.

But tie up your kerchief and ply up your nag,
Come dry up your grumbles and try not to lag;
Come with your steers from the long chaparral,
For we're far on the road to the railroad corral.

[43]

The afternoon shadows are starting to lean,
When the chuck wagon sticks in the marshy ravine;
The herd scatters farther than vision can look,
For you can bet all true punchers will help out the cook.

Come shake out your rawhide and shake it up fair;
Come break your old bronco to take in his share;
Come from your steers in the long chaparral,
For 'tis all in the drive to the railroad corral.

But the longest of days must reach evening at last,
The hills all climbed, the creeks all passed;
The tired herd droops in the yellowing light;
Let them loaf if they will, for the railroad's in sight.

So flap up your holster and snap up your belt,
And strap up your saddle whose lap you have felt;
Good-by to the steers from the long chaparral,
For there's a town that's a trunk by the railroad corral.

THE COWBOY'S DREAM*

"Singing a herd of five thousand cattle to sleep was not an unusual undertaking in the days when the old Chisholm Trail was the great driveway between Texas ranches and the railroad shipping points in Kansas. Round and round the herd the riders would go.

" 'Say, my voice is getting mighty tired,' one of the riders would call out. 'Can't one of you fellers tune up and give me a rest?' An-

* The song was a favorite of the Texas evangelist, Rev. Abe Mulkey, when urging the cowboys to "come up to the mourners' bench" at the frontier camp meetings.

    I. P. Skinner of Athens, Texas, surmises: "Charley Hart of Carrolton, Miss., was under the necessity of living (incognito) on the Black Ranch in Clay County, Texas, soon after the war. He found surcease of sorrow in writing, and composed this song, I think in 1873, with the title 'Drift to That Sweet By-and-By.' "

other rider would take up the song, and the cattle would slumber the night through. One of the favorites is 'The Dim Narrow Trail,' or 'The Cowboy's Dream.' "

—*San Antonio Express* (May 30, 1909).

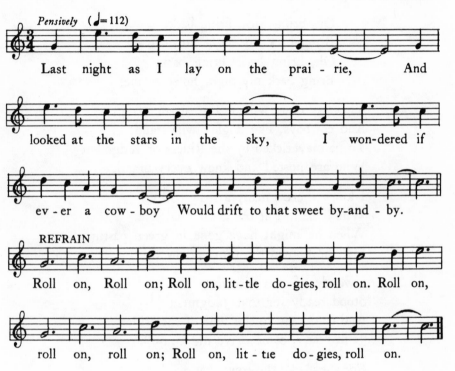

Last night as I lay on the prairie,
And looked at the stars in the sky,
I wondered if ever a cowboy
Would drift to that sweet by-and-by.

Roll on, roll on;
Roll on, little dogies, roll on.
Roll on, roll on, roll on;
Roll on, little dogies, roll on.

The road to that bright happy region
Is a dim narrow trail, so they say;
But the bright one that leads to perdition
Is posted and blazed all the way.

Oh, bring back, bring back,
Bring back my night horse to me.
Oh, bring back, bring back,
Bring back my night horse to me.

They say there will be a great round-up.
And cowboys, like dogies, will stand,
To be mavericked by the Riders of Judgment
Who are posted and know every brand.

I know there's many a stray cowboy
Who'll be lost at the great final sale,
When he might have gone in green pastures
Had he known the dim narrow trail.

I wonder if ever a cowboy
Stood ready for that Judgment Day
And could say to the Boss of the Riders,
"I'm ready, come drive me away."

For they, like the cows that are locoed,
Stampede at the sight of a hand,
Are dragged with a rope to the round-up,
Or get marked with some crooked man's brand.

And I'm scared that I'll be a stray yearling—*
A maverick, unbranded on high—

* A parallel stanza:

Oh, they say that the boss is a-coming,
To rope and to brand and earmark,
And will take all the cuts back to the Judgment
To be registered in his great Tally Book.

[46]

And get cut* in the bunch with the "rusties" †
When the Boss of the Riders goes by.

I often look upward and wonder
If the green fields will seem half so fair,
If any the wrong trail have taken
And will fail to be over there.

No maverick or slick will be tallied
In that great book of life in his home,
For he knows all the brands and the earmarks
That down through the ages have come.

But along with the strays and the sleepers,
The tailings must turn from the gate;
No road brand to give them admission,
But that awful sad cry, "Too late!"

For they tell of another big owner
Who's ne'er overstocked, so they say,
But who always makes room for the sinner
Who drifts from the strait narrow way.

They say he will never forget you,
That he knows every action and look;
So, for safety, you'd better get branded,
Have your name in his big Tally Book,

To be shipped to that bright mystic region,
Over there in the green pastures to lie,
And be led by the crystal still waters
To the home in the sweet by-and-by.

* By "cuts" the cowboy refers to cattle not suitable for driving up the trail, or not up to the standard of their class. "Maverick" and "slicks" are unbranded cattle. "Slicks" are young cattle lightly branded by thieves who plan to come back later and steal them.
† Underdeveloped, and therefore not acceptable, cattle; "sorry dogies."

[*Version 2*]

Pensively (♪=112)

Last night as I lay on the prai - rie, And looked at the stars in the sky, I won-dered if ev-er a cow - boy Would drift to that sweet by - and - by.

REFRAIN

Roll on, roll on; Roll on, lit-tle do-gies, roll on. Roll on, roll on, roll on; Roll on, lit - tle do-gies, roll on.

THE DYING COWBOY*

Slowly, with deep melancholy (♩=48)

"Oh, bur - y me not on the lone prai - rie." These
He had wailed in pain till o'er his brow Death's

words came low and mourn-ful-ly From the pal -lid lips of a
shad-ows fast were gath-'ring now; He thought of his home and his

* Amalgamated from thirty-six separate sources.

[48]

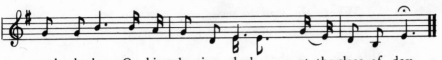

youth who lay   On his   dy - ing   bed   at the close of   day.
loved ones nigh   As the   cow-boys gath - ered   to   see   him die.

"Oh, bury me not on the lone prairie."
These words came low and mournfully
From the pallid lips of a youth who lay
On his dying bed at the close of day.

He had wailed in pain till o'er his brow
Death's shadows fast were gathering now;
He thought of his home and his loved ones nigh
As the cowboys gathered to see him die.

"Oh, bury me not on the lone prairie
Where the wild coyotes will howl o'er me,
In a narrow grave just six by three.
Oh, bury me not on the lone prairie."

"In fancy I listen to the well known words
Of the free, wild winds and the song of the birds;
I think of home and the cottage in the bower
And the scenes I loved in my childhood's hour.

"It matters not, I've oft been told,
Where the body lies when the heart grows cold;
Yet grant, oh, grant this wish to me:
Oh, bury me not on the lone prairie.

"Oh, then bury me not on the lone prairie,*
In a narrow grave six foot by three,

* The varying "choruses," or refrains, sung to the same melody, are printed to illustrate
the results of different composers of the song, not with pen and paper at hand, but evolved,
perhaps, as a cowboy rode alone over the prairie. We may read them now as another example
of the survival of the fittest.

Where the buffalo paws o'er a prairie sea.
Oh, bury me not on the lone prairie.

"I've always wished to be laid when I died
In the little churchyard on the green hillside;
By my father's grave there let mine be,
And bury me not on the lone prairie.

"Let my death slumber be where my mother's prayer
And a sister's tear will mingle there,
Where my friends can come and weep o'er me;
Oh, bury me not on the lone prairie.

"Oh, bury me not on the lone prairie
In a narrow grave just six by three,
Where the buzzard waits and the wind blows free;
Then bury me not on the lone prairie.

"There is another whose tears may be shed
For one who lies on a prairie bed;
It pained me then and it pains me now—
She has curled these locks, she has kissed this brow.

"These locks she has curled, shall the rattlesnake kiss?
This brow she has kissed, shall the cold grave press?
For the sake of the loved ones that will weep for me,
Oh, bury me not on the lone prairie.

"Oh, bury me not on the lone prairie
Where the wild coyotes will howl o'er me,
Where the buzzards sail and the wind goes free.
Oh, bury me not on the lone prairie.

"Oh, bury me not—" And his voice failed there.
But we took no heed of his dying prayer;
In a narrow grave just six by three
We buried him there on the lone prairie.

Where the dewdrops glow and the butterflies rest,
And the flowers bloom o'er the prairie's crest;
Where the wild coyote and winds sport free
On a wet saddle blanket lay a cowboy-ee.

"Oh, bury me not on the lone prairie
Where the wild coyotes will howl o'er me,
Where the rattlesnakes hiss and the crow flies free.
Oh, bury me not on the lone prairie."

Oh, we buried him there on the lone prairie
Where the wild rose blooms and the wind blows free;
Oh, his pale young face nevermore to see—
For we buried him there on the lone prairie.

Yes, we buried him there on the lone prairie.
Where the owl all night hoots mournfully,
And the blizzard beats and the winds blow free
O'er his lowly grave on the lone prairie.

And the cowboys now as they roam the plain—
For they marked the spot where his bones were lain—
Fling a handful of roses o'er his grave,
With a prayer to Him who his soul will save.

"Oh, bury me not on the lone prairie
Where the wolves can howl and growl o'er me;
Fling a handful of roses o'er my grave
With a prayer to Him who my soul will save."

DOGIE SONG

The cow-bosses are good-hearted chunks,
Some short, some heavy, more long;

But don't matter what he looks like,
They all sing the same old song.

On the plains, in the mountains, in the valleys,
In the south where the days are long,
The bosses are different fellows;
Still they sing the same old song.

"Sift along, boys, don't ride so slow;
Haven't got much time but a long round to go.
Quirt him in the shoulders and rake him down the hip;
I've cut you toppy mounts,* boys—now pair off and rip.
Bunch the herd at the old meet,
Then beat 'em on the tail;
Whip 'em up and down the sides
And hit the shortest trail."

THE TRAIL TO MEXICO†

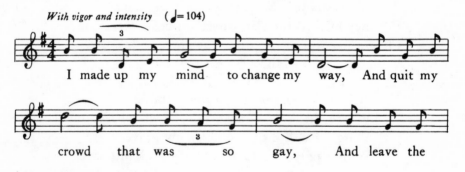

With vigor and intensity (♩ = 104)

I made up my mind to change my way, And quit my

crowd that was so gay, And leave the

* Most reliable cow horses.
† J. E. McCauley of Seymour, Texas, in sending in one of the thirteen versions of this song, wrote:
"I don't know how this come to be made up as I've knew it a long time and don't remember when I first heard it nor how long I have knew it."
The tune is from the Cowboy Band, San Angelo, Texas. It seems a modernized oldster.

[52]

girl who'd prom-ised me her hand, And head down

south of the Ri - o Grande, And when I

held her in my arms I knew she had ten thou-sand

charms; She prom - ised then she would be

true And wait for me as lov-ers do.

REFRAIN

I'm go - ing back to Mex - i - co where the long-horn.

steers and cac-tus grow Where the girls are good day af - ter

day and do not live just for your pay.

[53]

I made up my mind to change my way,
And quit my crowd that was so gay,
And leave the girl who'd promised me her hand,
And head down south of the Rio Grande.
And when I held her in my arms
I knew she had ten thousand charms;
She promised then she would be true
And wait for me as lovers do.

Refrain:

    I'm going back to Mexico,
    Where the longhorn steers and cactus grow,
    Where the girls are good day after day
    And do not live just for your pay.

It was in the year of eighty-three
That A. J. Stinson hired me.
He says, "Young feller, I want you to go
And drive this herd to Mexico."
And when I held her in my arms
I thought she had ten thousand charms;
Her kisses were soft, her lips were sweet,
Saying, "We'll get married next time we meet."

The first horse they gave me was an old black
With two big set-fasts on his back;
I padded him with gunny-sacks and my bedding all;
He went up, then down, and I got a fall.
The next they gave me was an old gray—
I'll remember him till my dying day;
And if I had to swear to the fact,
I believe he was worse off than the black.

Oh, it was early in the year
When I went on trail to drive the steer;

I stood my guard through sleet and snow
While on the trail to Mexico.
Oh, it was a long and toilsome go
As our herd rolled on to Mexico;
With laughter light and the cowboy's song
To Mexico we rolled along.

When I arrived in Mexico
I wanted to see my love but could not go;
So I wrote a letter, a letter to my dear,
But not a word from her could I hear.
When I arrived at my native home
I called for the darling of my own;
They said she had married a richer life,
Therefore, wild cowboy, seek another wife.

Oh, the girl is married I do adore,
And I cannot stay at home any more;
I'll cut my way to a foreign land
Or I'll go back West to my cowboy band.
I'll go back to the Western land,
I'll hunt up my old cowboy band—
Where the girls are few and the boys are true
And a false-hearted love I never knew.

"O Buddie, O Buddie, please stay at home,
Don't be forever on the roam.
There is many a girl more true than I,
So pray don't go where the bullets fly."
"It's curse your gold and your silver too,
Confound a girl that won't prove true;
I'll travel West where the bullets fly,
I'll stay on the trail till the day I die."

Refrain:

I'm going back to Mexico,
Where the longhorn steers and the cactus grow,
Where the girls are good day after day
And do not live just for your pay.

[*Version 2*]

NOTE.—This version is quoted from Newton Gaines, "Some Characteristics of Cowboy Songs," *Publications of the Texas Folk-Lore Society*, VII, 151.

THE TEXAS SONG*

I'm going to leave old Texas now,
For they've got no use for the longhorn cow;
They've plowed and fenced my cattle range,
And the people there are all so strange.
    Whoo-a-whoo-a—

I'll take my horse, I'll take my rope,
And hit the trail upon a lope,
Say "Adiós" to the Alamo,
And turn my head to Mexico.

I'll make my home on the wide, wide range.
The people there are not so strange,
The hard, hard ground will be my bed,
And the saddle seat will hold my head.

And when I waken from my dreams,
I'll eat my bread and my sardines,
And when my ride on earth is done,
I'll take my turn with the holy one.

I'll tell St. Peter that I know
A cowboy's soul ain't white as snow,
But in that far-off cattle land
He sometimes acted like a man.

* Four stanzas of one version, showing the influence of present-day conditions on the sentiment of the song, were sent in by John A. Erhard of Dallas, Texas, who heard them among the cowboys on the plains of Oklahoma. This song is sung to the same tune as the second version of "The Trail to Mexico."

THE GAL I LEFT BEHIND ME

A Cowboy Version

I struck the trail in seventy-nine,
The herd strung out behind me;
As I jogged along my mind ran back
To the gal I left behind me.
    That sweet little gal, that true little gal,
    The gal I left behind me!

That sweet little gal, that true little gal,
The gal I left behind me!

If ever I get off the trail
And the Indians they don't find me,
I'll make my way straight back again
To the gal I left behind me.
    That sweet little gal, that true little gal,
    The gal I left behind me!

When the night was dark and the cattle run,
With the boys coming on behind me,
My mind run back at my pistol's crack
To the gal I left behind me.
    That sweet little gal, that true little gal,
    The gal I left behind me!

The wind did blow, the rain did flow,
The hail did fall and blind me;
I thought of that gal, that sweet little gal,
That gal I'd left behind me!
    That sweet little gal, that true little gal,
    The gal I left behind me!

She wrote ahead to the place I said,
I was always glad to find it.
She says, "I'm true, when you get through
Ride back and you will find me."
    That sweet little gal, that true little gal,
    The gal I left behind me!

When we sold out I took the train,
I knew where I would find her;

When I got back we had a smack,
And that was no gol-darned liar.
That sweet little gal, that true little gal,
The gal I left behind me!

NIGHT–HERDING SONG

BY HARRY STEPHENS*

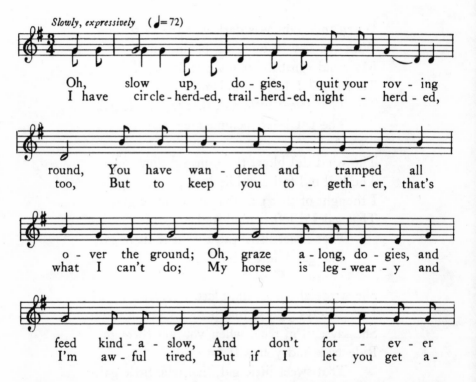

Slowly, expressively ($\quad$=72)

Oh, slow up, do - gies, quit your rov - ing
I have cir cle - herd-ed, trail - herd-ed, night - herd - ed,

round, You have wan - dered and tramped all
too, But to keep you to - geth - er, that's

o - ver the ground; Oh, graze a - long, do - gies, and
what I can't do; My horse is leg - wear - y and

feed kind - a - slow, And don't for - ev - er
I'm aw - ful tired, But if I let you get a -

* "I made up this song while I was night-herding for the Wylie Company, Yellowstone
Park." One morning in the spring of 1909 Harry leaned over the gate of my home on
the campus of the Agricultural and Mechanical College of Texas and called to me:
"Professor, I've come to say good-by. Grass is a-rising, and I've got to move on." Though
afterwards he has often written to me, I have never seen him since. He has left behind him
a beautiful "Night-Herding Song."

be   on   the   go   Oh,
way I'm sure to   get   fired   Bunch -

move   slow,   do - gies, move   slow.
up,   lit - tle   do - gies, bunch   up.

Oh, slow up, dogies, quit your roving round,
You have wandered and tramped all over the ground;
Oh, graze along, dogies, and feed kinda slow,
And don't forever be on the go—
Oh, move slow, dogies, move slow.

I have circle-herded, trail-herded, night-herded, too,
But to keep you together, that's what I can't do;
My horse is leg-weary and I'm awful tired,
But if I let you get away I'm sure to get fired—
Bunch up, little dogies, bunch up.

Oh, say, little dogies, when you goin' to lay down
And quit this forever siftin' around?
My limbs are weary, my seat is sore;
Oh, lay down, dogies, like you've laid before—
Lay down, little dogies, lay down.

Oh, lay still, dogies, since you have laid down,
Stretch away out on the big open ground;
Snore loud, little dogies, and drown the wild sound
That will all go away when the day rolls round—
Lay still, little dogies, lay still.

[61]

II

THE ROUND-UP

GITTIN'-UP HOLLERS

Wake up, snakes, and bite a biscuit.

* * * * *

Rise and shine, and give God the glory.

* * * * *

Roll out there, fellers, and hear the little birdies sing their praises to God.

* * * * *

Grub pile! Come a-runnin', boys!

* * * * *

Hungry enough to eat a saddle blanket.

TOAST

Up to my lips and over my gums;
Look out, guts, here she comes!

COWBOY GRACES

Eat your meat and save the skin;
Turn up your plates and let's begin.

* * * * *

Thar's the bread, thar's the meat;
Now, by Joe, let's eat.

* * * * *

Yes, we'll come to the table
As long as we're able,
And eat every damn thing
That looks sorta stable.

COWBOY TALKS TO A PITCHING HORSE

Come on, jughead! Get goin', cayuse!

* * * * *

Pick up your feet, sparkplug!

* * * * *

Do your stuff, brown!

* * * * *

Fan him! Spur him on the hairy side! Ride 'em, cowboy!

* * * * *

I'm a wild wolf, and my tail is draggin' the ground.

* * * * *

Born on the Colorado,
Sired by an alligator,
I'm a bold, bad man from Cripple Creek, Colorado.
When I get back, there'll be a tornado.
Git higher! Git higher!
The higher you git is too low for me!

* * * * *

Raised in a canebrake, and suckled by a lion,
Head like a bombshell and teeth made out of iron;
Nine rows of jaw teeth and holes punched for more.
I come from ourang-a-tang where the bullfrogs jump from north to south.

DIAMOND JOE*

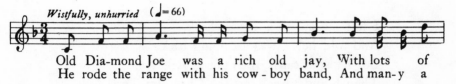

Old Dia-mond Joe was a rich old jay, With lots of
He rode the range with his cow-boy band, And man-y a

REFRAIN

cow-boys in his pay; Roll on, boys, roll, don't you roll so
mav'-rick got his brand.

slow, Roll on, boys, roll, don't you roll so slow.

Old Diamond Joe was a rich old jay,
With lots of cowboys in his pay;
He rode the range with his cowboy band,
And many a mav'rick got his brand.

Refrain:

Roll on, boys, roll, don't you roll so slow;
Roll on, boys, roll, don't you roll so slow;

I am a pore cowboy, I've got no home;
I'm here today and tomorrow I'm gone;

* J. D. Dillingham, Austin, Texas, who contributed this song, says that it was popular in central Texas sixty years ago. Diamond Joe wore big diamond buttons on his vest.

[65]

I've got no folks, I'm forced to roam;
Where I hang my hat is home sweet home.

If I was as rich as Diamond Joe,
I'd work today and I'd work no mo';
For they work me so hard and they pay so slow
I don't give a durn if I work or no.

I left my gal in a Texas shack,
And told her I was a-coming back;
But I lost at cards, then got in jail,
Then found myself on the Chisholm Trail.

I'll stay with the herd till they reach the end,
Then I'll draw my time and blow it in;
Just one more spree and one more jail,
Then I'll head right back on the lonesome trail.

I'll cross old Red at the Texas line,
And head straight back to that gal of mine;
I'll sit in the shade and sing my song,
And watch the herds as they move along.

When my summons come to leave this world,
I'll say good-by to my little girl;
I'll fold my hands when I have to go
And say farewell to Diamond Joe.

Refrain:

Roll on, boys, roll, don't you roll so slow;
Roll on, boys, roll, don't you roll so slow.
Ki—oo—e, I—oo—oh,
You roll like cattle never rolled before.

[66]

THE COWBOY

With a gentle, swinging pace ($\quad = 56$)

All day on the prai - rie in the sad - dle I ride, Not
I wash in a pool and I wipe on a sack; I

e - ven a dog, boys, to trot by my side; My
car - ry my ward - robe all on my back; For

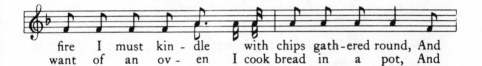

fire I must kin - dle with chips gath - ered round, And
want of an ov - en I cook bread in a pot, And

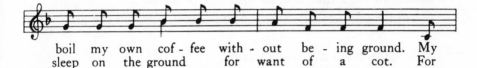

boil my own cof - fee with - out be - ing ground. My
sleep on the ground for want of a cot. For

fire I must kin - dle with chips gath - ered round, And
want of an ov - en I cook bread in a pot, And

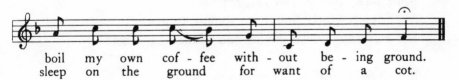

boil my own cof - fee with - out be - ing ground.
sleep on the ground for want of a cot.

All day on the prairie in the saddle I ride,
Not even a dog, boys, to trot by my side;
My fire I must kindle with chips gathered round,
And boil my own coffee without being ground.

[67]

My fire I must kindle with chips gathered round,
And boil my own coffee without being ground.

I wash in a pool and I wipe on a sack;
I carry my wardrobe all on my back;
For want of an oven I cook bread in a pot,*
And sleep on the ground for want of a cot.

My ceiling is the sky, my floor is the grass;
My music is the lowing of the herds as they pass;
My books are the brooks; my sermons, the stones;
My parson is a wolf on his pulpit of bones.

And then, if my cooking is not very complete,
You can't blame me for wanting to eat.
But show me a man that sleeps more profound
Than the big puncher-boy who stretches himself on the ground.

My books teach me ever consistence to prize;
My sermons, that small things I should not despise;
My parson remarks from his pulpit of bones
That Fortune favors those who look out for their own.

And then between me and love lies a gulf very wide;
Some lucky fellow may call her his bride.
My friends gently hint I am coming to grief,
But men must make money and women have beef.

But Cupid is always a friend to the bold,
And the best of his arrows are pointed with gold.
Society bans me so savage and dodge
That the Masons would ball me out of their lodge.

* In singing, repeat last two lines of each four-line stanza.

[68]

If I had hair on my chin, I might pass for the goat
That bore all the sins in the ages remote;
But why it is, I can never understand,
For each of the patriarchs owned a big brand.

Abraham emigrated in search of a range,
As water was scarce he wanted a change;
Old Isaac owned cattle in charge of Esau,
And Jacob punched cows for his father-in-law.

He started in business way down at bedrock,
And made quite a streak at handling stock;
Then David went from night-herding to using a sling;
And, winning the battle, he became a great king.
Then the shepherds, while herding the sheep on a hill,
Got a message from heaven of peace and good will.

[*Version 2*]

All day long on the prai-rie I ride, Not
e-ven a hound dog to trot by my side; My
fire it is kin-dled with chips gath-ered round; I
boil my own cof-fee with-out be-ing ground, I

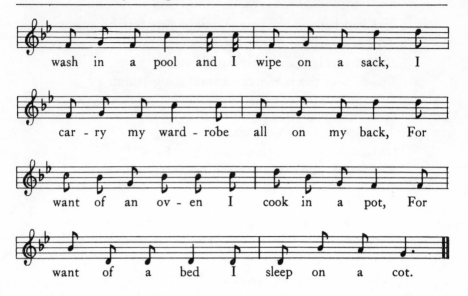

wash in a pool and I wipe on a sack, I

car-ry my ward-robe all on my back, For

want of an ov-en I cook in a pot, For

want of a bed I sleep on a cot.

A COW CAMP ON THE RANGE*

Oh, the prairie dogs are screaming
And the birds begin to sing.
See the heel fly chase the heifer, boys—
'Tis the first-class sign of spring.
The elm wood is a-budding
And the earth is turning green.
See the pretty things of nature
That make life a pleasant dream.

I'm just living through the winter
To enjoy the coming change,
For there is no place so homelike
As a cow camp on the range.
The boss is smiling radiant,
Radiant as the setting sun,

* Given to me by J. H. Strickland of Idaho, who had it from Jeff Hamilton of Virginia.

And we know he's stealing plenty,
For he ain't a-cussin' none.

The cook is at the chuck box
Whistling "Heifers in the Green,"
Making baking powder biscuits, boys,
While the pot is biling beans.
The boys are hobbling horses,
Then they untie their bedding
And unroll it on a run,
For they are in a monstrous hurry,
For the supper's getting done.

"Here's your bloody wolf bait,"
Cries the cook's familiar voice,
As he climbs a wagon wheel
To watch the boys rejoice.
Then all thoughts turn from reverence
To a plate of beef and beans,
As we graze on beef and biscuit,
Like yearlings on the range.

To the dickens with your city,
Where they herd the brainless brats
On a range so badly crowded
There ain't room to cuss the cat.
This life is not so sumptious,
I'm not longing for a change,
For there is no place so homelike
As a cow camp on the range.

TOP HAND*

While you're all so frisky I'll sing a little song—
Think a little horn of whisky will help the thing along.
It's all about the Top Hand, when he busted flat
Bummin' round the town, in his Mexican hat.
He's laid up all winter, and his pocketbook is flat,
His clothes are all tatters, but he don't mind that.

See him in town with a crowd that he knows,
Rollin' cigarettes and smokin' through his nose.
First thing he tells you, he owns a certain brand—
Leads you to think he is a daisy hand;
Next thing he tells you 'bout his trip up the trail,
All the way to Kansas, to finish out his tale.

Put him on a hoss, he's a handy hand to work;
Put him in the brandin'-pen, he's dead sure to shirk.
With his natural leaf tobacco in the pockets of his vest
He'll tell you his California pants are the best.
He's handled lots of cattle, hasn't any fears,
Can draw his sixty dollars for the balance of his years.

Put him on herd, he's a-cussin' all day;
Anything he tries, it's sure to get away.
When you have a round-up, he tells it all about
He's goin' to do the cuttin' an' you can't keep him out.
If anything goes wrong, he lays it on the screws,
Says the lazy devils were tryin' to take a snooze.

When he meets a greener he ain't afraid to rig,
Stands him on a chuck box and makes him dance a jig—
Waves a loaded cutter, makes him sing and shout—
He's a regular Ben Thompson when the boss ain't about.

* The story of a bogus top hand. The "top hand" is the most skillful cowboy.

When the boss ain't about he leaves his leggins in camp,
He swears a man who wears them is worse than a tramp.

Says he's not carin' for the wages he earns,
For Dad's rich in Texas—got wagonloads to burn;
But when he goes to town, he's sure to take it in,
He's always been dreaded wherever he's been.
He rides a fancy horse, he's a favorite man,
Can get more credit than a common waddie can.

When you ship the cattle he's bound to go along
To keep the boss from drinking and see that nothing's wrong.
Wherever he goes, catch on to his name,
He likes to be called with a handle to his name.
He's always primping with a pocket looking-glass,
From the top to the bottom he's a bold Jackass.

PINTO*

A notorious Texas desperado, murdered in El Paso, Texas.

I am a vaquero by trade;
To handle my rope I'm not afraid.
I lass' an *otero*† by the two horns,
Throw down the biggest that ever was born.
Whoa! Whoa! Whoa! Pinto, whoa!

My name to you I will not tell;
For what's the use, you know me so well.
The girls all love me, and cry
When I leave them to join the roder.
Whoa! Whoa! Whoa! Pinto, whoa!

* Sent to me by D. P. Lamereaux, Princeton, Calif.
† A steer as big as a mountain.

[73]

I am a vaquero, and here I reside;
Show me the bronco I cannot ride.
They say old Pinto with one split ear
Is the hardest jumping bronco on the roder.
Whoa! Whoa! Whoa! Pinto, whoa!

There strayed to our camp an iron-gray colt;
The boys were all 'fraid him, so on him I bolt.
You bet I stayed with him till cheer after cheer—
"He's the bronco twister that's on the roder."
Whoa! Whoa! Whoa! Pinto, whoa!

My story is ended, old Pinto is dead;
I'll go up to Laredo and paint the town red.
I'll go up to Laredo and set up the beer
To all the cowboys that's on the roder.
Whoa! Whoa! Whoa! Pinto, whoa!

WHEN THE WORK'S ALL DONE THIS FALL*

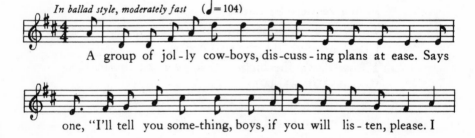

In ballad style, moderately fast ($\quarternote$=104)

A group of jol-ly cow-boys, dis-cuss-ing plans at ease. Says

one, "I'll tell you some-thing, boys, if you will lis-ten, please. I

* D. J. O'Malley of the S.A. ranch, near Miles City, Montana, claims to be the author
of this song. On October 6, 1893, the *Stock Growers Journal* of Miles City published
the words with the caption, "After the Round-up," giving the author as D. J. White.
Another informant, Lee Lytton of Fort Worth, Texas, supplied a full text with the remark
that the song originated on the Spotted Wood Trail, 140 miles out of Deadwood, Wyoming,
and was based on an actual happening. The words sometimes are sung to the tune of "After
the Ball Is Over."

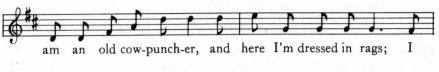

am an old cow-punch-er, and here I'm dressed in rags; I

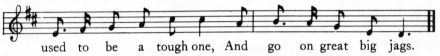

used to be a tough one, And go on great big jags.

A group of jolly cowboys, discussing plans at ease.
Says one, "I'll tell you something, boys, if you will listen, please.
I am an old cow-puncher and here I'm dressed in rags,
I used to be a tough one and go on great big jags.

Chorus:

"After the round-ups are over and after the shipping is done,
I am going right straight home, boys, ere all my money is gone.
I have changed my ways, boys, no more will I fall;
And I am going home, boys, when the work is done this fall.

"But I've got a home, boys, a good one, you all know,
Although I have not seen it since long, long ago.
I'm going back to Dixie once more to see them all;
I'm going back to see my mother when the work's all done this fall.

"When I left home, boys, my mother for me cried,
Begged me not to go, boys, for me she would have died;
My mother's heart is breaking, breaking for me, that's all,
And with God's help I'll see her when the work's all done this fall."

That very night this cowboy went out to stand his guard;
The night was dark and cloudy and storming very hard;
The cattle they got frightened and rushed in wild stampede;
The cowboy tried to head them, riding at full speed.

[75]

While riding in the darkness so loudly did he shout,
Trying his best to head them and turn the herd about,
His saddle horse did stumble and on him did fall,
The poor boy won't see his mother when the work's all done this fall.

His body was so mangled the boys all thought him dead,
They picked him up so gently and laid him on a bed;
He opened wide his blue eyes and looking all around
He motioned to his comrades to sit near him on the ground.

"Boys, send Mother my wages, the wages I have earned,
For I'm afraid, boys, my last steer I have turned.
I'm going to a new range, I hear my Master's call,
And I'll not see my mother when the work's all done this fall.

"Fred, you take my saddle; George, you take my bed;
Bill, you take my pistol after I am dead;
And think of me kindly when you look upon them all,
For I'll not see my mother when work is done this fall."

Poor Charlie was buried at sunrise, no tombstone at his head,
Nothing but a little board; and this is what it said:
"Charlie died at daybreak, he died from a fall,
And he'll not see his mother when the work's all done this fall."

THE DRIFTER*

    Oh, I am a rusty cowboy,
    And Pumpkin Creek is where I roam,
    But now I've got to leave it,
    And hunt another home;

* Written by a cowboy named Dave Hughes, known as *Old Arkansaw*. Written out by Miss Goldie Fowler, whose parents have kept it in a scrapbook for years. Sent by Professor C. K. Hoyt.

For the grangers are among us,
And I have got to go,
To some far distant country
Where I can have a show.

Refrain:

> Then fare you well, old Pumpkin Creek.
> I can no longer stay.
> Hard times and the granger
> Have driven me away;
> Hard times and the granger
> Have caused me to roam,
> For I am a rusty cowboy
> And Pumpkin Creek's my home.

Oh, it has not been longer
Than two years or more,
We'd saddle up our broncos
And rounding up we'd go.
We'd lasso the mavericks
And brand them one by one,
Till the granger got among us
And stopped that kind of fun.

But we always got good wages
For this kind of work,
Till the granger got among us
And took up all the dirt;
But now we've got to leave them,
Nor do we wish them harm,
For God will bless the granger
On the newly made farm.

I always liked the grangers,
For they are a jolly set,

[77]

They give us lots of chances,
And I'd stay with them yet;
But my pocketbook is empty
And I have got to go,
To some other country
Where I can have a show.

THE ZEBRA DUN*

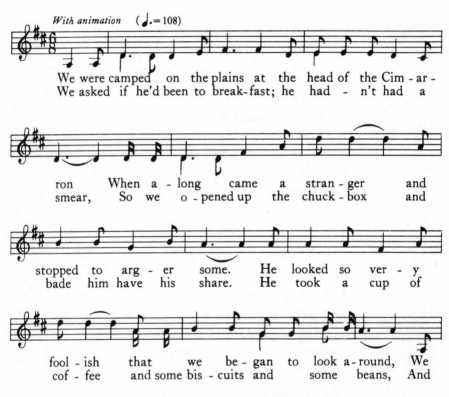

With animation ($\dotted\ =108$)

We were camped on the plains at the head of the Cim - ar -
We asked if he'd been to break-fast; he had - n't had a

ron When a - long came a stran - ger and
smear, So we o - pened up the chuck - box and

stopped to arg - er some. He looked so ver - y
bade him have his share. He took a cup of

fool - ish that we be - gan to look a - round, We
cof - fee and some bis - cuits and some beans, And

* This song is said to have been composed by Jake, the Negro camp cook for a ranch on
the Pecos River belonging to George W. Evans and John Z. Means. It was first sung to
me by W. Bogel, a student in the Agricultural and Mechanical College of Texas.

thought he was a green - horn that had just 'scaped from town.
then be - gan to talk and tell a-bout for - eign kings and queens.

We were camped on the plains at the head of the Cimarron
When along came a stranger and stopped to arger some.
He looked so very foolish that we began to look around,
We thought he was a greenhorn that had just 'scaped from town.

We asked if he had been to breakfast; he hadn't had a smear,
So we opened up the chuck-box and bade him have his share.
He took a cup of coffee and some biscuits and some beans,
And then began to talk and tell about foreign kings and queens,

About the Spanish War and fighting on the seas
With guns as big as steers and ramrods big as trees;
And about old Paul Jones, a mean-fighting son of a gun,
Who was the grittiest cuss that ever pulled a gun.

When he had finished eating and put his plate away,
He rolled a cigarette and asked the time of day;
He talked about the weather, the election, and such things,
But didn't seem to know much about the workings on the range;

Such an educated feller his thoughts just came in herds,
He astonished all them cowboys with them jaw-breaking words.
He just kept on talking till he made the boys all sick,
And they began to look around just how to play a trick.

He said he had lost his job upon the Santa Fe
And was going across the plains to strike the 7-D.
He didn't say how come it, some trouble with the boss,
But said he'd like to borrow a nice fat saddle hoss.

[79]

This tickled all the boys to death, they laughed way down in their
    sleeves—
"We will lend you a horse just as fresh and fat as you please."
Shorty grabbed a lariat and roped the Zebra Dun
And turned him over to the stranger and waited for the fun.

Old Dunny was a rocky outlaw that had grown so awful wild
That he could paw the white out of the moon every jump for a
    mile.
Old Dunny stood right still—as if he didn't know—
Until he was saddled and ready for to go.

When the stranger hit the saddle, old Dunny quit the earth
And traveled right straight up for all that he was worth.
Old Dunny, standing on his head, a-having wall-eyed fits,
His hind feet in the stirrups, his front ones in the bits.

We could see the tops of the mountains under Dunny every jump,
But the stranger he was growed there just like the camel's hump;
The stranger sat upon him and curled his black mustache
Just like a summer boarder waiting for his hash.

He thumped him in the shoulders and spurred him when he whirled,
To show them flunky punchers that he was the wolf of the world.
When the stranger had dismounted once more upon the ground,
We knew he was a thoroughbred and not a gent from town;

The boss, who was standing round watching of the show,
Walked right up to the stranger and told him he needn't go—
"If you can use the lasso like you rode old Zebra Dun,
You are the man I've been looking for ever since the year One."

Oh, he could twirl the lariat and he didn't do it slow,
He could catch them forefeet nine out of ten for any kind of dough,
And when the herd stampeded he was always on the spot
And set them to milling, like the stirrings of a pot.

There's one thing and a shore thing I've learned since I've been born,
That every educated feller ain't a plumb greenhorn.

[*Version* 2]

CHARLIE RUTLEDGE

This song was first published in the *Stock Growers Journal*, Miles City, Montana, July 11, 1891, signed D. J. White (D. J. O'Malley). Sung to the tune of "Lake Pontchartrain." The song was current in Texas, where I first found it.

Another good cow-puncher has gone to meet his fate,
I hope he'll find a resting place within the golden gate.
Another place is vacant on the ranch of the X I T,
'Twill be hard to find another that's liked as well as he.

The first that died was Kid White, a man both tough and brave,
While Charlie Rutledge makes the third to be sent to his grave,
Caused by a cow-horse falling while running after stock;
'Twas on the spring round-up—a place where death men mock.

He went forward one morning on a circle through the hills,
He was gay and full of glee, and free from earthly ills;
But when it came to finish up the work on which he went,
Nothing came back from him; for his time on earth was spent.

'Twas as he rode the round-up, an X I T turned back to the herd;
Poor Charlie shoved him in again, his cutting horse he spurred;
Another turned; at that moment his horse the creature spied
And turned and fell with him, and, beneath, poor Charlie died.

His relations in Texas his face nevermore will see,
But I hope he will meet his loved ones beyond in eternity.
I hope he will meet his parents, will meet them face to face,
And that they will grasp him by the right hand at the shining throne
    of grace.

THE COWBOY AT WORK

You may call the cowboy horned and think him hard to tame,
You may heap vile epithets upon his head;
But to know him is to like him, notwithstanding his hard name,
For he will divide with you his beef and bread.

If you see him on his pony as he scampers o'er the plain,
You would think him wild and woolly, to be sure;
But his heart is warm and tender when he sees a friend in need,
Though his education is but to endure.

When the storm breaks in its fury and the lightning's vivid flash
Makes you thank the Lord for shelter and for bed,
Then it is he mounts his pony and away you see him dash,
No protection but the hat upon his head.

Such is life upon a cow ranch, and the half was never told;
But you never find a kinder-hearted set
Than the cattleman at home, be he either young or old,
He's a "daisy from away back," don't forget.

When you fail to find a pony or a cow that's gone astray,
Be that cow or pony wild or be it tame,
The cowboy, like the drummer—and the bedbug, too, they say—
Brings him to you, for he gets there just the same.

BRONC PEELER'S SONG*

I've been upon the prairie,
I've been upon the plain,
I've never rid a steamboat,

* Sent by W. P. MacLaughlin, from Clovis, N. M., on March 15, 1911. He explained that this song was written down from the singing of a middle-aged cow-poke on the round-up.

Nor a double-cinched-up train.
But I've driv my eight-up to wagon
That were locked three in a row,
And that through blindin' sand storms,
And all kinds of wind and snow.

Chorus:

    Good-by, Liza, poor gal,
    Good-by, Liza Jane,
    Good-by, Liza, poor gal,
    She died on the plain.

There never was a place I've been
Had any kind of wood.
We burn the roots of bar-grass
And think it's very good.
I've never tasted home bread,
Nor cakes, nor muss like that;
But I know fried dough and beef
Pulled from red-hot tallow fat.

I hate to see the wire fence
A-closin' up the range;
And all this fillin' in the trail
With people that is strange.
We fellers don't know how to plow,
Nor reap the golden grain;
But to round up steers and brand the cows
To us was allus plain.

So when this blasted country
Is all closed in with wire,
And all the top, with crab grass,
Is burnin' in Sol's fire,

[84]

I hope the settlers will be glad
When rain hits the land.
And all us cowdogs are in hell
With a set* joined hand in hand.

WILD BRONC PEELER†

Well, I'm a wild cowboy, I've roved the West o'er,
Roped the balls of lightning, and shot up towns galore;
I've busted the wild broomtails,‡ with their heads plumb skinned,
And rode a slick saddle from beginning to end.

Chorus:

But I've got many a hard fall and bit the mighty dust,
Till my knees do quiver when the bronc I try to bust;
Yes, my teeth do rattle and my knees do curve,
Why, what the hell's the matter—have I lost my nerve?

I've ripped over pinnacles, flew through the brush,
Yes, I've rode the streets of hell in a mighty damn rush,
I've spurred my horse to congress, he's jumped from rim to rim,
Yes, I've rode my gad through places slick and slim.

I've roped the wild horse and tied him down quick;
Did the saddle act and forked him plumb quick;
I've jerked off the hackamore, fetched a cowboy whoop,
And let him come alive for to bawl and root.

I've let him paw the clouds down, and just sit up there,
Like I was by a fireside in a rockin'-chair.
Oh, when I wore a pistol just learning the trade,
I never dreamed of gettin' leary when a cowboy I made.

* "Set" means settler.   † Song sent in by Harry Stephens from California.
‡ Native wild horses of Spanish breed.

[85]

On a snaky sage tail I'm goin' high and handsome,
Whippin' him all over for a mighty small ransom;
He's jarrin' the earth and pawin' down the moon,
If he don't give up he'll get me soon;

For my head's a whip-cracker, my seat's a flyin'-squirrel,
Nose a-runnin' blood, mind's in a whirl;
The blinds were down and he went off a rim,
And left me hangin' to a boulder on the brim.

Still they're all alike to me this wide world o'er,
Shoot to me the mighty outlaw and of brucky* cattle more.
So still I live and I'm ridin' 'em on,
And I guess I'll keep it up till all the broncs are gone.

JESS'S DILEMMA

From the scrapbook of S. L. Thorne, Fort Worth, Texas, himself an old cowboy, who says: "As I kept a daily journal of this drive through towns, watering-places, etc., and I think I am correctly informed, this is the last herd that was ever worked across the United States." Date, probably 1891.

Jess, a wild cowboy, loves whisky and beer,
And can tail a small yearling or tie down a steer.
While standing night guard—for some fun, that was all—
He twined a wild yearling which loudly did bawl.

It prized and it bellowed and made such a noise,
Stampeded the cattle and woke up the boys.
In this terrible dilemma Jess called in a rush
For Moodie to loose it that the yearling might hush:

* Probably brushy cattle—cattle from the brush country in southwest Texas.

"For what could I say with this damn yearling tied
If the boss in anger approaching did ride.
Oh, Moodie, oh, Moodie, in haste turn it loose,
And give me a chance for a feeble excuse."

The cattle was running and drifting fast South,
When Moodie felt for his heart, but was up in his mouth;
But the yearling was loosed and Jess lightly sprang,
And he rolled and he flanked that feeble mustang.

And he rounded those cattle while under full run,
But soon, when the time suited, owned up to his fun.
The boss passed it up, for la! he knew it was all with the past,
And with all of the boys he joined in the laugh.

Come all you young cowboys, take warning by Jess,
Don't swing the lasso while on night guard too careless;
Nor don't be caught napping while driving the trail,
For some one will find you—it seldom will fail.

But keep an eye on the boss and two on the herd,
And a close lookout for each idle word;
And keep a close lookout for what's even worse:
That you're not caught idling, two riding one horse.*

And when you've made this year's drive for the year '89,
Don't say unthoughted it will be your last time;
For so many have said the very same thing.
Then go up the trail every chance in the spring.

* Bottle.

A PRISONER FOR LIFE

One day in 1909 a Negro former trail-driver sang this song to me in his home, about twenty miles east of Wichita Falls, Texas. His tune fits the flat loneliness of that country.

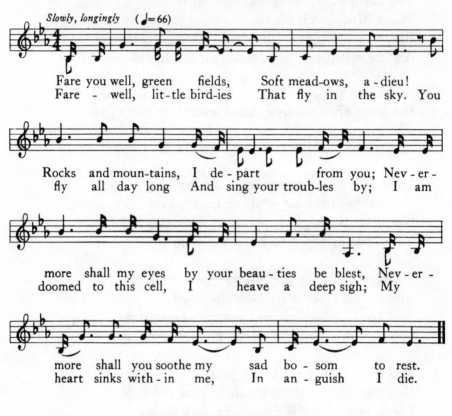

Slowly, longingly (♩ = 66)

Fare you well, green fields, Soft mead-ows, a-dieu!
Fare-well, lit-tle bird-ies That fly in the sky. You

Rocks and moun-tains, I de-part from you; Nev-er-
fly all day long And sing your troub-les by; I am

more shall my eyes by your beau-ties be blest, Nev-er-
doomed to this cell, I heave a deep sigh; My

more shall you soothe my sad bo-som to rest.
heart sinks with-in me, In an-guish I die.

Fare you well, green fields,
Soft meadows, adieu!
Rocks and mountains,
I depart from you;
Nevermore shall my eyes
By your beauties be blest,

Nevermore shall you soothe
My sad bosom to rest.

Farewell, little birdies
That fly in the sky,
You fly all day long
And sing your troubles by;
I am doomed to this cell,
I heave a deep sigh;
My heart sinks within me,
In anguish I die.

Fare you well, little fishes
That glide through the sea.
Your life's all sunshine,
All light, and all glee;
Nevermore shall I watch
Your skill in the wave.
I'll depart from all friends
This side of the grave.

What would I give
Such freedom to share,
To roam at my ease
And breathe the fresh air;
I would roam through the cities,
Through village and dell,
But I never would return
To my cold prison cell.

What's life without liberty,
I ofttimes have said,
Of a poor troubled mind

That's always in dread;
No sun, moon, and stars
Can on me now shine,
No change in my chamber
From twilight till dawn.

Fare you well, kind friends.
I am willing to own,
Such a wild outcast
Never was known;
I'm the downfall of my family,
My children, my wife;
God pity and pardon
The poor prisoner for life.

THE CONVICT

When slumbering in my convict cell my childhood days I see,
When I was Mother's little child and knelt at Mother's knee.
There my life was peace, I know; I knew no sorrow or pain.
Mother dear never did think, I know, I would wear a felon's chain.

Clink, clink, clink, clink, clink,
Ah, don't you near the clinking of my chain?
Clink, clink, clink, clink, clink,
Ah, don't you hear the clinking of my chain?

When I had grown to manhood, and evil paths I trod,
I learned to scorn my fellow man and even curse my God;
And in the evil course I ran for a great length of time
Till at last I ran too long and was condemned for a felon's crime.

My prison life will soon be o'er, my life will soon be gone—
May the angels waft it heavenward to a bright and happy home.
I'll be at rest, sweet, sweet rest; there is rest in the heavenly home.
I'll be at rest, sweet, sweet rest; there is rest in the heavenly home.

    Clink, clink, clink, clink, clink,
    Ah, don't you hear the clinking of my chain?
    Clink, clink, clink, clink, clink,
    Ah, don't you hear the clinking of my chain?

LITTLE JOE, THE WRANGLER

During 1907–1910 I found in Texas several versions of this song, and printed it anonymously in 1910. Later I discovered the song in a small collection of cowboy verse published in Estancia, New Mexico, by N. Howard (Jack) Thorp. Mr. Thorp says he wrote the song in 1898. See page 96 of "Songs of the Cowboys," by N. Howard Thorp.

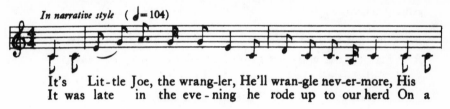

It's   Lit-tle Joe, the wrang-ler, He'll wran-gle nev-er-more, His
It was late   in the eve-ning he rode up to our herd On a

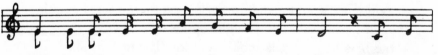

days   with the   re-mu-da they are   o'er;   'Twas a
lit-tle Tex   -   as po-ny he call'd Chaw;   With his

year   a-go last A-pril he rode in-to our camp,—Just a
bro-gan shoes and ov'-ralls, a tough-er look-in' kid   You

[91]

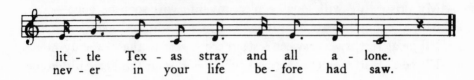

lit - tle   Tex - as   stray   and   all   a - lone.
nev - er   in   your   life   be - fore   had   saw.

It's little Joe, the wrangler, he'll wrangle nevermore,
His days with the *remuda* they are o'er;
'Twas a year ago last April he rode into our camp,—
Just a little Texas stray and all alone,—

It was late in the evening he rode up to our herd
On a little Texas pony he called "Chaw."
With his brogan shoes and ov'ralls, a tougher lookin' kid
You never in your life before had saw.

His saddle was a Texas "kack,"* built many years ago,
With an O. K. spur on one foot lightly swung;
His "hot roll" in a cotton sack so loosely tied behind,
And his canteen from his saddle-horn was swung.

He said that he had to leave home, his pa had married twice;
And his new ma whipped him every day or two;
So he saddled up old Chaw one night and lit a shuck this way,
And he's now trying to paddle his own canoe.

He said if we would give him work, he'd do the best he could,
Though he didn't know straight up about a cow;
So the boss he cut out a mount and kindly put him on,
For he sorta liked this little kid somehow;

Learned him to wrangle horses and to try to know them all,
And get them in at daylight if he could;
To follow the chuck-wagon and always hitch the team,
And to help the *cocinero* rustle wood.

* Slang. Very ordinary make.

[92]

We had driven to the Pecos, the weather being fine;
We had camped on the south side in a bend;
When a norther commenced blowin', we had doubled up our guard,
For it taken all of us to hold them in.

Little Joe, the wrangler, was called out with the rest;
Though the kid had scarcely reached the herd,
When the cattle they stampeded, like a hailstorm long they fled,
Then we were all a-ridin' for the lead.

'Midst the streaks of lightnin' a horse we could see in the lead,
'Twas Little Joe, the wrangler, in the lead;
He was riding Old Blue Rocket with a slicker o'er his head,
A-tryin' to check the cattle in their speed.

At last we got them milling and kinda quieted down,
And the extra guard back to the wagon went;
But there was one a-missin' and we knew it at a glance,
'Twas our little Texas stray, poor Wrangling Joe.

The next morning just at daybreak, we found where Rocket fell,
Down in a washout twenty feet below;
And beneath the horse, mashed to a pulp,—his spur had rung the
    knell,—
Was our little Texas stray, poor Wrangling Joe.

THE OLD COWBOY*

I rode a line on the open range,
When cow-punching wasn't slow;

* Sung to J. Frank Dobie by Charlie Johnson of Charco, Texas. Dobie printed it in his
article, "More Ballads and Songs of the Frontier Folk" (*Publications of the Texas Folk
Lore Society*, Vol. VII, p. 156).

I've turned the longhorn cow one way,
And the other the buffalo.

I went up the trail in the eighties—
Oh, the hardships I have stood! *
I've drank the water from cow tracks, boys,
When you bet it tasted good.

I've stood night guard many a night
In the face of a driving storm,
And sang to them a doleful song
When they rattled their hocks and horns.

I've been in many a stampede, too;
I've heard the rumbling noise;
And the light we had to turn them by
Was the lightning on their horns.

But many a boy I worked with then
Is sleeping on old Boot Hill; †
For his last cow drive was made to Dodge,
Over the Jones and Plummer trail.

They're building towns and railroads now,
Where we used to bed our cows;
And the man with the mule, the plow and the hoe
Is digging up our old bed grounds.

The old cowboy has watched the change,
Has seen the good times come and go—
But the old cowboy will soon be gone,
Just like the buffalo.

* "When the old cowpuncher talks about the hardships he has stood, he is generally wishing that he had a chance to re-stand them. He is not really trying to put up a monument to his own sacrifices. He had a bully good time and remembers it with gusto."
† "Boot Hill was the graveyard at Dodge City, Kansas, 'Cowboy Capitol,' where more than a few men were buried with their boots on."

THE PECOS PUNCHER

From an unsigned manuscript sent me more than twenty years ago. In November, 1935, I heard another version, incomplete, sung by Jeff and Herman Roberts on the Zweifel Farm, Hood County, Texas. They called their song "Three Jolly Cow-punchers"; these cow-punchers come from Yellowstone Flat, ride Frazier saddles and stamp a J. O. on the dogie's left shoulder. They, too, would go East like Wild Bill and play tough:

> Let our hair grow out longer and dance on the stage,
> And coin in the money at the White Sheet parade.

Furthermore they show their "jolly" spirit in this additional couplet:

> We steal out our horses, to dances we go;
> And if we get boozy, we pull off a show.

I'm a gay puncher, fresh from the Pecos Flat,
I wear the high heels, also the white hat,
I ride the Meyers saddle, my chaps* are the best,
My bits, boots, and spurs can't be beat in the West.

I'm noted in Texas out on the Staked Plains,
Also from the Pecos to the Rio Grande range;
I ride up the trail and take down the rawhide,
And there never was a bronco but what I could ride.

I ride in the wagon, I ride in pursuit,
To hear the cook holler, "Chuck away, grab a root."
We roll out our bedding on the ground cold and hard,
For shortly we have to stand three hours guard.

* Leather leggins.

[95]

Next morning at daybreak in a circle we ride,
We round up the dogies, take down the rawhide;
We rope them and brand them like in days of old,
Upon the left shoulder we stamp the Eight-O.

I've worked for the Mallets, also the Long S,
But as for the Eight-O's, I think them the best;
The nights are so dark, can hardly see at all,
As I ride to the sound of some maverick's bawl.

Now as for maverick stealing, I confess true enough,
But to the young cowman it seems mighty tough;
But what cares the puncher as he rides the range o'er?
The cowman will get there or else make a roar.

Now as for bronc riding, I've got quite enough,
I'll go East like Wild Bill and there play the tough;
Let my beard grow long and dance on the stage,
I'll tell they eat cactus out West and chew sage.

As for saddle and bridle I have no more use,
I'll ride to the home ranch and turn my bronc loose;
I'll hang up my saddle where it will keep dry,
For I may need it in the sweet by-and-by.

THE U–S–U RANGE

Said to have been composed by G. W. Barr, Stamford, Texas.

Oh, come, cowboys, and listen to my song!
I'm in hopes I'll please you and not keep you long;
I'll sing of things you may think strange
About west Texas and the U-S-U range.

You may go to Stamford and there see a man
Who wears a white shirt and is asking for hands;

You may ask him for work and he'll answer you short,
He will hurry you up, for he wants you to start.
He will put you in a wagon and be off in the rain,
You will go up on Tongue River on the U-S-U range.

You will drive up to the ranch and there you will stop.
It's a little sod house with dirt all on top.
You will ask what it is and they will tell you out plain
That it's the ranch house on the U-S-U range.

You will go in the house and he will begin to explain;
You will see some blankets rolled up on the floor;
You may ask what it is and they will tell you out plain
That it is the bedding on the U-S-U range.

You are up in the morning at the daybreak
To eat cold beef and U-S-U steak,
And out to your work, no matter if it's rain—
And that is the life on the U-S-U range.

You work hard all day and come in at night,
And turn your horse loose, for they say it's all right,
And set down to supper and begin to complain
Of the chuck that you eat on the U-S-U range.

The grub that you get is beans and cold rice
And U-S-U steak cooked up very nice;
And if you don't like that you needn't complain,
For that's what you get on the U-S-U range.

Now, kind friends, I must leave you, I no longer can remain,
I hope I have pleased you and given you no pain.
But when I am gone, don't think me strange,
For I have been a cow-puncher on the U-S-U range.

[97]

THE DYING COWBOY OF RIM ROCK RANCH

Good-by to my pals of the prairie,
Good-by to the cattle and the trail,
Good-by to the cards and the drinking,
Good-by to the prairies and the vale.

Refrain:

    For I'm riding away on my Brown Girl
    Where the sun is sinking low;
    For I'm riding away on my Brown Girl,
    Where the sun is sinking low.

[98]

Good-by to the cracking of the pistol,
Good-by to the clinking of the spur,
Good-by to the cards and the drinking,
Good-by to the wild Irish girl.

Good-by to the yapping of the coyote,
Good-by to the call of the dove,
Good-by to the Rim Rock Ranch,
Good-by to the girl that I love.

Oh, boys, when you're far from Rim Rock,
You know there's a cabin on that shore,
You can think of the spot where I left you
For the round-up where we all must go.

THE STAMPEDE*

When the hot sun smiles on the endless miles
    That lead to the distant mart,
And the cattle wail down the well-worn trail,
    And moan till it grips the heart,
And they gasp for air in the dust clouds there,
    As they jostle their way along
With uplifted ear so that they may hear
    The cow-puncher's evening song.

Far up at the head rode old "Texas Red"—
    A man of determined face—
And his keen gray eye took in earth and sky
    As he rode with a centaur's grace.
On the left was Joe on his white pinto;
    Jim Smith patrolled on the right.

* First published in *Wild West Weekly* (Street and Smith, 79 Seventh Ave., New York).

[99]

66897

And the other tricks took an even six,
  And we needed them all that night.

And to quench our thirst we had dared the worst
  And fought for a nester's well;
But he had a girl with a witching curl,
  And she cast a golden spell.
So our shots went wide from the sinner's hide
  As he faded from our view,
And the charming miss blew old Red a kiss
  And smiled as his pony flew.

'Twas a pretty play, but he spurred away,
  His face like a prairie blaze.
And he hit the dirt as he plied his quirt
  Till lost in the friendly haze,
While the bawling shrilled as the cattle milled,
  And their eyes grew shot with fear—
For they knew right well that a merry hell
  Lurked in the gathering smear.

In the north black clouds like funeral shrouds
  Rolled down with an icy breath,
And we faced a fight on a brutal night
  With odds on the side of death;
For a trailing herd when it's rightly stirred
  Is a thing for a man to shun,
And no coward band ever holds command
  When the norther's on the run.

In the ghostly hush that precedes the rush
  Of the wild wind-driven flood,
We made our dash to the thunder's crash,
  Spurs set till they drew the blood;

But the Storm King struck to our bitter luck,
    We rode in the lightning's glare,
And the north wind whirled through a watery world,
    And laughed at our puny dare.

Then the cattle swerved as a mob unnerved
    And shrank from a raging thing,
And they drifted back on the beaten track,
    Tail to the norther's sting.
We fought like men, but 'twas useless then—
    They plunged down the backward track.
Theirs a single creed—'twas the dread stampede—
    Straight at the nester's shack!

There was death at stake, and 'twas make or break
    In the rush of that frenzied mob;
But we'd risked our lives in a hundred drives,
    And we figured to know our job.
Then a sudden hail on the whistling gale
    And a horse went slithering by—
'Twas old Texas Red, and we knew he sped
    To the girl of the flashing eye.

With a wicked grip on his biting whip,
    He smoked down on the heaving ranks,
And his searching eye set to do or die
    As he fanned at his pony's flanks;
And we gazed aghast when we saw at last—
    Old Tex at the head of the ruck,
And we made a prayer for the rider there,
    Just a wish for a hero's luck.

Straight she stood and still, at the storm's wild will,
    Close by the nester's well,

And her eyes were kissed by the driving mist
　　As she faced that living hell,
But when Texas Red, 'crost his pony's head,
　　Erect in his stirrups rose,
Like a sprite she sprung—to his shoulder clung—
　　A rod from the leader's nose.

'Twas a gallant race, but he held his pace
　　As he edged to the leeward side.
Not a moment's slip of his strong arm's grip,
　　As he led that bawling tide;
And his noble steed, knowing well the need,
　　Gave of his stout heart's best,
And he brought them free from that maddened spree,
　　And slid—in the mud—to rest.

Yes, we found the two where the north wind blew,
　　Her black hair across his breast;
In his arms she clung as his big heart sung
　　Under his calfskin vest.
And the lucky brute made us each salute,
　　And she kissed us one by one,
And we all went wild till old Tex got riled
　　And threatened to pull a gun.

On the trail we lay at the break of day,
　　Deep in the Texas mud—
Dog-tired we dragged as the cattle lagged,
　　Cooling their racing blood;
'Twas a weary trek to the river's neck,
　　And we longed for the scorching sun,
And we drank Red's luck as we downed our chuck,
　　And we sang—for the night was done!

[102]

A KANSAS COWBOY

Words and music sent by Gene Boardman Hoover (Mrs. A. B. Hoover), Kansas City, Missouri, who says: "Years ago an older brother of mine came riding 'out of the West,' singing this cowboy song with much gusto. It seems to have made a tremendous impression upon my childish mind, for it is still galloping through my subconscious. In recalling it, I also call to mind a daring, golden-haired youth, who loved the mountains, the plains, and the cattle of the old West, and who liked nothing better than for 'night to overtake him with his saddle and his gun,' even though he might have 'nowhere to lay his head.'" (May, 1937.)

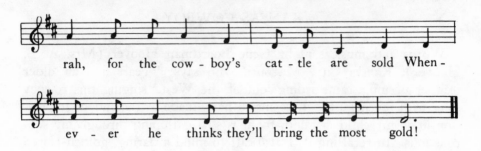

rah, for the cow - boy's cat - tle are sold When -
ev - er he thinks they'll bring the most gold!

Where the cowboys roost on the green rolling prairie,
    And the cattle are grazing all day,
Oh, when you get there just call around and see,
    And for you I'll surely make a way.

Refrain:
    Hurrah for the cowboy riding so bold,
    Hurrah, for the cowboy never grows old,
    Hurrah, for the cowboy's cattle are sold
    Whenever he thinks they will bring the most gold!

When heel flies come, the cattle they will run,
    For a little pool of water they will break,
They will stand in there till the setting of the sun,
    Not a single bite of grass will they take.

Oh, a cowboy's life is just like a dog's,
    And he sometimes wishes he was dead,
When night overtakes him with his saddle and his gun,
    And he has nowhere to lay his head.

Oh, a cowboy's brave, and a cowboy's bold,
    With snakes and coyotes he will browse,
But he never knows Sunday from any other day,
    For it's always "Huahy, Huahy!" to the cows.

You may talk about your dudes in cities of the East,
But I wouldn't give a cent for them all;
I'd rather be a cowboy riding in the West,
Than say grace in a legislative hall.

THE RUSTLER*

When first I started out cow-driving, I drove them on the square;
My friends they all went back on me, I hardly thought it fair;
I was forced to leave my country, although against my will,
But I'm bound to be a cowboy, let luck be what it will.

Oh, the captain of the hoodoos,† his name is Powell's Buck,
And if he lives another year you bet he'll be in luck;
For when he meets a lonely cowboy he thinks he is mighty wise
But when he meets us at Hugh's ranch he wants to compromise.

Oh, when you go cow-driving, oh, drive them on the rush;
Corne off all roads, boys, and haze them through the brush;
For the hoodoos are a plenty, and Goliad is nigh,
We'll feed them on Winchester balls and pile them up to die.

Oh, the hoodoos have chased me and still I am not broke,
I'm going to the mountains and think I am doing well;
I am going to the mountains some cattle for to sell,
And I hope to see the hoodoos dead and damn them all in hell.

PANHANDLE COB‡

He was only a common puncher, such as the punchers were,
When life was life on the prairies and people didn't care;
When there wasn't no derned wire fences from the strip to the Rio
Grande,

* From D. L. Browning.   † Cow thieves.
‡ "Wrote" by H. D. Maclachlan, Panhandle, Texas.

[105]

When the cutter answered an insult and a boy could burn a
  brand;
Only an old-time cowboy with ways that would shorely jar
On the nerves that come in with the railroads, the nester, the bum
  and box-car.

He could ride a blame streak o' lightnin', was a cracker-jack at a
  dance;
He loved poker better'n eatin', and he'd hob you if airy a
  chance;
He could cuss the worl' by sections when you had him halfway
  mad;
He'd drink an' shoot up the city when the whisky was extra bad.
His wealth was a horse an' saddle, pair o' spurs an' the clothes he
  wore,
An' a dollar or two in his pocket, but oftener less than more.

In fact, he was just a cow-puncher, an' that ain't no rose-water
  job.
Colbert Seth was his name—don't forget it—an' for short we called
  him Cob.
But for all he was rough on the outside an' didn't live by rule,
He'd a heart in his breast as big, sir, as the biggest kind of a
  mule.
If he met a pard in a tight he'd divide up all he had
An' to help out a woman (you know it!) he'd shoot himself an' be
  glad.

He hadn't got no religion; but top o' the golden stair
There'll be heap o' church members missin', but Cob you bet'll be
  there.
This ain't no lie I'm tellin' an', jest to prove it ain't,
I'll tell you a little story with nary a lick o' paint.

It was up at the ranch—the O-X's—this 'ere Cob fell foul o' the
    boss.
How it begun, I forget now, but seems like it was long o' a hoss.

Anyhow, they had it goin' an' comin', too, you bet,
Till the Rod, he was always cranky, jist told old Cob to "get";
So Cob went an' he saddled his pony, for he seen it wasn't no
    bluff,
An' came down to the lot where the boss was to get him a check for
    his stuff.
Now that day they were doin' some brandin' an' the dust was flyin'
    about,
An' Cob had to look for a minute before he could make the boss
    out.

When he did, 'twas to see him a-flyin' round the lot like a cyclone on
    wheels,
An' the rest o' the boys all a-makin' for the fence with a clean pair
    o' heels.
An' the reason why all the derned outfit to the fence had so sud-
    denly took
Was that right in the midst o' the lot was little old steer on the
    hook.
It was a-pawin' the ground an' a-snuffin' like an engine goin'
    upgrade;
Yep, it jist taken charge o' the lot, sir, as if it had bought it an'
    paid.

So Cob, catchin' on to the racket, hops right on the fence like the
    rest;
For, whenever a steer gets to proddin', the very top rail is the best;
An' he jist had time to straddle across it, as if it had been an old
    hoss,

[107]

When through the fence, right where he's sittin', creeps Sissy, the
  child o' the boss.
She was laughin' an' hollerin', "Daddy," an' didn't know nothin'
  'bout cows,
'Cept them as her mammy was milkin', an' them a cyclone wouldn't
  rouse.

So she saw the old steer a-cavortin', an' thinkin' it's jist feelin' good,
Cries, "Daddy, oh, Dad, lookee yonder," an' makes tracks for where
  the brute stood.
That there was the first as we seen o' her an' you bet it made us feel
  queer—
A kiddy of three in the lot there, alone with a wild Texas steer;
An' we hadn't no breath left to holler, for the brute had his eyes on
  the kid,
An' was comin' a-foggin' right for her, a-meanin' business if ever a
  steer did.

The boss gasps out, "Run," in a terror—as well he'd 'a' saved his
  breath,
For the kiddy don't savvy an' stands there a-smilin' an' waitin' for
  death;
Yes, sir, jest a-smilin' an' waitin', an' us boys settin' round like blame
  fools,
An' never liftin' a finger no more than if we'd been so many mules.
In two seconds more a new angel would have flew to them realms
  o' bliss
When we seen some one drop from the fence rail an' make tracks like
  the wind straight for Sis.

It was Cob, an' the steer had the start; but he knowed it was life or
  death,

An' greased lightnin' wasn't in it with that run of old Cob Seth;
For he beat the steer by a yard, jest enough to save the kid,
By throwin' himself right between them, yes, sir, that's what he did;
Threw himself right in the gap there, an' when the steer made his
    hook
It wasn't the little kiddy but the puncher what he took.

It took him clean in the side an' we seen a trickle of red,
An' we knowed there was danger in it by the layin' o' Cob's head.
That called us to our senses an' a shot brought down the steer—
Could ha' done that at the outset if we'd not been crazed with
    fear.
In a minute we'd picked up the kiddy, it was only kinder scared;
Then we turned to where Cob was lyin' to see how he had fared.

There he lay where he had fallen, all limber an' white an' still,
With the red blood oozin', oozin', an' our eyes began to fill.
As we watched his face grow whiter an' seen his fight for breath,
An' we knowed that had but one meanin', an' that one meanin',
    death.
We did all that human could do, but all was done in vain,
For Cob was booked for up yonder, out o' the dust an' pain.

We could only stand an' watch him, could only stand an' wait,
For the beat o' the angel's white wings an' the swing o' the Golden
    Gate.
At last they came; we couldn't hear, but that's what the preachers
    say,
An' Cob sure heard something yonder, for he smiled as he passed
    away.
Such a smile—so soft an' tender—like the breathin' o' a prayer,
Seemed like it wasn't Cob, boys, but an angel that lay there.

But, boys, you must excuse me. I'm feelin' kinder queer,
My eyes are gettin' misty, there's a lump in my throat right here.
It's a cold I've got, I reckon. Anyways, you've heard the story,
How Cob gave his life for the kiddy an' went straight up to glory.

SALTY DOGS

Sent by W. P. McLaughlin, Clovis, New Mexico, who writes:
" 'Salty dog' in the Southwest is an expression that covers everything that is worthy of emulation. 'Salty dog' is a figure of speech and comes from the moving camps of this neck of the plain. Bacon is 'dog.' If it is salty, it is the only thing that is brought into camp that is continually salty. As bacon is different from everything else, so is the character to whom this name 'salty dog' applies. He may be vivacious, adventurous, a dare-devil, or a bad man with peculiar methods, a card shark, or an especially good bronco-peeler. Or he may have a reputation as a marksman. Whatever his line, if he is a specialist and remarkable for prowess, and if his specialty pertains to the ranges of the Southwest, he is a 'salty dog.' Salty dogs are divided into several kinds. There's the cow-punchin' dog, the bronco-peelin' dog, the sheep-herdin' dog, the freightin' dog, the bullfightin' dog, the hog-leg dog (six-shooter), the scoutin' dog, the steer-tyin' dog. If they are masters of their line they are salty dogs."

Eph Kate was a cow-punchin' boy:
To throw a steer was his only joy;
He could rope and tie a maverick
In the wink of an eye and make it stick.

Refrain:
Baby, won't you come and be my salty dog?
Eph, baby, come and be my salty dog;
I love you true, indeed I do.
Oh, Eph, babe, won't you come and be my salty dog?

[110]

Clare Neat was a rough-and-tumble lad,
He'd rather fight and do what was bad.
He could shoot the diamonds out any old "gray's" eye,
Say, that's the kind wear their boots when they die.

Bob Kelly was the truest rider that ever came
Out in the sixties from Texas to this plain;
He never found one that he couldn't ride
Without touching leather and with one hand tied.

Ezek Aranda was a Mexican bold;
The sheep he'd sheared nobody knowed;
He'd followed the lambs all of his life
And allus got the devils in without any strife.

Bill Laughlin was the "eight-up" in our camp,
He never was without a job, never would tramp;
He could turn a team in a needle's eye.
In a saddle, jerkin' a team, old Bill will die.

Abe Martin was the musical lad,
He could sing anything good or bad;
He could play any instrument he ever seen
And in band contests he was the cream.

Mike Arnold was the drinkin' boy of this here plain,
He made Governor Hogeman take the first train;
He downed Mills and Jeff and Praeger alike,
Although they drank their soda and his whisky they did spike.

Maw Perkins is the best camp cook
Who ever came in this neck by the tattoo book;
He could make more stuff with grease and flour
Than three cookees, and cook it in a hour.

[111]

Max Amonett was the dancin' kid,
He took all the prizes and put on the lid;
He knew all the figures and buck and wings,
And when he got through he danced the Highland Fling.

Walt Burkhorn was the race stock man,
He could scent a pony that always outran;
He never found a sporty guy he couldn't take in
By beatin' him in any race, be he Mex or Injin.

JIM FARROW

From Roy Bedichek, San Angelo, Texas. The song slyly intimates that the Farrows were cattle thieves.

It's Jim Farrow and John Farrow and little Simon, too,
Have plenty of cattle where I have but few.
Marking and branding both night and day—
It's "Keep still, my boys, and you'll all get your pay."
It's up to the courthouse, the first thing they know,
Before the Grand Jury they'll have to go.
They'll ask you about earmarks, they'll ask you about brand,
But tell them you were absent when the work was on hand.

Jim Farrow brands J. F. on the side;
The next comes Johnnie who takes the whole hide;
Little Simon, too, has H. on the loin—
All stand for Farrow, but it's not good for Sime.
You ask for the mark, I don't think it's fair,
You'll find the cow's head but the ear isn't there,
It's a crop and a split and a sort of a twine—
All stand for F., but it's not good for Sime.

"Get up, my boys," Jim Farrow will say,
"And out to horse hunting before it is day."
So we get up and are out on the way
But it's damn few horses we find before day.
"Now saddle your horses and out on the peaks
To see if the heifers are out on the creeks."
We'll round 'em today and we'll round 'em tomorrow,
And this ends my song concerning the Farrows.

WINDY BILL*

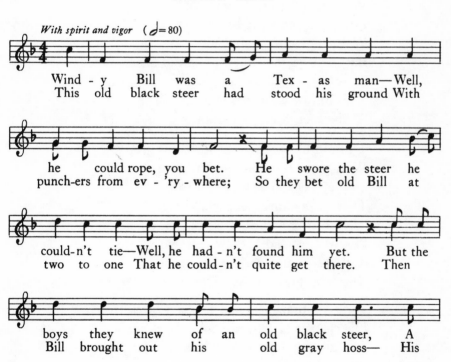

With spirit and vigor (♩=80)

Wind - y Bill was a Tex - as man—Well,
This old black steer had stood his ground With

he could rope, you bet. He swore the steer he
punch-ers from ev - 'ry - where; So they bet old Bill at

could-n't tie—Well, he had-n't found him yet. But the
two to one That he could-n't quite get there. Then

boys they knew of an old black steer, A
Bill brought out his old gray hoss— His

* Sent by Birdsall Briscoe, 620 Crawford St., Houston, Texas, who said he learned it in
New Mexico.

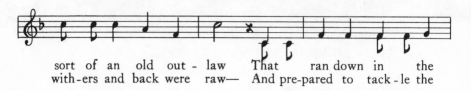

sort of an old out - law That ran down in the
with-ers and back were raw— And pre-pared to tack - le the

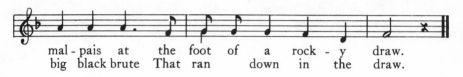

mal - pais at the foot of a rock - y draw.
big black brute That ran down in the draw.

Windy Bill was a Texas man—
Well, he could rope, you bet.
He swore the steer he couldn't tie—
Well, he hadn't found him yet.
But the boys they knew of an old black steer,
A sort of an old outlaw
That ran down in the malpais
At the foot of a rocky draw.

This old black steer had stood his ground
With punchers from everywhere;
So they bet old Bill at two to one
That he couldn't quite get there.
Then Bill brought out his old gray hoss—
His withers and back were raw—
And prepared to tackle the big black brute
That ran down in the draw.

With his Brazos bit and his Sam Stack tree,*
His chaps and taps to boot,
And his old maguey† tied hard and fast,
Bill swore he'd get the brute.

* The frame or "tree" of a saddle was made from wood covered with rawhide. The
"Sam Stack tree," a famous make of saddles.
† Rope made from fibre of the Mexican maguey.

[114]

Now, first Bill sort of sauntered round,
Old Blackie began to paw,
Then threw his tail straight in the air
And went driftin' down the draw.

The old gray plug flew after him,
For he'd been eatin' corn;
And Bill, he piled his old maguey
Right round old Blackie's horns.
The old gray hoss he stopped right still;
The cinches broke like straw,
And the old maguey and the Sam Stack tree
Went driftin' down the draw.

Bill, he lit in a flint rock pile,
His face and hands were scratched.
He said he thought he could rope a snake,*
But he guessed he'd met his match.
He paid his bets like a little man
Without a bit of jaw,
And 'lowed old Blackie was the boss
Of anything in the draw.

There's a moral to my story, boys,
And that you all must see.
Whenever you go to tie a snake
Don't tie it to your tree;
But take your dolly welters†
'Cordin' to California law,
And you'll never see your old rim-fire‡
Go drifting down the draw.

* Snake=bad steer.
† Dolly welter=rope around the wrapped horn of the saddle. Spanish, *dar la vuelta*. Other words used for a turn or two of the rope around the horn of the saddle are "daling," "vuelting," "felting," "dale vuelting."
‡ Saddle with two girths.

ONLY A COWBOY*

Away out in old Texas, that great Lone Star State,
Where the mocking bird whistles both early and late;
It was in western Texas on the old N A range,
The boy fell a victim on the old staked plains.

> He was only a cowboy gone on before,
> He was only a cowboy, we will never see more;
> He was doing his duty on the old N A range
> But now he is sleeping on the old staked plains.

His crew they were numbered twenty-seven or -eight,
The boys were like brothers, their friendship was great,
When "O God, have mercy" was heard from behind—
The cattle were left to drift on the line.

He leaves a dear wife and little ones, too.
To earn them a living, as fathers oft do;
For while he was working for the loved ones so dear
He was took without warning or one word of cheer.

And while he is sleeping where the sun always shines,
The boys they go dashing along on the line;
The look on their faces it speaks to us all
Of one who departed to the home of the soul.

> He was only a cowboy gone on before,
> He was only a cowboy, we will never see more;
> He was doing his duty on the old N A range,
> But now he is sleeping on the old staked plains.

* From D. L. Browning, Garner, Texas.

WHOSE OLD COW?*

'Twas the end of round-up, the last day of June,
Or maybe July, I don't remember,
Or it might have been August, 'twas some time ago,
Or perhaps 'twas the first of September.

Anyhow, 'twas the round-up we had at Mayou
On the Lightning Rod's range, near Cayo;
There were some twenty wagons, more or less, camped about
On the temporal in the cañon.

First night we'd no cattle, so we only stood guard
On the horses, somewhere near two hundred head;
So we side-lined and hoppled, we belled and we staked,
Loosed our hot-rolls and fell into bed.

Next morning 'bout daybreak we started our work,
Our horses, like 'possums, felt fine.
Each one "tendin' knittin'," none tryin' to shirk!
So the round-up got on in good time.

Well, we worked for a week till the country was clean
And the bosses said, "Now, boys, we'll stay here.
We'll carve and we'll trim 'em and start out a herd
Up the east trail from old Abilene."

Next morning all on herd, and but two with the cut,
And the boss on Piute, carving fine,
Till he rode down his horse and had to pull out,
And a new man went in to clean up.

* From *Cowboy Songs*, by N. Howard Thorp (Boston: Houghton, Mifflin).

[117]

Well, after each outfit had worked on the band
There was only three head of them left;
When Nig Add from L F D outfit rode in,—
A dictionary on earmarks and brands.

He cut the two head out, told where they belonged;
But when the last cow stood there alone
Add's eyes bulged so he didn't know just what to say,
'Ceptin', "Boss, dere's something here monstrous wrong!

"White folks smarter'n Add, and maybe I'se wrong;
But here's six months wages dat I'll give
If anyone'll tell me when I reads dis mark
To who dis longhorned cow belong!

"Overslope in right ear an' de underbit,
Lef' ear swaller fork an' de undercrop,
Hole punched in center, an' de jinglebob
Under half crop, an' de slash an' split.

"She's got O Block an' Lightnin' Rod,
Nine Forty-Six an' A Bar Eleven,
T Terrapin an' Ninety-Seven,
Rafter Cross an' de Double Prod.

"Half circle A an' Diamond D,
Four Cross L and Three P Z,
B W I bar, X V V
Bar N cross an' A L C.

"So, if none o' you punchers claims dis cow,
Mr. Stock 'Sociation needn't git 'larmed;
For one more brand more or less won't do no harm,
So old Nigger Add'll just brand her now."

THE HORSE WRANGLER

The original of this song was published in the Miles City (Montana) *Stock Growers' Journal*, February 3, 1894, under the pseudonym of R. J. Stovall. The author's real name is D. J. O'Malley, and he lives at Eau Claire, Wisconsin. The song grew to wide popularity, being well known in Texas. The second melody is adapted from Pat Rooney's tune in the *New York Mercury*, April 10, 1902. Some slight changes in words make them fit the version I print.

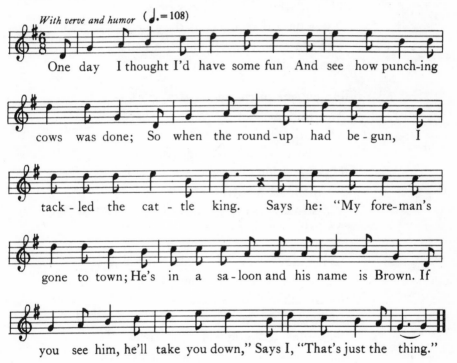

With verve and humor (♩.=108)

One day I thought I'd have some fun And see how punch-ing
cows was done; So when the round-up had be-gun, I
tack-led the cat-tle king. Says he: "My fore-man's
gone to town; He's in a sa-loon and his name is Brown. If
you see him, he'll take you down," Says I, "That's just the thing."

One day I thought I'd have some fun,
And see how punching cows was done;
So when the round-up had begun
I tackled the cattle king.

Says he: "My foreman's gone to town;
He's in a saloon and his name is Brown.
If you see him, he'll take you down."
Says I, "That's just the thing."

We started for the ranch next day;
Brown argered me most all the way.
He said that cow-punching was nothing but play,
That it was no work at all,—
That all you had to do was ride,
'Twas only drifting with the tide;
The son of a gun, oh, how he lied!
Don't you think he had his gall?

He put me in charge of a cavyard,
And told me not to work too hard,
That all I had to do was guard
The horses from getting away;
I had one hundred and sixty head,
I sometimes wished that I was dead;
When one got away, Brown's head turned red,
And there was the devil to pay.

Sometimes one would make a break,
Across the prairie he would take,
As if running for a stake,—
It seemed to them but play;
Sometimes I could not head them all,
Sometimes my horse would catch a fall
And I'd shoot on like a cannon ball
Till the earth came in my way.

They saddled me up an old gray hack
With two set-fasts on his back,

They padded him down with a gunny sack
And used my bedding all.
When I got on he quit the ground,
Went up in the air and turned around,
And I came down and busted the ground,—
I got one hell of a fall.

They took me up and carried me in
And rubbed me down with an old stake pin.
"That's the way they all begin;
You're doing well," says Brown.
"And in the morning, if you don't die,
I'll give you another horse to try."
"Oh, say, can't I walk?" says I.
Says he, "Yes, back to town."

I've traveled up and I've traveled down,
I've traveled this country round and round,
I've lived in city and I've lived in town,
But I've got this much to say:
Before you try cow-punching, kiss your wife,
Take a heavy insurance on your life,
Then cut your throat with a barlow knife—
For it's easier done that way.

[Version 2]

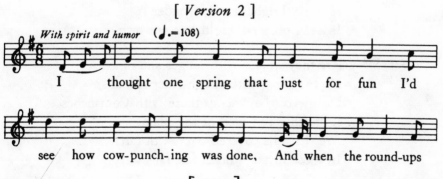

With spirit and humor (♩.=108)

I thought one spring that just for fun I'd
see how cow-punch-ing was done, And when the round-ups

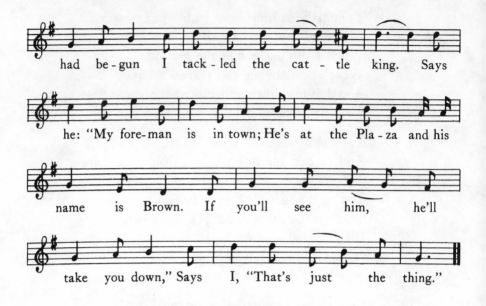

had be-gun I tack-led the cat-tle king. Says
he: "My fore-man is in town; He's at the Pla-za and his
name is Brown. If you'll see him, he'll
take you down," Says I, "That's just the thing."

THE COWBOY'S MEDITATION

At midnight when cattle are sleeping
On my saddle I pillow my head,
And up at the heavens lie peeping
From out of my cold, grassy bed.
Often and often I wondered
At night when lying alone
If every bright star up yonder
Is a big peopled world like our own.

Are they worlds with ranges and ranches?
Do they ring with rough rider refrains?
Do the cowboys scrap there with Comanches
And other red men of the plains?
Are the hills covered over with cattle
In those mystic worlds far, far away,

Do the ranch houses ring with the prattle
Of sweet little children at play?

At night in the bright stars up yonder
Do the cowboys lie down to their rest?
Do they gaze at this old world and wonder
If rough riders dash over its breast?
Do they list to the wolves in the canyons?
Do they watch the night owl in its flight,
With their horse their only companion
While guarding the herd through the night?

Sometimes when a bright star is twinkling
Like a diamond set in the sky,
I find myself lying and thinking,
It may be God's heaven is nigh.
I wonder if there I shall meet her,
My mother whom God took away;
If in the star-heavens I'll greet her
At the round-up that's on the last day.

In the east the great daylight is breaking
And into my saddle I spring;
The cattle from sleep are awaking,
The heaven-thoughts from me take wing,
The eyes of my bronco are flashing,
Impatient he pulls at the reins,
And off round the herd I go dashing,
A reckless cowboy of the plains.

HOME, SWEET HOME*

J. Frank Dobie writes: "One of the best and most honorably known names in the cattle country is that of Slaughter." Sung to the tune of "Home, Sweet Home."

We were lying on a prairie on Slaughter's ranch one night,
With our heads upon our saddles while the fire was burning bright.
Some were telling stories and some were singing songs,
While others were idly smoking as the long hours rolled along.
At last we fell to talking of distant friends so dear,
When a boy raised up in his saddle and brushed away a tear.
"Now though it's only a Kansas dugout I left behind to roam,
I'd give my saddle and pony to be at home, sweet home."

We all asked why he had left his home, if it was so dear to him,
He looked the rough crowd over and spoke in a voice that was
    dim:
"I fell in love with a neighbor girl, her cheeks were soft and
    white;
Another feller loved her too; it ended in a fight.
This feller his name was Thomas Jones, we'd known each other from
    boys;
We had rode each other's horses, we had shared each other's joys.
Tom was tall and slender, his face was young and fair;
His eyes were the color of heaven, he had dark curly hair.

"Oh, now it makes me shudder to think of that awful night;
When Tom and I began fighting, I stuck him with my knife.
I fell right down on my knees and tried to stop the blood
That from his side came spurting all in a crimson flood.

* From "Texas and Southwestern Lore" (*Publications of the Texas Folk Lore Society*, Vol. VI). Mrs. Bob Criswell of the Swenson Ranch, Throckmorton, Texas, sang me a slightly different version.

And now whenever I sleep, I dream I hear him say:
'Bob, old boy, you'll be sorry—I'll be gone before it's day.'
Now, boys, you can see the reason why I am compelled to roam;
But I'd give my pony and saddle to be at home, sweet home."

UTAH CARROLL*

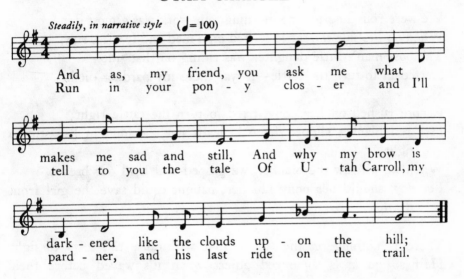

And as, my friend, you ask me what makes me sad and still,
And why my brow is darkened like the clouds upon the hill;
Run in your pony closer and I'll tell to you the tale
Of Utah Carroll, my pardner, and his last ride on the trail.

'Mid cactus and the thistles of Mexico's fair land,
Where the cattle roam in thousands, a-many a herd and brand,
There is a grave with neither headstone, neither date nor name—
There lies my pardner, sleeping in the land from which I came.

* Part of this song was given to the compiler by F. C. Thorne of Fort Worth, Texas. J. T.
Shirley of San Angelo, Texas, says that a cowboy on the Curve T Ranch in Schleicher
County wrote this song.

Side by side we've rode the ranges, cut out, roped and burned the
    brand,
And through the storm and dreary darkness joined the night-herd's
    weary stand.
We rode the range together and had rode it side by side;
I loved him as a brother; I wept when Utah died.

We were rounding up one morning, our work was almost done,
When on the side the cattle started on a mad and fearless run;
The boss man's little daughter was riding on that side—
Started in to turn the cattle—it was there my pardner died.

Lenore rushed on her pony, tried to turn the cattle right;
Her red blanket slipped from beneath her, catching in her stirrup
    tight;
When we all saw the blanket, we gasped and held our breath,
For now should her pony fail her, naught could save the girl from
    death.

There is nothing on the ranges that will cause the cows to fight
Half so quick as some red object when it's waved before their
    sight;
When the cattle saw the blanket almost dragging on the ground
They were maddened in a moment and they charged it in a
    bound.

Then Lenore saw the threatening danger, quickly turned her pony's
    face,
And, in leaning from her saddle, tried her blanket to displace;
When she leaned she lost her balance, fell in front of this wild
    tide—
"Lie still, Lenore, I am coming!" were the words my pardner
    cried.

[126]

Fifty yards or more behind her Utah Carroll came riding fast;
Little did he think that moment that the ride would be his last.
Many a time from out the saddle he had caught the trailing rope;
Now to raise the girl at full speed he thought her only hope.

As his horse approached the maiden, sure of foot with steady bound,
Low he bent from out his saddle to catch the child from off the
　　ground;
As his horse approached the maiden everyone there held his
　　breath,
For the race that he was running was a race of life and death.

Low he swept as fast he passed her; he had caught her in his
　　arms.
And I thought he was successful and safe from future harm.
But such weight upon those cinches had ne'er been put before,
And the hind cinch snapped asunder, and he lay beside Lenore.

As the girl fell from her pony she had dragged the blanket down,
And it lay there close beside her as she lay upon the ground.
Utah picked up the blanket. "Lie still," again he said,
Then he raced across the prairie and waved the blanket o'er his
　　head.

As he ran across the prairie every cowboy gave a cry,
"He has saved the boss's daughter, though we know he's bound to
　　die.
He has turned those maddened cattle from Lenore, his little
　　friend!"
And now they rushed upon him and he stopped to play his hand.

Quickly then from out the scabbard Utah Carroll his pistol
　　drew,
He was bound to die a-fighting, as all brave cowboys do.

His pistol flashed like lightning, the reports were loud and clear,
Still the herd came rushing onward, though he'd dropped the leading steer.

Soon the cattle were upon him and my pardner had to fall,
Nevermore to cinch a bronco, nor to give a cattle call.
There he died upon the ranges, though it seemed most awful hard
That I could not make the distance in time to save my pard.

When we broke into the circle, upon the ground my pardner lay;
From a hundred wounds and bruises he had passed his life away.
It was there I knelt beside him, though I knew his life was o'er;
Still I thought I heard him murmur, "I am coming—lie still,
Lenore."

Every boy upon the cow ranch knew how bravely Utah died,
And they passed his grave in sorrow and they spoke his name with
pride;
For he died as a cowboy, never bending, never a fear
When the cattle were upon him and the rush of death was near.

"And in some future morning," I heard the preacher say,
"I hope we'll all meet Utah at the round-up far away."
Then we wrapped him in a blanket sent by his little friend,
And it was that very red blanket that brought him to his end.

TEN THOUSAND CATTLE*

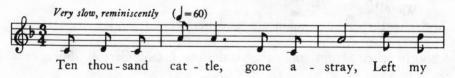

Very slow, reminiscently (♩ = 60)

Ten thou-sand cat-tle, gone a-stray, Left my

* From *Singing Cowboy* by Margaret Larkin, p. 151 (New York: Knopf).

[128]

range, and trav-eled a-way, And the sons-of-
guns, I'm here to say, Have left me dead broke, dead broke
to-day. In gam-bling hells de-lay-ing,
Ten thou-sand cat-tle stray-ing, stray-ing.

Ten thousand cattle, gone astray,
Left my range and traveled away,
And the sons-of-guns, I'm here to say,
Have left me dead broke, dead broke today.

Refrain:
    In gambling hells delaying,
    Ten thousand cattle straying, straying.

And my gal, she has gone away,
Left my shack and traveled away,
With a son-of-a-gun from Ioway,
And left me a lone man, a lone man today.

Refrain:
    In gambling hells delaying,
    Ten thousand cattle straying, straying.

She was awful sweet and loved me so
But the Ioway fellow made her go;
Now my heart is broke, and I'm weak and low,
And to drink my life away is all I know.

Refrain:

>In gambling hells delaying,
>Ten thousand cattle straying, straying.

I had a ranch and cattle on the plains
And every year my business showed a gain
But when she left me, it caused me ache and pain
And I'll never try to build a home again.

Refrain:

>In gambling hells delaying,
>Ten thousand cattle straying, straying.

TEN THOUSAND GOD–DAMN CATTLE*

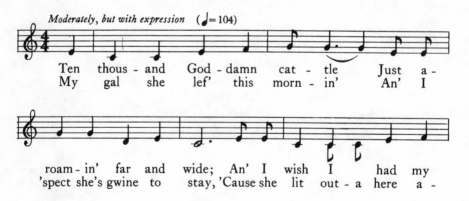

Moderately, but with expression (♩ = 104)

Ten thous - and God - damn cat - tle Just a -
My gal she lef' this morn - in' An' I

roam - in' far and wide; An' I wish I had my
'spect she's gwine to stay, 'Cause she lit out - a here a -

* With apologies to Daca's Bookstore, Greenwich Village, New York City.

hon - ey
run - nin'
With a
Lay - in'
son - of - a - bitch from I
by my
- o -

side.
way.
Lone
Lone
man,
man,
lone
lone
man.
man.

Ten thousand God-damn cattle,
Just a-roamin' far an' wide;
An' I wish I had my honey
Layin' by my side.
Lone man! Lone man!

My gal she lef' this mornin'
An' I spect she's gwine to stay,
'Cause she lit outa here a-runnin'
With a son-of-a-bitch from Ioway.
Lone man! Lone man!

Dead broke!

III

DODGE CITY, THE END OF THE TRAIL

The lions on the mountains I've drove them to their lairs;
The wildcats are my playmates and I've wrestled grizzly bears;
I'm wild and woolly and full of fleas,
And I've never been curried above the knees.
Whoopee! It's my night to h-o-w-l.

* * * * *

And when my work is over, to Cheyenne then I'll head,
Fill up on beer and whiskey and paint the damn town red,
I'll gallop through the front streets with many a frightful yell;
I'll rope the slant old heathen and then yank them straight to hell.

* * * * *

Oh, bury me beside my knife and six-shooter,
My spurs on my heels, my rifle at my side;
And place on my coffin a bottle of brandy,
That the cowboys may drink as they carry me along.

* * * * *

The sheriff followed hard and fast, a muy hombre he,
He had a posse at his back, a rifle at his knee;
But when he turned his sixes loose, we let him know
It took a Jim Dandy to bring us back from New Mexico.

THE BOASTING DRUNK IN DODGE

When a group of cowboys reached Dodge City from Texas, they had not slept in a bed for months; nor had they shaved or enjoyed a hot bath or a haircut. Their clothing was dirty, often ragged. They had not seen a woman perhaps for half a year. The saloons of Dodge never shut their doors (on the opening day the proprietor threw away the keys). The red lights in back of the saloons beckoned. First the cowboys got rid of their extra hair, bought new outfits of clothing, and then they tanked up. They were ready to go. Some were quiet in their dissipation. Others talked—perhaps to keep up their courage—as does the "Boasting Drunk." Dodge was the toughest town known in 1883.

Raised on six-shooters till I get big enough to eat ground shot-
    guns,
When I'm cool I warm the Gulf of Mexico and bathe therein,
When I'm hot there's an equinoxical breeze that fans me fevered
    brow,
The moans of widows and orphans is music to me melancholy
    soul.

Me the boy that chewed the wad the goat eat that butted the goat
    off the bridge,
Born in the Rocky Mountains, suckled by a grizzly bear,
Ninety-nine rows of jaw teeth and not a single hair.

Thirty-two inches 'tween the eyes and they feed me with a shovel,
Mount the wild ass and leap from crag to crag,

[135]

And roar like laughter in a tomb,
Jump from precipice to precipice and back to pice again.

Snatched him bald-headed and spit on the place where the hair
    come off;
Take a leg off him and beat him over the head with the bloody end
    of it,
Slap his head up to a peak and then knock the peak off,
Take his eye out and eat it for a grape.

Gimme one hundred yards start and I'll run plumb to Honolulu
    without even wettin' my feet,
Shoulder five hundred bushel of shot and wade through solid rocks
    up to my shoulder blades.
Any damn man don't believe it . . .

I'll lick him on a sheep hide and never tromp on the tail,
Knock a belch out of him that'll whiz like a nail,
Knock a belch out of him longer'n a rail,
Sharp enough to stick a pig with.

DRINKING SONG

J. B. Jones of Los Angeles heard Bob Walker, "a wanderer, half
Seminole Indian and half Negro," sing this song. "Walker learned
this somewhere in the West."

> Drink that rotgut, drink that rotgut,
> Drink that redeye, boys;
> It don't make a damn wherever we land,
> We hit her up for joy.
>
> We've lived in the saddle and ridden trail,
> Drink old Jordan, boys.

[136]

We'll go whooping and yelling, we'll all go a-helling,
Drink her to our joy.

Whoopee! drink that rotgut, drink that red nose,
Whenever you get to town;
Drink it straight and swig it mighty,
Till the world goes round and round!

THE DESPERADO

I'm a howler from the prairies of the West.
If you want to die with terror, look at me.
I'm chain-lightning—if I ain't may I be blessed.
I'm the snorter of the boundless prairie.

    He's a killer and a hater!
    He's the great annihilator!
    He's a terror of the boundless prairie.

I'm the snoozer from the upper trail!
I'm the reveler in murder and in gore!
I can bust more Pullman coaches on the rail
Than any one who's worked the job before.

    He's a snorter and a snoozer.
    He's the great trunk-line abuser.
    He's the man who puts the sleeper on the rail.

I'm the double-jawed hyena from the East,
I'm the blazing, bloody blizzard of the States.
I'm the celebrated slugger; I'm the Beast.
I can snatch a man bald-headed while he waits.

[137]

He's a double-jawed hyena!
He's the villain of the scena!
He can snatch a man bald-headed while he waits.

THE BAD MAN FROM THE BRAZOS*

I'm a blizzard from the Brazos on a tear, hear me hoot;
I'm a lifter of the flowing locks of hair, hear me toot;
    I'm a rocker from the Rockies
    And of all the town the talk is,
"He's a pirate from the Pampas on the shoot."

Sometimes I meet a city unprotected, paint it red;
Choke the sheriff, stand the marshal upside-down, on his head;
    Call for drinks for all the party,
    And if chinned by any smarty
Pull my gun right out and freely pay in lead.

Those who love me call me Little Dynamite, I'm a pet;
I'm walking, stalking terror of the night, you can bet;
    By my nickel-plated teasers
    Many a rusty-featured greaser's,
Many a rusty-featured greaser's sun has set.

I'm a coyote of the prairie dude, hear me zip;
In the company of gentlemen I'm rude with my lip;
    Down in front remove that nigger,
    Or I'll perforate his figger;
I'm a fighter, I am fly, and I am flip.

* Sent by Mrs. Louis Meilcarek, Chicago, Ill., whose father brought it home from Texas
in '83 or '84, having learned it from a copy of *Texas Siftings.* "He sang it to the tune of
'La-da-da.'"

THE COWBOY*

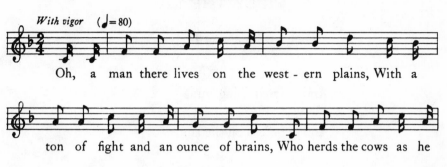

Oh, a man there lives on the west - ern plains, With a
ton of fight and an ounce of brains, Who herds the cows as he
robs the trains and goes by the name of cow - boy.

Oh, a man there lives on the Western plains,
With a ton of fight and an ounce of brains,
Who herds the cows as he robs the trains
And goes by the name of cowboy.

He laughs at death and scoffs at life;
He feels unwell unless in some strife.
He fights with a pistol, a rifle, or knife,
This reckless, rollicking cowboy.

He sets up drinks when he hasn't a cent;
He'll fight like hell with any young gent.
When he makes love, he goes it hell-bent,
Oh, he's some lover, this cowboy.

He shoots out lights in a dancing hall;
He gets shot up in a drunken brawl.
Some coroner's jury then ends it all,
And that's the last of the cowboy.

* From *Cowboy Sings* (p. 69), edited by Kenneth Clark (New York: Paull-Pioneer Music Corporation).

BILLY THE KID

[*Version 1**]

Billy was a bad man
And carried a big gun,
He was always after Greasers
And kept 'em on the run.

He shot one every morning,
For to make his morning meal.
And let a white man sass him,
He was shore to feel his steel.

He kept folks in hot water,
And he stole from many a stage;
And when he was full of liquor
He was always in a rage.

He kept things boilin' over,
He stayed out in the brush,
And when he was full of dead eye,
T'other folkses better hush.

But one day he met a man
Who was a whole lot badder.
And now he's dead,
And we ain't none the sadder.

* Sent in 1911 to John B. Jones by Jim Marby, who inhabited a place near Tucson, Arizona, with Sam Niggertoe, his pet coyote, an animal Jim found a whole lot easier than any of his wives.

[140]

[*Version 2**]

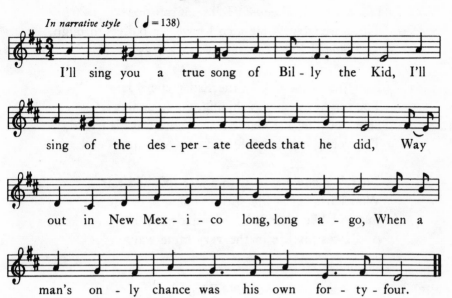

In narrative style (♩ = 138)

I'll sing you a true song of Bil-ly the Kid, I'll sing of the des-per-ate deeds that he did, Way out in New Mex-i-co long, long a-go, When a man's on-ly chance was his own for-ty-four.

> I'll sing you a true song of Billy the Kid,
> I'll sing of the desperate deeds that he did,
> Way out in New Mexico long, long ago,
> When a man's only chance was his own 44.
>
> When Billy the Kid was a very young lad,
> In the old Silver City he went to the bad;
> Way out in the West with a gun in his hand
> At the age of twelve years he first killed his man.
>
> Fair Mexican maidens play guitars and sing
> A song about Billy, their boy bandit king,
> How ere his young manhood had reached its sad end
> He'd a notch on his pistol for twenty-one men.

* From Victor Record No. 20396 and *American Ballads and Folk Songs*, pp. 137-138 (New York: Macmillan).

'Twas on the same night when poor Billy died
He said to his friends: "I am not satisfied;
There are twenty-one men I have put bullets through,
And Sheriff Pat Garrett must make twenty-two."

Now this is how Billy the Kid met his fate:
The bright moon was shining, the hour was late,
Shot down by Pat Garrett, who once was his friend,
The young outlaw's life had now come to its end.

There's many a man with a face fine and fair
Who starts out in life with a chance to be square,
But just like poor Billy he wanders astray
And loses his life in the very same way.

QUANTRELL

[*Version 1**]

With spirit and enthusiasm (♩. = 66)

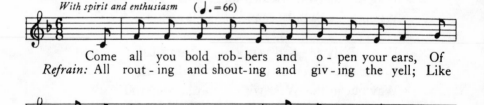

Come all you bold rob-bers and o - pen your ears, Of
Refrain: All rout - ing and shout-ing and giv-ing the yell; Like

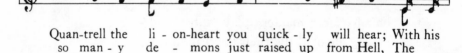

Quan-trell the li - on-heart you quick - ly will hear; With his
so man - y de - mons just raised up from Hell, The

---

* From *American Ballads and Folk Songs* (New York: Macmillan). Quantrell is said to
have gone up the trail with Texas cattle in 1866 (*Trail Drivers of Texas*, p. 38, col. 2).

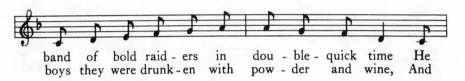

band of bold raid - ers in   dou - ble - quick time   He
boys they were drunk - en with pow - der   and wine, And

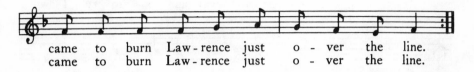

came to   burn Law - rence just   o - ver the   line.
came to   burn Law - rence just   o - ver the   line.

Come all you bold robbers and open your ears,
Of Quantrell the lion-heart you quickly will hear;
With his band of bold raiders in double-quick time
He came to burn Lawrence just over the line.

Chorus:

All routing and shouting and giving the yell,
Like so many demons just raised up from hell,
The boys they were drunken with powder and wine
And came to burn Lawrence just over the line.

They came to burn Lawrence, they came not to stay,
They rode in one morning at breaking of day,
Their guns were a-waving, their horses a-foam,
And Quantrell a-riding his famous big roan.

They came to burn Lawrence, they came not to stay.
Jim Lane he was up at the break of the day;
He saw them a-coming and got in a fright,
Then crawled in a corncrib to get out of sight.

Oh, Quantrell's a fighter, a bold-hearted boy,
A brave man or woman he'll never annoy;
He'd take from the wealthy and give to the poor,
For brave men there's never a bolt to his door.

[143]

[*Version 2**]

With a good swing (♩.=92)

It is of a fear-less high-way-man a sto-ry I will

tell. His name was Char - lie Quan-trell, and in

Kan - sas he did dwell; It was on the Kan - sas

plains he com-menced his wild ca - reer; And man - y weal-thy

gen - tle - men be - fore him stood with fear......

REFRAIN

Char - lie Quan-trell - o...... Char - lie Quan-trell - o - o-

o. Bold, gay, and dar - ing stood old Char-lie Quan-trell-o.....

* From Mrs. Cora Burgess and Mrs. George White, Grand Saline, Texas. Mrs. Burgess says: "I learned this song from my mother, who learned it from her boy friend fifty years ago. He learned it 'out West.' "

It is of a fearless highwayman a story I will tell.
His name was Charlie Quantrell, and in Kansas he did dwell;
It was on the Kansas plains he commenced his wild career,
And many wealthy gentlemen before him stood with fear.

Refrain:
    Charlie Quantrell-o, Charlie Quantrell-o-o-o-o,
    Bold, gay, and daring stood old Charlie Quantrell-o.

With a brace of loaded pistols he carried both night and day,
Though he never robbed a poor man while on the highway,
But what he taken from the rich, like tops and like best,
He always did divide it with the widow in distress.

One night he met a packman whose name was Tideo Brown,
And they traveled on together till the day began to dawn;
When the packman found his money gone, likewise his watch and
    chain,
He at once encountered Quantrell and he robbed him back again.

Now Charlie saw the packman as good a man as he;
He asked him as a comrade on the highway for to be;
The packman he consented without a word's delay,
And he proved a loyal comrade until his dying day.

As Charles went out to walk one day, 'twas early on one morn,
He met the mayor of Casmeyer just outside of town;
Now the mayor knew his features, and "Your name," he said, "must
    be,
Oh, your name is Charlie Quantrell, you must come along with me."

Now Charlie's wife to town had gone provisions for to buy;
When she saw her Charlie taken, she began to weep and cry;

"Oh, I wish I had a dollar," said he. No sooner had he spoke,
Than she handed him a blunderbus from underneath her coat.

Now with this loaded blunderbus, the truth it must be told,
It caused the mayor to tremble and it robbed him of his gold;
Five thousand pounds were there laid down and then preëmpted
    there,
And with his horse and saddle to the mountains did repair.

Now Charlie being an outlaw, upon the mountain high,
With both infantry and cavalry to take him they did try.
But he hid among the brush that grew thick upon the field,
And received nine wounds before he would yield.

It was at a little prairie the place they call Lamar,
Where Charlie and his comrade were forced to suffer sore;
The jury found them guilty and the judge gave this reply,
"For robbing on the highway you're both condemned to die."

"Now farewell, dear wife and my little children three,
And you, my aged father who sheds those tears for me,
And likewise my dear old mother," who tore gray hair and cried,
Saying, "It were better, Charlie, in your cradle you had died."

Refrain:
    Charlie Quantrell-o, Charlie Quantrell-o-o-o-o,
    Brave, gay, and daring stood old Charlie Quantrell-o.

ROY BEAN*

Known as "The Law West of the Pecos"

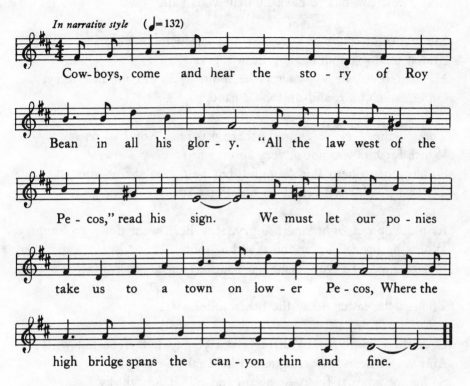

Cowboys, come and hear the story of Roy Bean in all his glory.
"All the law west of the Pecos," read his sign.
We must let our ponies take us to a town on lower Pecos
Where the high bridge spans the canyon thin and fine.

He was born one day in Toyah, where he learned to be a lawyer,
A teacher and a barber and the mayor.

* From *American Ballads and Folk Songs* (New York: Macmillan, 1934). The words came from Slim Critchlow, Utah Buckaroos, Salt Lake City, Utah. Recently Charles J. Finger of Fayetteville, Arkansas, modestly confessed that he wrote this metrical story of some of the activities of Roy Bean.

He was cook and old-shoe mender, sometimes preacher and bartender,
And it cost two-bits to have him cut your hair.

He was right smart of a hustler and considerable a rustler,
And at mixing up an eggnog he was grand;
He was clever, he was merry, he could drink a Tom and Jerry,
On occasion at a round-up took a hand.

Though the story isn't funny, there was once Roy had no money,
Which for him was not so very strange or rare;
So he went to help Pop Wyndid, but he got so absent-minded
That he put his RB brand on old Pop's steer.

As old Pop got right smart angry, Roy Bean went down to Langtry,
Where he opened up an office and a store.
Where he'd sell you drinks or buttons or another rancher's mut-
tons,
Though the latter made the other feller sore.

Once there came from Austin City a young dude reported witty,
And out of Bean he sorta guessed he'd take a rise;
So he got unusual frisky as he up and called for whisky
Sayin', "Bean, now hurry up, gol durn your eyes."

Then down he threw ten dollars, which the same Roy quickly col-
lars,
And the same Roy holds to nine and hands back one;
Then the dude he gave a holler, when he saw that single dollar,
And right then began the merriment and fun.

The dude he slammed the table just as hard as he was able,
The price of whisky was too high, he swore.

Said Roy Bean, "For all your fussin' and your most outrageous
    cussin'
You are fined the other dollar by the law.

"On this place I hold a lease. I'm the Justice of the Peace,
And the law west of the Pecos all is here,
And you've acted very badly." Then the dude he went off sadly
While down his lily cheek there rolled a tear.

One fine day they found a dead man who in life had been a red
    man,
Though it's doubtless he was nothing else than bad.
They called Bean to view the body. First he took a drink of toddy,
Then he listed all the things the dead man had.

For a red man he was tony, for he had a pretty pony
And a dandy bit and saddle and a rope;
He'd a very fine Navajo rug and a quart within his jug
And a pony that was dandy on the lope.

So the find it was quite rare-o, for he'd been a cocinero*
And his Pay-day hadn't been so far away.
He'd a brand-new fine white Stetson and a silver Smith and Wes-
    son,
While a purse of forty dollars jingled gay.

Said Roy Bean: "You'll learn a lesson, for you have a Smith and
    Wesson,
And to carry implements of war is wrong.
Forty dollars I will fine you, for we couldn't well confine you,
As already you've been layin' round too long."

* Cook.

[149]

Now, you boys have heard the story of Roy Bean in all his glory;
He's the man who was the justice and the law,
He was handy with his hooks, and he was ornery in his looks,
And just now I ain't gonna tell you any more.

SAM BASS

Vigorously (♩=92)

Sam Bass was born in In - di - an - a, it
Sam used to deal in race stock, one

was his na - tive home, And at the age of sev-en-teen, young
called the Den - ton mare; He matched her in scrub rac - es and

Sam be - gan to roam. Sam first came out to Tex - as a
took her to the fair. Sam used to coin the mon-ey and

cow - boy for to be; A
spent it just as free, He

kind - er-heart - ed fel - low you sel - dom ev - er see.
al - ways drank good whis-ky wher - ev - er he might be.

Sam Bass was born in Indiana, it was his native home,
And at the age of seventeen, young Sam began to roam.
Sam first came out to Texas a cowboy for to be—
A kinder-hearted fellow you seldom ever see.

Sam used to deal in race stock, one called the Denton mare;
He matched her in scrub races and took her to the fair.
Sam used to coin the money and spent it just as free,
He always drank good whisky wherever he might be.

Sam left the Collins ranch in the merry month of May
With a herd of Texas cattle the Black Hills for to see,
Sold out in Custer City and then got on a spree—
A harder set of cowboys you seldom ever see.

On their way back to Texas they robbed the U.P. train,
And then split up in couples and started out again.
Joe Collins and his partner were overtaken soon,
With all their hard-earned money they had to meet their doom.

Sam made it back to Texas all right side up with care;
Rode into the town of Denton with all his friends to share.
Sam's life was short in Texas; three robberies did he do:
He robbed all the passenger, mail, and express cars too.

Sam had four companions—four bold and daring lads—
They were Richardson, Jackson, Joe Collins, and Old Dad;
Four more bold and daring cowboys the rangers never knew,
They whipped the Texas Rangers and ran the boys in blue.

Sam had another companion, called Arkansas for short,
Was shot by a Texas Ranger by the name of Thomas Floyd;
Oh, Tom is a big six-footer and thinks he's mighty fly,
But I can tell you his racket—he's a deadbeat on the sly.

Jim Murphy was arrested, and then released on bail;
He jumped his bond at Tyler and then took the train for Terrell;
But Mayor Jones had posted Jim and that was all a stall,
'Twas only a plan to capture Sam before the coming fall.

Sam met his fate at Round Rock, July the twenty-first,
They pierced poor Sam with rifle balls and emptied out his purse.
Poor Sam he is a corpse and six foot under clay,
And Jackson's in the bushes trying to get away.*

Jim had borrowed Sam's good gold and didn't want to pay,
The only shot he saw was to give poor Sam away.
He sold out Sam and Barnes and left their friends to mourn—
Oh, what a scorching Jim will get when Gabriel blows his horn! †

And so he sold out Sam and Barnes and left their friends to mourn.
Oh, what a scorching Jim will get when Gabriel blows his horn!
Perhaps he's got to heaven, there's none of us can say,
But if I'm right in my surmise he's gone the other way.

JESSE JAMES

[*Version 1*]

Steadily, in strict narrative style (♩=92)

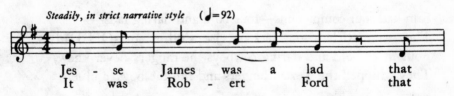

Jes - se James was a lad that
It was Rob - ert Ford that

* Jackson has not been seen, hide nor hair, since that day.
† "I can call to memory Jim Murphy. He was near my age, for we was once schoolboys together. This Jim Murphy gave Sam and his outfit away, and I was told by a man present in the neighborhood where Jim Murphy died that Jim contracted sore eyes because some of Sam's friends slipped deadly poison in Jim's eye medicine and caused him to die a raving maniac."—J. M. Thorne, Fort Worth, Texas.

killed a-ma-ny a man; He robbed the Dan-ville
dir-ty lit---tle coward, I won-der how he does

train. But that dir-ty lit-tle cow-ard that
feel, For he ate of Jes-se's bread and he

shot Mis-ter How-ard Has laid poor Jes-se in his grave.
slept in Jes-se's bed, Then laid poor Jes-se in his grave.

REFRAIN

Poor Jes-se had a wife to mourn for his life, Three

chil-dren they were brave; But that dir-ty lit-tle cow-ard that

shot Mis-ter How-ard Has laid poor Jes-se in his grave.

Jesse James was a lad that killed a-many a man;
He robbed the Danville train.
But that dirty little coward that shot Mr. Howard
Has laid poor Jesse in his grave.

Poor Jesse had a wife to mourn for his life,
Three children, they were brave;
But that dirty little coward that shot Mr. Howard
Has laid poor Jesse in his grave.*

It was Robert Ford, that dirty little coward,
I wonder how he does feel,
For he ate of Jesse's bread and he slept in Jesse's bed,
Then laid poor Jesse in his grave.

Jesse was a man, a friend to the poor,
He never would see a man suffer pain;
And with his brother Frank he robbed the Chicago bank,
And stopped the Glendale train.

It was his brother Frank that robbed the Gallatin bank,
And carried the money from the town;
It was in this very place that they had a little race,
For they shot Captain Sheets to the ground.

They rallied out West for to live upon the best,
The Fletchers asked their names;
They laughed and smiled as they made their reply,
"We are Frank and Jesse James."

It was on Wednesday night, the moon was shining bright,
They robbed the Glendale train;
The people they did say, for many miles away,
It was robbed by Frank and Jesse James.

It was on Saturday night, Jesse was at home
Talking to his family brave,

* A variant refrain runs:
　　　　Jesse's wife was a lady all her life,
　　　　Three children, they were brave;
　　　　But the dirty little Ford, he beat her of his board
　　　　And laid poor Jesse in his grave.

[154]

Robert Ford came along like a thief in the night*
And laid poor Jesse in his grave.

The people held their breath when they heard of Jesse's death,
And wondered how he ever came to die.
It was one of the gang called little Robert Ford,
He shot poor Jesse on the sly.

Jesse went to his rest with his hand on his breast;
The devil will be upon his knee.
He was born one day in the County of Clay
And came from a solitary race.

Jesse went down to the old man town,
Thinking he would do as he'd please;
But he will dwell in the City of Hell
And he'll go to the devil on his knees.

This song was made by Billy Gashade,†
As soon as the news did arrive;
He said there was no man with the law in his hand
Who could take Jesse James when alive.

[*Version 2*‡]

Jesse James was a man who traveled through the land,
Stealin' an' robbin' wuz 'is trade;
But a dirty little coward by the name of Robert Howard
Laid Jesse James in 'is grave.

* "Robert Ford's pistol ball knocked him tumbling from the wall." Jesse was hanging a picture as Ford, a guest and supposed friend, shot him from behind.
† The last stanza was made by a Missouri Negro.
‡ From eastern Tennessee mountain whites, from memory, as given by C. H. Perrow, "Songs and Rhymes of the South," *Journal of American Folk Lore,* Vol. XXV, p. 137.

Pore Jesse James! Pore Jesse James!
　Laid Jesse James in 'is grave;
En a dirty little coward by the name of Robert Howard
　Laid Jesse James in 'is grave.

Oh, the people of the West, when they heard of Jesse's death,
　Wondered how the hero come ter die;
But a dirty little coward by the name of Robert Howard
　Laid Jesse James in his grave.

It wuz late one Saddy night when the moon wuz shinin' bright
　That Jesse robbed the Danville train;
But thet Smith an' Wesson ball knocked por Jesse frum the wall
　En laid Jesse James in 'is grave.

[*Version 3**]

Oh! Jesse was the man, he traveled through the land,
　For money Jesse never suffered pain;
Jesse and his brother Frank, they robbed the Chicago bank
　And stopped the Danville train.

Jesse said to his brother Frank, "Will you stand by my side
　Till the Danville train passes by?"
"Yes, I'll stand by your side and fight one hundred men till I die
　And the Danville train has rolled by."

Oh, Robert Ford was the man, he traveled through the land,
　He never robbed a train in his life;
But he told the courts his aim was to kill Jesse James,
　And to live in peace with his wife.

* From eastern Kentucky mountain whites, MS. of C. B. House, as given by C. T. Perrow, "Songs and Rhymes of the South," *Journal of American Folk Lore*, Vol. XXV, p. 137.

Ten thousand dollars reward was given Robert Ford
    For killing Jesse James on the sly;
Poor Jesse has gone to rest with his hands upon his breast,
    And I'll remember Jesse James till I die.

[*Version 4**]

Jesse James was a boy that downed many a man,
    He held up the Danville train,
He robbed from the rich and he gave to the poor,
    He'd a hand and a heart and a brain.

Chorus:

    Poor Jesse left a wife to mourn all her life,
        His children three were brave,
    But the dirty little coward that shot Mr. Howard,
        He laid poor Jesse in his grave.

Jesse's brother Frank cleaned out Gallatin Bank
    And he took all the cash from the place,
And they shot Captain Sheets in the public streets,
    For it was a lively race.

Jess went to the depot the agent for to see,
    And there they surrendered the keys
To Jesse James and Frank who had cleaned out the bank,
    And the agent was on his knees.

And that same midnight when the moon was shining bright,
    They stopped the Glenville train,
They were bold hearts there and they did it without fear,
    It was planned by Jesse's brain.

* As sung by Jim Welsh; reported in *Frontier Ballads*, by Charles J. Finger (New York: Doubleday, Page, 1927).

Then the sad, sad thing what we have to sing,
When Jesse with his family in his shack
Was reading the Book then Robert Ford took
A shot at poor Jesse James.

JUAN MURRAY*

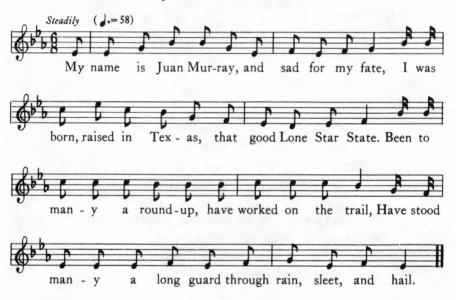

My name is Juan Mur-ray, and sad for my fate, I was
born, raised in Tex - as, that good Lone Star State. Been to
man - y a round-up, have worked on the trail, Have stood
man - y a long guard through rain, sleet, and hail.

My name is Juan Murray, and sad for my fate,
I was born, raised in Texas, that good Lone Star State.
Been to many a round-up, have worked on the trail,
Have stood many a long guard through rain, sleet, and hail.

I am a jolly cowboy and have roamed all over the West,
And among the bronco riders I rank among the best.
But when I left old Midland, with voice right then I spoke:
"I never will see you again until the day I croak."

* From T. C. Thornton, Fort Worth, Texas.

But since I left old Texas so many sights I have saw,
A-traveling from my native state way out to Mexico—
I am looking all around me and cannot help but smile
To see my nearest neighbors all in the Mexican style.

I left my home in Texas to dodge the ball and chain.
In the State of Sonora I will forever remain.
Farewell to my mother, my friends that are so dear,
I would like to see you all again, my lonesome heart to cheer.

I have a word to speak, boys, only another to say:
Don't never be a cow-thief, don't never ride a stray;
Be careful of your line, boys, and keep it on your tree—
Just suit yourself about it, for it is nothing to me.

But if you start to rustling you will come to some sad fate,
You will have to go to prison and work for the state.
Don't think that I am lying and trying to tell a joke,
For the writer has experienced just every word he's spoke.

It is better to be honest and let others' stock alone
Than to leave your native country and seek a Mexican home.
For if you start to rustling you will surely come to see
The State of Sonora—be an outcast just like me.

BOW DOWN YOUR HEAD AND CRY

Tune, "The Boston Burglar"

A cowboy ballad of northwest Texas, which seems to be a "cattalo"
—"The Fair Maid Freed from the Gallows" being the cow and
"The Boston Burglar" the buffalo bull.

[159]

I went down to the river, poor boy,
To see the ships go by;
My sweetheart stood on the deck of one,
She waved to me good-bye.

Refrain:
Bow down your head and cry, poor boy,
Bow down your head and cry;
Stop thinking of the girl you love,
Bow down your head and cry.

I followed her for months and months
And offered her my hand;
She was just about to have me, when
She ran off with a gambling man. (*Refrain.*)

He came at me with a jackknife,
I went at him with lead,
And when the fight was over,
He lay beside me dead. (*Refrain.*)

They took me to the jail-house,
The days and days rolled by;
The jury found me guilty,
And the judge says, "You must die." (*Refrain.*)

"Oh, do you bring me silver, poor boy,
Or do you bring me gold?"
"I bring you neither," said the man,
"I bring you a hangman's fold." (*Refrain.*)

"Oh, do you bring my pardon, poor boy,
To turn me a-loose?"
"I bring you nothing," said the man,
"Except a hangman's noose." (*Refrain.*)

And yet they call this justice!
And justice let it be!
I only killed the man that was
Just fixing to kill me. (*Refrain.*)

I went down to the river,
To see the ships go by;
My sweetheart stood on the deck of one
She waved to me good-bye. (*Refrain.*)

THE BAD BOY

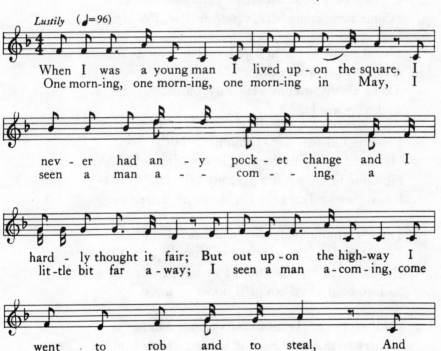

When I was a young man I lived up-on the square, I
One morn-ing, one morn-ing, one morn-ing in May, I

nev-er had an-y pock-et change and I
seen a man a-- com--ing, a

hard-ly thought it fair; But out up-on the high-way I
lit-tle bit far a-way; I seen a man a-com-ing, come

went to rob and to steal, And
rid-ing up to me. "Come

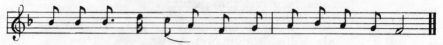

when I met   a ped-dler, oh, how   hap-py   I   did feel!
here, come here, young fel - low, I'm   af - ter you to - day."

When I was a young man I lived upon the square,
I never had any pocket change and I hardly thought it fair;
But out upon the highway I went to rob and to steal,
And when I met a peddler, oh, how happy I did feel!

One morning, one morning, one morning in May
I seen a man a-coming, a little bit far away;
I seen a man a-coming, come riding up to me.
"Come here, come here, young fellow, I'm after you today."

He taken me to the new jail, he taken me to the new jail,
And I had to walk right in.
There all my friends went back on me
And also my kin.

I had an old rich uncle, who lived in the West,
He heard of my misfortune, it wouldn't let him rest;
He came to see me, he paid my bills and score—
I have been a bad boy, I'll do so no more.

There's Minnie and Alice and Lucy likewise,
They heard of my misfortune, brought tears to their eyes.
I've told 'em my condition, I've told it o'er and o'er;
So I've been a bad boy, I'll do so no more.

I will go to east Texas to marry me a wife,
And try to maintain her the balance of my life;
I'll try to maintain; I'll lay it up in store
I've been a bad boy, I'll do so no more.

Young man, you robber, you had better take it fair,
Leave off your marshal killing and live on the square;
Should you meet the marshal, just pass him by;
And travel on the muscular, for it's root hog or die.

When I drew my money I drew it all in cash
And off to see my Susan, you bet I cut a dash;
I spent my money freely and went it on a bum,
And I love the pretty women and am bound to have my fun.

I used to sport a white hat, a horse and buggy fine,
Courted a pretty girl and always called her mine;
But all my courtships proved to be in vain,
For they sent me down to Huntsville to wear the ball and chain.

Along came my true love, about twelve o'clock,
Saying, "Henry, O Henry, what sentence have you got?"
The jury found me guilty, the judge would allow no stay,
So they sent me down to Huntsville to wear my life away.

RYE WHISKY*

With gusto (♩.= 58)

I'll eat when I'm hun-gry, I'll drink when I'm dry; If the

hard times don't kill me, I'll live till I die.

* The second musical version, transcribed from a recent recording, employs the second
stanza of this version as a refrain. The various stanzas and refrains, however, can be used
interchangeably.

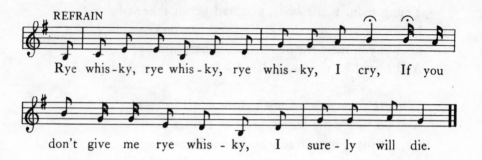

REFRAIN

Rye whis-ky, rye whis-ky, rye whis-ky, I cry, If you

don't give me rye whis-ky, I sure-ly will die.

I'll eat when I'm hungry, I'll drink when I'm dry;
If the hard times don't kill me, I'll live till I die.

Refrain:

Rye whisky, rye whisky, rye whisky, I cry,
If you don't give me rye whisky, I surely will die.

I'll tune up my fiddle, and I'll rosin my bow,
And make myself welcome wherever I go.

Beefsteak when I'm hungry, red liquor when I'm dry,
Greenbacks when I'm hard up, and religion when I die.

They say I drink whisky; my money's my own,
All them that don't like me can leave me alone.

Sometimes I drink whisky, sometimes I drink rum,
Sometimes I drink brandy, at other times none.

But if I get boozy, my whisky's my own,
And them that don't like me can leave me alone.

Jack o' diamonds, jack o' diamonds, I know you of old,
You've robbed my poor pockets of silver and gold.

[164]

Oh, whisky, you villain, you've been my downfall;
You've kicked me, you've cuffed me, but I love you for all.

If the ocean was whisky and I was a duck
I'd dive to the bottom and get one sweet suck.

But the ocean ain't whisky and I ain't a duck,
So we'll round up the cattle and then we'll get drunk.

Sweet milk when I'm hungry, rye whisky when I'm dry,
If a tree don't fall on me, I'll live till I die.

I'll buy my own whisky, I'll make my own stew;
If I get drunk, madam, it's nothing to you.

I'll drink my own whisky, I'll drink my own wine;
Some ten thousand bottles I've killed in my time.

I'll drink and I'll gamble, my money's my own,
And them that don't like me can leave me alone.

My foot in the stirrup, my bridle in my hand,
A-courting fair Mollie, to marry if I can.

My foot's in my stirrup, my bridle's in my hand;
I'm leaving sweet Mollie, the fairest in the land.

Her parents don't like me, they say I'm too poor;
They say I'm unworthy to enter her door.

I've no wife to quarrel, no babies to bawl;
The best way of living is no wife at all.

Way up on Clinch Mountain I wander alone;
I'm as drunk as the devil. Oh, let me alone.

You may boast of your knowledge, and brag of your sense,
'Twill all be forgotten a hundred years hence.

[*Version 2*]

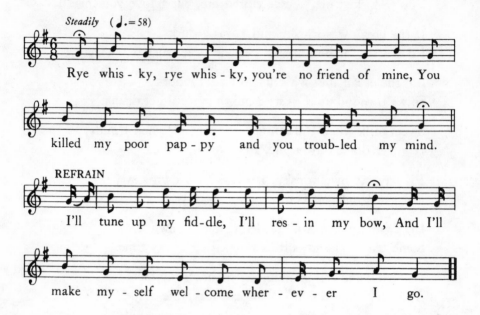

Steadily (♩.= 58)

Rye whis - ky, rye whis - ky, you're no friend of mine, You

killed my poor pap - py and you troub-led my mind.

REFRAIN

I'll tune up my fid-dle, I'll res - in my bow, And I'll

make my - self wel - come wher - ev - er I go.

O–BAR COWBOY*

Another "Rye Whisky"

I will drink, I will gamble, I will play wild again,
Oh, I'm a wild cowboy from the branding pen.

I will rope them, I will throw them, I will soon have them tied,
I will stamp the O-Bar right on their left side.

I have worked for the Bar-H's, the Three Times Nine,
But the O-Bar yearlings are the worst I can find.

They will ring and they will jar, they will raise old hell,
When one leaves the round-up, he sure bids it farewell.

* "Composed" and sung by Bill Wagon, Sierra Blanca, Texas.

Out over the prairie he will snuff and he will glide—
If I rope that yearling, I will sure have to ride.

But the O-Bar ponies their gaits they have got,
From the speed of the lightning to a slow turkey trot.

Jerk down my bedcord, my line I will swing,
I'm goin' to lasso that yearlin', rope him on the wing.

When I rope him, I'll throw him, I'll have him hog-tied,
I'll burn the O-Bar right on his side.

Oh, the O-Bar are snaky and the O-Bar are wild,
But they can't show no tricks to this here child.

I will gamble, I will drink, I will play wild again,
I will drag up the yearlings in the O-Bar pen.

THE WILD MONTANA BOY *

There was a wild Montana boy, Jack Nolan was his name;
He lived in old Montana, close to the Canadian line.
He was his father's only pride, his mother's only joy,
And dearly did these parents love that wild Montana boy.

At the early age of sixteen Jack left his happy home,
For the sunny shores of Texas he was inclined to roam.
He robbed the rich and helped the poor, the farms he did destroy.
He was a terror to old Texas, this wild Montana boy.

At the early age of eighteen Jack began his wild career
With a heart that felt no harm and that knew no fear.

* Compare "Jack Donahoe," in "Cowboy Songs and Other Frontier Ballads" (New York: Macmillan, 1910). "The Wild Montana Boy" was sent by Mrs. Alberta Head of Missouri to "Fiddlin' Joe's Song Corral" in the *Wild West Weekly*.

[167]

He robbed the rich and helped the poor, he stopped George McRoy,
Who trembling gave his gold unto the wild Montana boy.

Jack bid the squire good morning and told him to beware,
And not arrest a poor boy while acting on the square;
And not to rob a mother of her only pride and joy,
For she might go a-rambling like her wild Montana boy.

One day Jack was a-riding on the prairie all alone,
Listening to the mockingbirds that sang their mournful songs,
Up to him there rode a mounted troop, Cole, Davis, and Fritz
    McRoy,
They started to capture him, that wild Montana boy.

"Surrender now, Jack Nolan—you know there's three to one.
Surrender to your government, you are its plundering son."
Jack snatched a pistol from his breast, and waved the little toy.
"I'll die but I'll not surrender," said the wild Montana boy.

He first fired at Fritz McRoy, which took him to the ground;
Then he fired on Davis, which gave him a deathly wound.
A bullet pierced Jack's proud heart from the weapon of Fritz
    McRoy,
And that's the way they captured him, that wild Montana boy.

THE COWBOY*

By the Cowboy Poet Lariat

It was only a few short years ago
When we were in our prime,
When a bunch of us went up the trail

* From *Bill Jones of Paradise Valley, Oklahoma and the Great Southwest* (p. 177), copyright 1914 by John J. Callison, Kingfisher, Okla.

To have a jolly good time.
It was hot July when we got to Dodge,
That wickedest little town; *
And we started in to have some fun
Just as the sun went down.

We killed a few of the worst bad men
For the pleasure of seeing them kick;
We rode right into a billiard hall,
And I guess we raised Old Nick.
The bartender left in wonderful haste
On that hot and sultry day;
He never came back to get his hat
Until we were miles away.

We went from Dodge to the town Caldwell,
As we wished to prolong the fun;
When the marshal there caught sight of us,
You ought to have seen him run.
We rode right into a big dance hall
That opened upon the street;
The music and dancing both were fine,
And the girlies sure looked sweet.

We drank all the Caldwell whisky,
We ate everything in sight;
We took in all the dances,
And they say we had a fight.
Charles Siringo was shot in the leg,
Dick Smith was shot in the neck;
Bill Jones was shot in the pocket,
As also was Henry Peck.

* "The toughest town on the map" in 1882.

[169]

We found in the Indian country
We must fight our way across,
For the reds were on the warpath,
Under old Chief Crazy Hoss.
When we landed back in Texas
After a lonesome trip,
We met some Texas Rangers
And I guess we had to skip.

We worked for King & Kennedy,
We worked for Shanghai Pierce,
We worked for the Slaughter brothers
When they were at their worst.
We worked on many another ranch,
As we wandered to and fro,
And back and forth and up and down,
From Dodge to Mexico.

Most of the boys have passed and gone
With whom we used to ride,
Into the unknown Valley of Peace,
Just over the Great Divide.
And when the final round-up comes,
The count shall be fair and straight,
As they enter the big corral above,
Through the heavenly Golden Gate.

BUCKSKIN JOE

'Twas a calm and peaceful evening in a camp called Arapahoe,
And the whisky was a-running with a soft and gentle flow,
The music was a-ringing in a dance hall 'cross the way,
And the dancers was a-swinging just as close as they could lay.

People gathered round the tables, a-betting with their wealth,
And near by stood a stranger who had come there for his health,
He was a peaceful little stranger though he seemed to be unstrung;
For just before he'd left his home he'd separated with one lung.

Near by at a table sat a man named Hankey Dean—
A tougher man, says Hankey, buckskin chaps had never seen.
But Hankey was a gambler, and he was plumb sure to lose;
For he had just departed with a sun-dried stack of blues.

He rose from the table, on the floor his last chip flung,
And cast his fiery glimmers on the man with just one lung.
"No wonder I've been losing every bet I made tonight
When a sucker and a tenderfoot was between me and the light.

"Look here, little stranger, do you know who I am?"
"Yes, and I don't care a copper-colored damn."
The dealers stopped their dealing, and the players held their breath,
For words like those to Hankey were a sudden flirt with death.

"Listen, gentle stranger, I'll read my pedigree;
I'm known on handling tenderfeet and worser men than thee,
The lions on the mountains, I've drove them to their lairs;
The wild-cats are my playmates, and I've wrestled grizzly bears.

"Why, the centipedes can't mar my tough old hide,
And rattlesnakes have bit me and crawled off and died.
I'm as wild as the horse that roams the range;
The moss grows on my teeth, and wild blood flows through my veins.

"I'm wild and woolly and full of fleas
And never curried below the knees.

[171]

Now, little stranger, if you'll give me your address—
How would you like to go, by fast mail or express?"

The little stranger who was leaning on the door
Picked up a hand of playing cards that were scattered on the floor.
Picking out the five of spades, he pinned it to the door
And then stepped back some twenty paces or more.

He pulled out his life-preserver and, with a "One, two, three, four,"
Blotted out a spot with every shot;
For he had traveled with a circus and was a fancy pistol shot.
"I have one more left, kind sir, if you wish to call the play."

Then Hankey stepped up to the stranger and made a neat apology:
"Why, the lions in the mountains—that was nothing but a joke.
Never mind about the extra, you are a bad shooting man,
And I'm a meek little child and as harmless as a lamb."

THE KILLER*

Dobe Bill, he came a-riding
    From the canyon, in the glow
Of a quiet Sunday morning
    From the town of Angelo;
Ridin' easy on the pinto
    That he dearly loved to straddle,
With a six-gun and sombrero
    That was wider than his saddle.
And he's hummin' as he's ridin'
    Of a simple little song

* Source unknown; first published in the *Wild West Weekly*.

That's a-rumblin' through the cactus
    As he's gallopin' along:

"Oh, I've rid from San Antony
    Through the mesquite and the sand,
I'm a r'arin', flarin' bucko,
    Not afraid to play my hand.
I'm a hootin', shootin' demon
    And I has my little fun
With my pinto called Apache
    And Adolphus—that's my gun."

Straight to Santa Fe he drifted,
    And he mills around the town,
Sorta gittin' of his bearin's
    While he pours his liquor down.
But he's watchin'—always watchin'—
    Every hombre in the place,
Like he's mebbe sorta lookin'
    For some certain hombre's face.

Then one night he saunters careless
    To the place of "Monte Sam,"
And he does a bit of playin'
    Like he doesn't give a damn.
All at once it's still and quiet
    Like a calm before a blow,
And the crowd is tense and nervous,
    And the playin's stopped and slow.

At the bar, a man is standin'
    Sneerin' as his glances lay.
Like a challenge did he fling 'em,
    Darin' 'em to make a play.

"Two-Gun" Blake, the Pecos killer,
  Hated, feared wherever known,
Stood and drank his glass of mescal
  With assurance all his own.

Then the eyes of Blake, the killer,
  Caught the glance of Dobe Bill,
And they held each one the other
  With the steel of looks that kill.
Then the tones of Blake came slowly,
  With a sneer in every word:
"Well, you've found me!" But the other
  Gave no sign he saw or heard.

Walkin' calmly toward the speaker,
  He advanced with steady pace.
Then he grinned and quick as lightnin'
  Slapped him squarely in the face.
"Shoot, you snake!" he whispered hoarsely.
  "Shoot, you lily-livered cur!
Draw! You're always strong for killin';
  Now I'm here to shoot for her!"

Some there was that claimed they saw it,
  As the killer tried to draw—
But there's no one knows for certain
  Just exactly what they saw.
I'll agree the shootin' started
  Quick as Blake had made his start—
Then a brace of bullets hit him
  Fair and certain through the heart.

As he fell, his hand was graspin'
  Of the gun he'd got too late,

With the notches on it showin'
　　Like the vagaries of Fate.
And the man who stood there lookin'
　　At the killer as he lay,
Murmured: "Nell, I've kept my promise.
　　I have made the scoundrel pay!"

Dobe Bill, he went a-ridin'
　　From the town of Santa Fe
On a quiet Sunday morning,
　　Goin' happy on his way,
Ridin' happy on that pinto
　　That he dearly loved to straddle,
With his six-gun and sombrero
　　That was wider than his saddle.
And he's hummin' as he's goin'
　　Of a simple little song
That's a-boomin' through the cactus
　　As he's gallopin' along:

"Oh, I'm goin' down the valley,
　　Through the mesquite and the sand.
I'm a r'arin', flarin' bucko,
　　Not afraid to play my hand.
I'm a hootin', shootin' demon
　　And I has my little fun
With my bronco called Apache
　　And Adolphus—that's my gun."

THE DURANT JAIL

The Du-rant jail beats no jail at all, If you

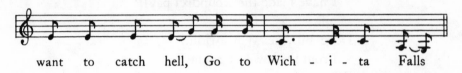

want to catch hell, Go to Wich-i-ta Falls

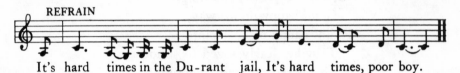

It's hard times in the Du-rant jail, It's hard times, poor boy.

The Durant jail beats no jail at all,
If you want to catch hell go to Wichita Falls.

Refrain:

It's hard times in the Durant jail,
It's hard times, poor boy.

There's a big bull ring in the middle of the floor,
And a damned old jailer to open the door.

Your pockets he'll pick, your clothes he will sell,
Your hands he will handcuff, Goddam him to hell!

It's both of my feet bound in the cell,
My hands tied behind, Goddam him to hell!

And here's to the cook, I wish he was dead,
It's old boiled beef and old corn bread.

The chuck they give us is beef and corn bread,
As old as hell and as heavy as lead.

[176]

We pop it down in us within our cells,
Just like the pop from heaven to hell.

The coffee is rough and the yard is full of hogs,
And we are guarded by two bulldogs.

No longer than yesterday I heard the jailer say,
He was feeding the prisoners at two dollars a day.

The times are hard at such poor pay,
He couldn't feed 'em grub but two times a day.

Our bed is made of old rotten rugs;
When we lay down we are all covered with bugs;

And the bugs they swear if we don't give bail,
We are bound to get lousy in the Tucson jail.

The nits and the lice climb in the jist,
One fell down and hollered "Jesus Christ!"

I said, "Mister Jailer, please led me your knife,
For the lice and the bedbugs have threatened my life."

Old Judge Simpkins will read us the law,
The damnedest fool judge you ever saw.

IV

CAMPFIRE AND BUNKHOUSE

Out upon the round-up, boys, tell you what you get:
Little chunk o' bread and a little chunk o' meat;
Little black coffee, boys, and gravel in your eye,
So it's doctor up your cinches, oil your slicker and your guns,
For it's out on the round-up when the green grass comes.

* * *

My sweetheart's a mule in the mines,
I drive her without any lines,
As on the bumper I sit, tobacco I spit
All over my sweetheart's behind.

* * *

William Jake Hall
Got a buck and a fall,
Killed as dead as a slug
By a Texas plug;
Born in Georgy.
'48, Anno Domini.

Oh, where's that girl that will go with me
And live in that pretty place?
How happy we would be!
We will build a little log cabin,
Take the dirt for the floor,
A sheepskin for the window,
And a blanket for the door!
We will chase the antelope over the plain,
The buffalo calf we will tie with a chain,
And the wild gazelle with his silvery feet,
I will give thee for a playmate, sweet.

* * *

There was Hep and Texas an' Bronco Jack,
Jiggers and me and Bean,
An' we loved a gal by the name of Sal,
A regular rancho queen.

* * *

Oh, it's treat the cook with a pleasant look;
It's sleep in the prickly pear;
It's all day-o on the ro-day-o,
An' you bet you we'll be there.

RED RIVER SHORE

As is the case with many of the songs and ballads in this volume, *Red River Shore* is a composite, put together from several "incomplete" versions that I have collected. Most of these stanzas come from Slim Critchlow, Utah Buckaroos, Salt Lake City, Utah. The sixth stanza is taken from an unsigned manuscript. The last stanza was taken from the singing of Tim Hight of Oklahoma, and the fourth from the singing of Mrs. Minta Morgan of Bells, Texas.

In another, doubtless older, version of this ballad, the hero destroys the wicked father's henchman with a broadsword.

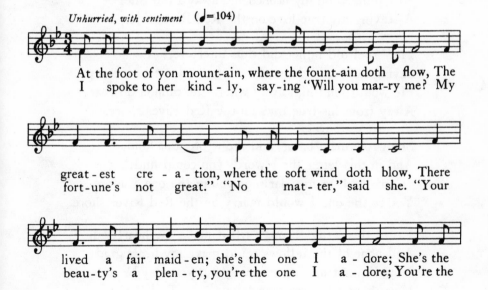

At the foot of yon mount-ain, where the fount-ain doth flow, The
I spoke to her kind-ly, say-ing "Will you mar-ry me? My

great-est cre - a - tion, where the soft wind doth blow, There
fort-une's not great." "No mat-ter," said she. "Your

lived a fair maid-en; she's the one I a - dore; She's the
beau-ty's a plen-ty, you're the one I a - dore; You're the

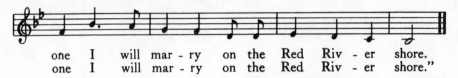

one I will mar - ry on the Red Riv - er shore.
one I will mar - ry on the Red Riv - er shore."

At the foot of yon mountain, where the fountain doth flow,
The greatest creation, where the soft wind doth blow,
There lived a fair maiden; she's the one I adore,
She's the one I will marry on the Red River shore.

I spoke to her kindly, saying, "Will you marry me?
My fortune's not great." "No matter," said she.
"Your beauty's a plenty, you're the one I adore;
You're the one I will marry on the Red River shore."

I asked her old father, if he'd give her to me.
"No, sir, she shan't marry no cowboy," said he.
So I jumped on my bronco and away I did ride
A-leaving my true love on the Red River side.

Her cruel old father did thus interfere,
Saying he would deprive her of the dearest so dear;
He would send him away where the cannon do roar
Away from his true love on the Red River shore.

She wrote me a letter, and she wrote it so kind,
And in this letter these words you could find:
"Come back to me, darling: you're the one I adore.
You're the one I would marry on the Red River shore.

I read this letter through till it made my heart sad,
And none of the fellows could make my heart glad;
Now I'm not used to stoppin', and you may be sure,
I was bound for my true love on the Red River shore.

[182]

So I jumped on my bronco and away I did ride
To marry my true love on the Red River side.
But her dad knew the secret, and with twenty and four
Came to fight this young cowboy on the Red River shore.

I drew my six-shooter, spun around and around
Till six men were wounded and seven were down.
No use for an army of twenty and four;
I'm bound for my true love on the Red River shore.

Such is the fortune of all womenkind,
They are always controlled, they are always made mind;
Controlled by their parents until they become wives,
And slaves of their husbands the rest of their lives.

Hard luck in this world for all womenkind;
To those who are single the world o'er I find—
Confined with their parents until they are wives,
And stay with their husbands the rest of their lives.

THE WILD RIPPLING WATER*

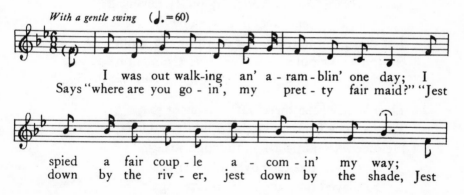

With a gentle swing (♩. = 60)

I was out walk-ing an' a - ram - blin' one day; I
Says "where are you go - in', my pret - ty fair maid?" "Jest

spied a fair coup - le a - com - in' my way;
down by the riv - er, jest down by the shade, Jest

* The words are those of Alex Moore of Austin, Texas [Library of Congress Record
59A1], supplemented in stanzas 4 and 5 by words sent in by E. N. Bowan of Abilene, Texas,
whose tune is recorded on disc 937A1, Library of Congress.

[183]

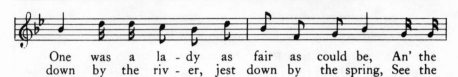

One was a la - dy as fair as could be, An' the
down by the riv - er, jest down by the spring, See the

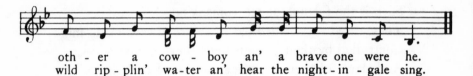

oth - er a cow - boy an' a brave one were he, An' the
wild rip - plin' wa - ter an' hear the night-in - gale sing, See the

oth - er a cow - boy an' a brave one were he.
wild rip - plin' wa-ter an' hear the night-in - gale sing.

I was out walking an' a-ramblin' one day;
I spied a fair couple a-comin' my way;
One was a lady as fair as could be,
An' the other a cowboy, an' a brave one were he,
An' the other a cowboy, an' a brave one were he.

Says, "Where are you goin', my pretty fair maid?"
"Jest down by the river, jest down by the shade,
Jest down by the river, jest down by the spring,
See the wild ripplin' water an' hear the nightingale sing,
See the wild ripplin' water an' hear the nightingale sing."

They hadn't been there but an hour or so
Till he drew from his satchel a fiddle and bow;
He tuned his fiddle all on the high string,
An' he played this tune over an' over again,
An' he played this tune over an' over again.

"Now," said the cowboy, "I should have been gone."
"No, no," said the pretty maid, "jest play one more song.

I'd rather hear the fiddle jest played on one string,
As to see the water glide by an' hear the nightingale sing,
As to see the water glide by an' hear the nightingale sing."

He tuned up his fiddle and he rosined his bow;
He played her a lecture, he played it all o'er;
He played her a lecture that made the valley ring.
"Hark! Hark!" said the fair maid. "Hear the nightingale sing."
"Hark! Hark!" said the fair maid. "Hear the nightingale sing."

She said, "Dear cowboy, will you marry me?"
He said: "Dear lady, that could never be.
I have a wife in Arizona, an' a lady is she;
One wife on a cow-ranch is a plenty for me,
One wife on a cow-ranch is a plenty for me.

"I'll go to Mexico, I'll stay there one year;
I'll drink sweet wine an' I'll drink lotta beer.
If I ever return here, it will be in the spring,
To see the bright ripplin' water, hear the nightingale sing,
See the bright ripplin' water, hear the nightingale sing."

"Come all you young maidens, take warning from me;
Never place your affections in a cowboy too free;
He'll go away an' leave you like mine did me;
Leave you to rock cradles, sing 'Bye-o-babee';
Leave you to rock cradles, sing 'Bye-o-babee.' "

THE RANGE RIDERS*

Come all you range riders and listen to me.
I relate you a story of the saddest degree;

* Sent by M. B. Wight, Fort Thomas, Ariz.

[185]

Relate you a story of the deepest distress;
I love my poor Lula, boys, of all girls the best.

When you are out riding, boys, upon the highway,
You meet a fair damsel, a lady so gay,
With her red rosy cheeks and her sparkling dark eyes,
Just think of my Lula, boys, and your bosom will rise.
While you live single, boys, you are just in your prime;
You have no wife to scold, you have nothing to bother your
    minds;

You can roam this world over, and do just as you will,
Hug and kiss pretty girls and be your own still.
But when you get married, boys, you are done with this life,
You have sold your sweet comfort for to gain you a wife;
Your wife she will scold you, and the children will cry,
It will make those fair faces look withered and dry.

You can scarcely step aside, boys, to speak to a friend,
Your wife is at your elbow saying, "What do you mean?"
With her nose turned upon you, it looks like sad news;
I advise you by experience that life to refuse.

Come fill up your bottles, boys, drink bourbon around;
Here is luck to the single, wherever they are found;
Here is luck to the single, and I wish them success,
Likewise to the married, and I wish them no less.

I have one more request to make, boys, before we part:
Never place your affection on a charming sweetheart;
She is dancing before you your affections to gain;
Just turn your back on her with scorn and disdain.

LACKEY BILL*

Come all you good old boys and listen to my rhymes,
We are west of eastern Texas and mostly men of crimes;
Each with a hidden secret well smothered in his breast,
Which brought us out to Mexico, way out here in the West.

My parents raised me tenderly, they had no child but me,
Till I began to ramble and with them could never agree.
My mind being bent on rambling did grieve their poor hearts sore,
To leave my aged parents them to see no more.

I was borned and raised in Texas, though never come to fame,
A cowboy by profession, C. W. King by name.
Oh, when the war was ended I did not like to work,
My brothers were not happy, for I had learned to shirk.

In fact I was not able, my health was very bad,
I had no constitution, I was nothing but a lad.
I had no education, I would not go to school,
And living off my parents I thought it rather cool.

So I set a resolution to travel to the West,
My parents objected, but still I thought it best.
It was out on the Seven Rivers all out on the Pecos stream,
It was there I saw a country I thought just suited me.

I thought I would be no stranger and lead a civil life,
In order to be happy would choose myself a wife.
On one Sabbath evening in the merry month of May
To a little country singing I happened there to stray.

* Sent by B. O. White of Roswell, N.M., and T. M. Hargis of Munday, Texas. "Lackey
Bill" can be sung to the tune of "The Rambling Cowboy."

[187]

It was there I met a damsel I never shall forget,
The impulse of that moment remains within me yet.
We soon became acquainted, I thought she would fill the bill;
She seemed to be good-natured, which helps to climb the hill.

She was a handsome figure though not so very tall;
Her hair was red as blazes—I hate it worst of all.
I saw her home one evening in the presence of her pap,
I bid them both good evening with a note left in her lap.

And when I got an answer I read it with a rush.
I found she had consented, my feelings was a hush.
But now I have changed my mind, boys, I am sure I wish her well;
Here's to that precious jewel, I'm sure I wish her well.

This girl was Miss Mollie Walker who fell in love with me,
She was a lovely Western girl, as lovely as could be:
She was so tall, so handsome, so charming, and so fair,
There is not a girl in this whole world with her I could compare.

She said my pockets would be lined with gold, hard work then I'd
      leave o'er,
If I'd consent to live with her and say I'd roam no more.
My mind began to ramble, and it grieved my poor heart sore
To leave my darling girl, her to see no more.

I asked if it made any difference if I crossed o'er the plains;
She said it made no difference if I returned again.
So we kissed, shook hands, and parted; I left that girl behind.
She said she'd prove true to me till death proved her unkind.

I rode in the town of Vagus, all in the public square;
The mail coach had arrived, the postboy met me there.

[188]

He handed me a letter that gave me to understand
That the girl I loved in Texas had married another man.

So I read a little farther and found those words were true.
I turned myself around, not knowing what to do.
I'll sell my horse, saddle, and bridle, cow-driving I'll resign,
I'll search this world from town to town for the girl I left behind.

Here the gold I find in plenty, the girls to me are kind,
But my pillow is haunted with the girl I left behind.
It's trouble and disappointment is all that I can see,
For the dearest girl in all the world has gone square back on me.

THE PEELER'S LAMENT*

Tune: "Wearin' o' the Green."

She had no business doin' it, but she come out o' the East;
The fust time I scanned her face, her eyes were all my feast;
And when I come to tell her "Mornin'," a lump clim' up my
    throat
That made me feel like a maverick, or more like our camp goat.

I loved the gal, nor dared to tell, couldn't strike love's talkin' trail,
Till one fine day with trappin's on I blurted out my tale;
I landed on her with my rope, and choked her into submission.
With 'bout the ease and grace the devil uses when he's fishin'.

And here's what I slipped in her hand—remember, my fine buck—
"If you's no objections, lady, to the parson you'll be tuck."

* Sent by W. P. MacLaughlin of Clovis, N.M., in 1911, who writes, "I have heard this ditty from Pecos City, New Mexico, on south."

Whoop! She just stuck out her hand and says to me, "Old Pard,
You're the lad for me, I'm sure, and you have played the right card.

"I always have wished for the cowboy's daring,
And a hell-roarin' life I have forever been craving."
So I lifted her into the right stirrup astride,
And we doubled that horse to parson's warm side!

But, hell, she didn't last longer—that gal—
Than the dry hot winds came and the sandstorms fell;
She wrote them out East to wire her the money,
And now, for all I know, she is some financier's honey.

Dirge:
But—"I love her with the passion put to use
     In my old griefs, and with my childhood's faith."
And—"I love her with the love I seem to lose
     With my lost saints—yes, with the breath,
     Smiles, tears of all my life; and if God choose,
     I shall but love her better after death."

There is no need of tellin' any punchin'-dog "Beware!"
For the best thing you could tell him is just to get his share;
'Cause the only thing will cure him is a bit of calico,
And when he gets his needin's he will be a wiser beau.

There's no use a-lyin', for I'm glad I saw that gal,
And if she's doin' any stunts, she still will be my pal;
'Cause this is no place for her, I know that very well,
For the devil, after prospectin' round, called it a damn poor place for
    hell.

[190]

THE OLD–TIME COWBOY*

Ofttimes I get to thinking of the changes time has wrought,
Since upon these Western ranges long ago I cast my lot.
I was young and full of ginger in the days of long ago;
Now my limbs are all rheumatic and my hair is touched with snow.
In them days the Sioux Indians were wandering everywhere,
And it made us feel somewhat uneasy for the safety of our hair.

Ofttimes I get to comparing the cowboys of today
With those weather-tanned old riders, now respectable and gray.
We had no dandy riders with their fancy brown shirts,
And we had no love-knot ribbons tied by girls upon our quirts.
We had no shindigs at the ranch-houses as they have them nowa-
    days,
With a lot of pretty cowgirls to join in our hurrays.

We lived in tents and dugouts with our blankets for a bed,
And our saddles for a pillow on which to lay our head.
Our rifles and revolvers beside us we would lay,
To get them poco pronto if the Indians made a play.
Oh, you bet you never saw us—and it's true as preachin', boss—
With a hundred-dollar saddle on a twenty-dollar hoss.

Ofttimes I get to thinking of old Bean Stew Maxine,
And a lot of my old companions now away up on the line.
Texas Jack, the holy terror, reckless, brave, and bold,
Is a high-toned legislator up in Denver, I am told.
Lightning Jack, who was always a-spoiling for a fight,
In the church of Kansas City is a bright and shining light.

* From "Texas and Southwestern Lore," ed. J. Frank Dobie (*Publications of the Texas Folk Lore Society*, Vol. VI). The song was sent to Mr. Dobie by Miss Flora Eckert of Fredericksburg, Texas, who secured it from cowboys of the Junction country.

Andy Dozen, who used to maverick, I'm surprised to hear,
Has a government position and a fortune every year.
Hungry Tom, a fiend for eating, got quite rich, I understand;
He is now up in Congress, playing style to beat the band.
But the news that surprises me is of little Tommie Dell,
Who used to swear to heaven and could crack a joke on hell,

The toughest boy on all the ranches, with our outfit of tough old
      boys,
He's preaching of the gospel up in southern Illinois.
Jim's the only sole survivor of the cowboys of the past
Who has stayed to cowboy custom and will hold it to the last.
Oh, I wonder if they would know me, recognize old Shaw,
Who was with them punching cattle on the Little Arkansas.

Oh, I wonder if they will own me, though I'm not so stylish dressed,
When the wicked rise from heaven and the weary are at rest.

THE RAMBLING COWBOY

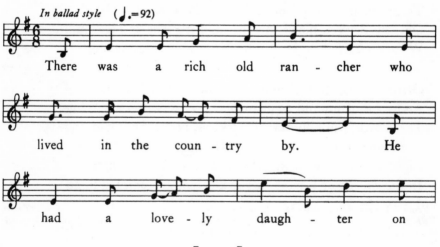

In ballad style (♩.=92)

There was a rich old ran - cher who
lived in the coun - try by. He
had a love - ly daugh - ter on

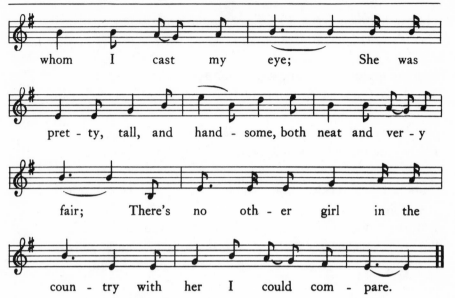

whom I cast my eye; She was
pret - ty, tall, and hand - some, both neat and ver - y
fair; There's no oth - er girl in the
coun - try with her I could com - pare.

There was a rich old rancher who lived in the country by,
He had a lovely daughter on whom I cast my eye;
She was pretty, tall, and handsome, both neat and very fair;
There's no other girl in the country with her I could compare.

I asked her if she would be willing for me to cross the plains;
She said she would be truthful until I returned again;
She said she would be faithful until death did prove unkind.
So we kissed, shook hands, and parted, and I left my girl behind.

I left the State of Texas, for Arizona was bound,
I landed in Tombstone City, I viewed the place all round.
Money and work were plentiful, and the cowboys they were kind;
But the only thought of my heart was the girl I left behind.

One day as I was riding across the public square
The mail coach it had just come in, and I met the driver there;

[193]

He handed me a letter which gave me to understand
That the girl I left in Texas had married another man.

I turned myself all around and about not knowing what to do,
But I read on down some further and it proved the words were
    true.
Hard work I have laid over, it's gambling I have designed,
I'll ramble this wide world over for the girl I left behind.

Come all you reckless and rambling boys who have listened to this
    song,
If it hasn't done you any good, it hasn't done you any wrong;
But when you court a pretty girl, just marry her while you can,
For if you go across the plains she'll marry another man.

THE RATTLESNAKE

A Ranch Haying Song

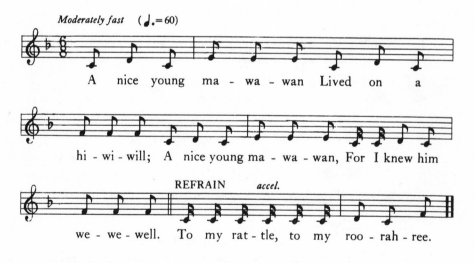

A nice young ma-wa-wan lived on a hi-wi-will;
A nice young ma-wa-wan, for I knew him we-we-well.

Refrain:
    To my rattle, to my roo-rah-ree!

He farmed it on-wy-on his father's far-wa-arm,
And never thou-wy-ought he'd come to ha-wa-arm.

He worked away-way from morn till dar-wa-ark
And then his sweetha-wa-art he did spar-wa-ark.

Her cheeks were re-we-ed, her hair the sa-wa-ame,
And Sallie Blan-wa-and it was her na-wa-ame.

This nice young ma-wa-wan went out to mo-wo-wow
To see if he-we-we could make a sho-wo-wow.

He scarcely mo-wo-wowed half round the fie-we-wield
Till up jumped—come a rattle, come a sna-wa-wake and bit him on the
    he-we-weel.

He lay right dow-wo-wown upon the gro-wo-wownd
And shut his ey-wy-wyes and looked all aro-wo-wound.

He took his scy-wy-wythe and with a blo-wo-wow
He laid the pe-we-wesky serpent lo-wo-wow.

He lay right dow-wo-own upon the gro-wo-wound
And shut his ey-wy-wyes and looked all ro-wo-wound.

"Oh, pappy da-wa-wad, go tell my ga-wa-wal
That I'm going to di-wi-wie for I know I sha-wa-wall.

"Oh, pappy da-wa-wad, go spread the ne-wu-wews;
And here come Sa-wa-wal without her sho-woo-woes."

He took the ser-we-erpent on his ha-wa-wand
And straightway we-we-went to Sally Bla-wa-wand.

"Oh, Sally, oh, Sa-wa-wally, here you se-we-wee
The pesky ser-we-erpent what bit me-we-we."

Then to the ho-wo-wouse the lad did go-wo-wo
With the rattlesna-wa-wake hanging to his toe-wo-woe.

"Oh, John, oh, John-wa-won, why did you go-wo-wo
Way down in the mea-we-weadow for to mow-wo-wow?"

"Oh, Sal, oh, Sa-wa-wal, why, don't you kno-wo-wow
When the grass is ri-wi-wipe it must be mo-wo-wowed?"

Poor Sallie screa-we-eamed in mortal fri-wi-ight
When she obser-we-erved the sarpint's bi-wi-ite.

"Oh, Johnny dea-we-ear, you'll surely di-wi-ie
Unless you dri-wi-ink some good old ry-wy-ye."

He drank old whi-wi-isky by the pa-wai-ail,
Alas, it proo-woo-ooved of no a-wi-vail.

And Sallie we-we-ept a week or mo-wo-ore,
And blackest bomba-zi-wi-ine she wo-wo-ore.

She could not da-wi-ance or sing or lau-wi-augh
Till she had wr-wi-it an epita-wi-aph.

The young man di-wi-ied, gave up the gho-wo-wost
To Abraham's bo-wo-osom he did po-wo-ost.

Poor Sallie dea-we-ear, she had a fai-wai-aint
And went to hea-we-ven like a sai-wa-aint.

Come all young gi-wi-irls, and shed a tea-we-ear
For this young ma-wa-wan that died right he-we-ere.

Come all young me-we-wen and warning ta-wa-wake,
And don't get bi-wi-wit by a rattlesna-wa-wake.

Poor John he di-wi-wied, and went to hea-wa-weaven,
And he's down there ye-we-wet, if he hasn't come ba-wa-wack.

The seventh of Au-wu-gust sixty-one-a-wone
This fatal ac-ci-dent was done-e-wone.

Let this be a war-wi-ning be to all-we-wall
To be prepa-we-ared when God does call-a-wall.

To my rattle, to my roo-rah-ree.

BILL VENERO*

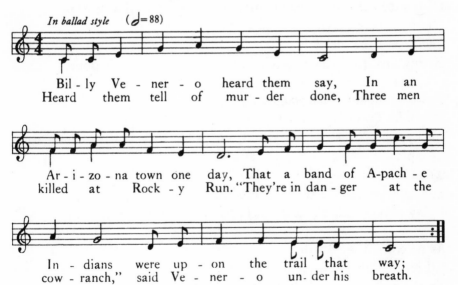

In ballad style (♩=88)

Bil - ly Ve - ner - o   heard them   say,   In   an
Heard   them   tell   of   mur - der   done, Three men

Ar - i - zo - na town one   day, That   a   band of A-pach - e
killed   at   Rock - y   Run. "They're in dan - ger   at   the

In - dians   were up - on   the   trail   that   way;
cow - ranch,"   said Ve - ner - o   un- der his   breath.

* In other versions "Paul Venerez."

Bill Venero heard them say,
In an Arizona town one day,
That a band of Apache Indians were upon the trail that way;
Heard them tell of murder done,
Three men killed at Rocky Run.
"They're in danger at the cow-ranch," said Venero under his breath.

The cow-ranch, forty miles away,
Was a little place that lay
In a deep and shady valley of the mighty wilderness;
Half a score of homes were there,
And in one a maiden fair
Held the heart of Bill Venero: Bill Venero's little Bess.

So no wonder he grew pale
When he heard the settler's tale
Of the men that he'd seen murdered yesterday at Rocky Run.
"Sure as there's a God above,
I will save the girl I love;
By my love for little Bessie I will see that something's done."

Not a moment he delayed
When his brave resolve was made.
"Why, man," his comrades told him when they heard of his daring
    plan,
"You are riding straight to death."
But he answered: "Save your breath.
I may never reach the cow-ranch, but I'll do the best I can."

As he crossed the alkali
All his thoughts flew on ahead
To the little band at cow-ranch thinking not of danger near;
With his quirt's unceasing whirl

And the jingle of his spurs
Little brown Chapo bore the cowboy o'er the far-away frontier.

Lower and lower sank the sun;
He drew rein at Rocky Run.
"Here those men met death, my Chapo"—and he stroked his glossy
    mane.
"So will those we go to warn
Ere the coming of the morn
If we fail—God help my Bessie." And he started on again.

Sharp and clear a rifle shot
Woke the echoes of the spot.
"I am wounded," cried Venero, as he swayed from side to side.
"While there's life there's always hope;
Slowly onward I will lope—
If I fail to reach the cow-ranch, Bessie Lee shall know I tried.

"I will save her yet," he cried.
"Bessie Lee shall know I tried."
And for her sake then he halted in the shadow of a hill;
From his buckskin shirt he took
With weak hands a little book;
Tore a blank leaf from its pages saying, "This shall be my will."

From a limb a pen he broke,
And he dipped his pen of oak
In the warm blood that was spurting from a wound above his
    heart.
"Rouse," he wrote before too late.
"Apache warriors lie in wait.
Good-by, Bess, God bless you darling," and he felt the cold tears start.

Then he made his message fast,
Love's first message and its last;
To the saddle horn he tied it, and his lips were white with pain.
"Take this message, if not me,
Straight to little Bessie Lee."
Then he leaned down in the saddle and clutched the sweaty mane.

Just at dusk a horse of brown
Wet with sweat came panting down
The little lane at the cow-ranch, stopped in front of Bessie's door;
But the cowboy was asleep,
And his slumber was so deep
Little Bess could never wake him though she tried for evermore.

You have heard the story told
By the young and by the old,
Away down yonder at the cow-ranch the night the Apaches came;
Of that sharp and bloody fight,
How the chief fell in the flight
Of the panic-stricken warriors when they heard Venero's name.

In an awed and reverent way
As men utter, "Let us pray,"
As we speak the name of heroes thinking how they lived and died,
So the heavens and earth between
Keep a little flower green
That little Bess had planted ere they laid her by his side.

MACAFFIE'S CONFESSION

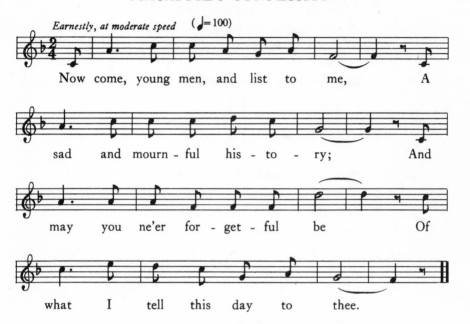

Earnestly, at moderate speed (♩=100)

Now come, young men, and list to me, A

sad and mourn - ful his - to - ry; And

may you ne'er for - get - ful be Of

what I tell this day to thee.

> Now come, young men, and list to me,
> A sad and mournful history;
> And may you ne'er forgetful be
> Of what I tell this day to thee.
>
> Oh, I was thoughtless, young, and gay
> And often broke the Sabbath day;
> In wickedness I took delight
> And sometimes done what wasn't right.
>
> I'd scarcely passed my fifteenth year,
> My mother and my father dear
> Were silent in their deep, dark grave,
> Their spirits gone to Him who gave.

'Twas on a pleasant summer day
When from my home I ran away,
And took unto myself a wife,
Which step was fatal to my life.

Oh, she was kind and good to me,
As ever woman ought to be,
And might this day have been alive no doubt,
Had I not met Miss Hatty Stout.

Ah, well I mind the fatal day
When Hatty stole my heart away;
'Twas love for her controlled my will
And did cause me my wife to kill.

'Twas on a brilliant summer's night
When all was still; the stars shone bright.
My wife lay still upon the bed
And I approached to her and said:

"Dear wife, here's medicine I've brought,
For you this day, my love, I've bought.
I know it will be good for you
For those vile fits—pray take it, do."

She cast on me a loving look
And in her mouth the poison took;
Down by her infant on the bed
In her last, long sleep she laid her head.

Oh, who could tell a mother's thought
When first to her the news was brought?
The sheriff said her son was sought
And into prison must be brought.

Only a mother standing by
To hear them tell the reason why
Her son in prison, he must lie
Till on the scaffold he must die.

My father, sixty years of age,
The best counsel did engage,
To see if something could be done
To save his disobedient son.

So, farewell, Mother, do not weep,
Though soon with demons I will sleep;
My soul now feels its mental hell
And soon with demons I will dwell.

.   .   .   .   .   .

The sheriff cut the slender cord,
His soul went up to meet its Lord;
The doctor said, "The wretch is dead,
His spirit from his body's fled."

His weeping mother cried aloud,
"O God, do save this gazing crowd,
That none may ever have to pay
For gambling on the Sabbath day."

THE BOSTON BURGLAR

In narrative style ($\downarrow$.=72)

I was born in Bos - ton cit - y,   a   cit - y

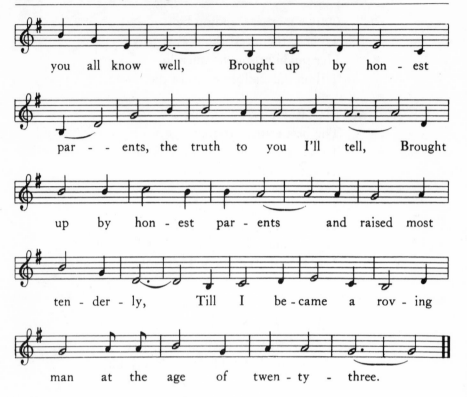

you all know well, Brought up by hon - est

par - - ents, the truth to you I'll tell, Brought

up by hon - est par - ents and raised most

ten - der - ly, Till I be - came a rov - ing

man at the age of twen - ty - three.

I was born in Boston city, a city you all know well,
Brought up by honest parents, the truth to you I'll tell,
Brought up by honest parents and raised most tenderly,
Till I became a roving man at the age of twenty-three.

My character was taken then, and I was sent to jail.
My friends they found it was in vain to get me out on bail.
The jury found me guilty, the clerk he wrote it down,
The judge he passed me sentence and I was sent to Charleston town.

You ought to have seen my aged father a-pleading at the bar,
Also my dear old mother a-tearing of her hair,

Tearing of her old gray locks as the tears came rolling down,
Saying, "Son, dear son, what have you done, that you are sent to
    Charleston town?"

They put me aboard an eastbound train one cold December day,
And every station that we passed, I'd hear the people say,
"There goes a noted burglar, in strong chains he'll be bound—
For the doing of some crime or other he is sent to Charleston town."

There is a girl in Boston, she is a girl that I love well,
And if I ever gain my liberty, along with her I'll dwell;
And when I regain my liberty, bad company I will shun,
Night-walking, gambling, and also drinking rum.

Now, you who have your liberty, pray keep it if you can,
And don't go around the streets at night to break the laws of man;
For if you do you'll surely rue and find yourself like me,
A-serving out my twenty-one years in the penitentiary.

FULLER AND WARREN*

Ye sons of Co-lum-bia, your at-ten-tion I do crave, While a
A gold ring he gave her in to-ken of his love; On the

sor-row-ful sto-ry I do tell, Which
face was the im-age of the dove. They

* Given by H. E. Crowley of Fort Worth, Texas, who learned the song between '79 and
'83 on the headwaters of the Colorado.

hap-pened of late in this In - di - an - a state, To a
mu-tual - ly a - greed to get mar-ried with speed, And were

he - ro not man - y could ex - cel, Like
pro - mised by the powers a - bove; But the

Sam-son he court - ed, made choice of the fair, And in -
fick - le - mind-ed maid - en vowed a - gain to wed To young

tend - ed to make her his wife; But
War - ren who lived in that place. It

she, like De - li - lah, his heart did en-snare, Which
was a fa - tal blow that caused his o - ver-throw And

cost him his hon - or and his life.
add ed to her shame and dis - grace.

Ye sons of Columbia, your attention I do crave,
While a sorrowful story I do tell,
Which happened of late in this Indiana state,
To a hero not many could excel;
Like Samson he courted, made choice of the fair,
And intended to make her his wife;
But she, like Delilah, his heart did ensnare,
Which cost him his honor and his life.

A gold ring he gave her in token of his love;
On the face was the image of the dove.
They mutually agreed to get married with speed,
And were promised by the powers above;
But the fickle-minded maiden vowed again to wed
To young Warren who lived in that place.
It was a fatal blow that caused his overthrow
And added to her shame and disgrace.

When Fuller came to hear he was deprived of his dear,
Whom he vowed by the powers to wed,
With his heart full of woe unto Warren he did go,
And smilingly unto him he said:
"Young man, you have injured me to gratify your cause
By reporting that I left a prudent wife.
Acknowledge now that you have wronged me, for though I
        break the laws,
Young Warren, I'll deprive you of your life."

Then Warren, he replied: "Your request must be denied,
For your darling to my heart she is bound;
And further I can say that this is our wedding day
In spite of all the heroes in town."

[207]

Then Fuller, in the passion of his love and anger bound—
Alas! it caused many to cry—
At one fatal shot killed Warren on the spot,
And smiling said, "I'm ready now to die."

The time was drawing nigh when Fuller had to die
He was tried and condemned by an honorable court,
And in Lawsdale he is waiting now to die;
An ignominious death for to hang above the earth
Like a garment on the gallows high;
But there is one consolation, let it long remembered be,
As the gallows waved above his head:
He did believe and was baptized, from sin he was set free,
And his spirit to glory now has fled.

The time was drawing nigh when Fuller had to die;
He bid the audience adieu.
Like an angel he did stand, for he was a handsome man,
On his breast he had a ribbon blue.
Ten thousand spectators did smite them on the breast,
And the guards dropped a tear from the eye,
Saying, "Cursed is she who caused this misery.
Would to God in his stead she had to die."

The gentle God of Love looked down with anger from above,
And the rope flew asunder like the sand.
Two doctors for the pay they murdered him, they say,
They hung him by the main strength of hand.
But the corpse it was buried, and the doctors lost their prey.
Oh, that harlot was bribed, I do believe;
Bad women to a certainty are the downfall of men,
As Adam was beguiled by Eve.

You may look through Judges, through Samuel, Paul, and Job,
And the truth of my doctrine you will find:
That woman is essentially the downfall of man.
Come all you loving husbands that have a prudent wife,
Treat her with honor and be true.
Oh, marriage is a lottery and few that win the prize,
It is pleasing to the heart and to the eye,
But those who live the single life might as well be called wise.
So, ladies and gentlemen, good-by.

JACK DONAHOE

These words were sung by a Negro undertaker in Austin, Texas, who had been a camp cook on the cattle trail. Such songs were probably brought to Texas by Australian cowboys.

Come, all you bold undaunted men,
You outlaws of the day,
It's time to beware of the ball and chain,
And also slavery.
Attention pay to what I say,
And verily if you do,
I will relate you the actual fate
Of bold Jack Donahoe.*

Refrain:

Then come, my hearties, we'll roam the mountains high!
Together we will plunder, together we will die!
We'll wander over mountains, we'll wander over plains,
For we scorn to live in slavery, bound down with iron
chains.

* Pronounced Donahoo.

[209]

He took to rob on the King's Highway;
We heard the people say
They were afraid to go that road
By either night or day!
And every day the newspapers
Were filled with something new
Concerning this bold highwayman
Whom they called Jack Donahoe.

He scarcely had landed, as I tell you,
Upon Australia's shore,
Than he became a real highwayman,
As he had been before.
There was Underwood and Mackerman,
And Wade and Westley too,
These were four associates
Of bold Jack Donahoe.

But Donahoe was taken
In the middle of his prime,
And he was sentenced to be shot
For an outrageous crime;
He left the police behind him
And several soldiers too;
Until the fatal day came round
They lost bold Donahoe.

Jack Donahoe who was so brave
Rode out one afternoon,
Knowing not that the pain of death
Would overtake him soon.
So quickly then the horse police
From Sydney came to view;

"Begone from here, you cowardly dogs,"
Says bold Jack Donahoe.

Says Donahoe to his comrade,
"If you'll prove true to me
We'll either fight until we die
Or gain the victory!
Be of good courage, stout and bold;
Be loyal, firm, and true,
For today we'll fight for victory!"
Said bold Jack Donahoe.

"Oh, no!" said cowardly Westley.
"To that I can't agree.
Cannot you see there's nine of them
Against just you and me?
But if we wait we'll be too late,
The battle we'll surely rue."
"Begone from me, you cowardly whelp,"
Said bold Jack Donahoe.

The captain and the sergeant
Stopped then to decide.
"Do you intend to fight us,
Or unto us resign?"
"To surrender to such cowardly dogs
Is more than I will do;
This day I'll fight if I lose my life,"
Says bold Jack Donahoe.

The captain and the sergeant
The men they did divide.
They fired from behind him
And also from each side;

It's six police he did shoot down
Before the fatal ball
Did pierce the heart of Donahoe
And cause bold Jack to fall.

"I'd rather roam these hills and dales
Like a wolf or kangaroo,
Than one hour for government!"
Cries bold Jack Donahoe.
And when he fell, he closed his eyes,
He bid the world adieu.
Come, all you boys, and sing the song
Of bold Jack Donahoe.

YOUNG COMPANIONS

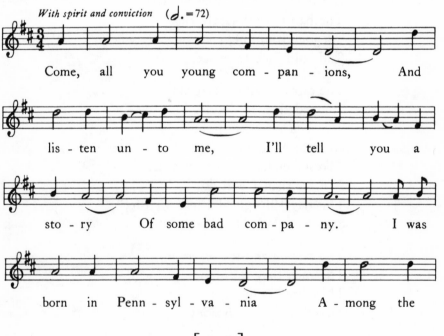

With spirit and conviction ($\frac{1}{2}$. = 72)

Come, all you young com - pan - ions, And lis - ten un - to me, I'll tell you a sto - ry Of some bad com - pa - ny. I was born in Penn - syl - va - nia A - mong the

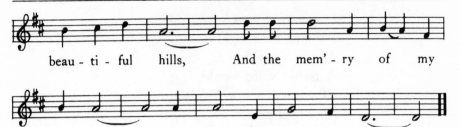

beau - ti - ful   hills,   And the mem' - ry   of   my

child - hood   Is warm with - in   me   still.

Come, all you young companions,
And listen unto me,
I'll tell you a story
Of some bad company.
I was born in Pennsylvania
Among the beautiful hills,
And the memory of my childhood
Is warm within me still.

I did not like my fireside,
I did not like my home;
I had in view far rambling,
So far away did roam.
I had a feeble mother,
She oft would plead with me;
And the last word she gave me
Was to pray to God in need.

I had two loving sisters,
As fair as fair could be;
And oft beside me kneeling
They oft would plead with me.
I bid adieu to loved ones,
To my home I bid farewell,
And I landed in Chicago
In the very depth of hell.

[213]

It was there I took to drinking,
I sinned both night and day,
And there within my bosom
A feeble voice would say:
"Then fare you well, my loved one.
May God protect my boy,
And blessings ever with him
Throughout his manhood joy."

I courted a fair young maiden.
Her name I will not tell,
For I should ever disgrace her
Since I am doomed for hell.
It was on one beautiful evening,
The stars were shining bright,
And with a fatal dagger
I bid her spirit flight.

So justice overtook me,
You all can plainly see,
My soul is doomed forever
Throughout eternity.
It's now I'm on the scaffold,
My moments are not long;
You may forget the singer,
But don't forget the song.

BROWN-EYED LEE

With spirit (♩.=96)

Kind friends, if you will lis-ten, a sto-ry I will tell A-

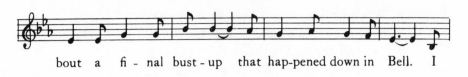

bout a fi-nal bust-up that hap-pened down in Bell. I

court-ed a brown-eyed maid-en known by the name of Lee; And

when I popped the ques-tion, she said she'd mar-ry me.

Kind friends, if you will listen, a story I will tell
About a final bust-up, that happened down in Bell.
I courted a brown-eyed maiden, known by the name of Lee;
And when I popped the question, she said she'd marry me.

I out and bought the license, March, eighteen-eighty-nine,
Expecting in a few days that darling would be mine.
But her mother grew quite angry and said it could not be,
She said she had another man picked out for Brown-Eyed Lee.

She talked to friends and neighbors, she said that she would fight,
She'd get her old six-shooter out and put old Red to flight;
But lovers laugh at shooters and the old she-devil, too—
I said I'd have my darling, if she didn't prove untrue.

I borrowed Dad's old buggy and got Jim's forty-one,
And started down to Kearn's to have a little fun.
I'm not one to crawfish when I'm in a tight;
I said, "I'll have my angel and not be put to flight."

[215]

I went on down to Kearn's with the devil in my head,
I said, "I'll have my darling or I'll leave the old folks dead."
Good fortune fell upon me; my darling proved untrue,
I give her back her letters and bid her a fond adieu.

I pressed her to my aching heart and kissed her a last farewell,
And prayed a permanent prayer to God to send her ma to hell.
I sold my cows to J. M. G. and my corn to K. M. P.,
And cursed the day that I first met that darling angel, Lee.*

I sold my horse and saddle and caught the northbound train,†
Leaving that darling girl behind that I had loved in vain.
When I got up next morning to see what I could see,
Well, every sound that I could hear would speak the name of
    Lee.

I stepped into a billiard hall. Thinks I, "I'll have a game."
But every ball that I could knock would speak the same dear name.
Although I'm broken-hearted, there's one thing I know well,
That the one that caused this bust-up will some day scorch in hell.

She'll cast her eyes to heaven, to Jesus on his throne,
And ask for a drop of water to cool her scorching tongue;
But Jesus will answer her: "Go to Old Scratch,
You are the very hypocrite that busted up this match.

"Depart from me, ye cursed, you are the Devil's own;
Old Red shall have a resting place on the right hand of my
    throne."

* Up to this point, from p. 50, *Sing 'Em, Cowboy, Sing 'Em*, ed. W. J. Glassmacher (New York: Amsco Music Sales Co., Inc.).
† From this line on the stanzas come from Margaret Larkin's *Singing Cowboy*.

And every night I go to bed, I pray a permanent prayer
For the girl I loved so well with dark brown eyes and hair.

BONNIE BLACK BESS

Said to have been the most popular song among the cowboys in the Indian Territory.

When fortune's blind goddess
Had fled my abode,
And friends proved unfaithful
I took to the road;

To plunder the wealthy
And relieve my distress,
I bought you to aid me,
My Bonnie Black Bess.

No vile whip nor spur
Did your sides ever gall,
For none did you need,
You would bound at my call;
And for each act of kindness
You would me caress.
Thou art never unfaithful,
My Bonnie Black Bess.

When dark, sable midnight
Her mantle had thrown
O'er the bright face of nature,
How oft we have gone
To the famed Hounslow heath,
Though an unwelcome guest
To the minions of fortune,
My Bonnie Black Bess!

How silent you stood
When the carriage I stopped!
The gold and the jewels
Its inmates would drop.
No poor man I plundered
Nor e'er did oppress
The widows or orphans,
My Bonnie Black Bess.

When Argus-eyed justice
Did me hot pursue,

From York town to London
Like lightning we flew.
No toll bars could stop you,
The waters did breast,
And in twelve hours we made it,
My Bonnie Black Bess.

But hate darkens o'er me,
Despair is my lot,
And the law does pursue me
For the many I've shot;
To save me, poor brute,
Thou hast done thy best,
Thou art worn out and weary,
My Bonnie Black Bess.

Hark! they never shall have
A beast like thee;
So noble and gentle
And brave, thou must die,
My dumb friend,
Though it does me distress.
There! There! I have shot thee,
My Bonnie Black Bess.

In after years
When I am dead and gone,
This story will be handed
From father to son;
My fate some will pity,
And some will confess
'Twas through kindness I killed thee,
My Bonnie Black Bess.

No one can e'er say
That ingratitude dwelt
In the bosom of Turpin—
'Twas a vice never felt.
I will die like a man
And soon be at rest;
Now, farewell forever,
My Bonnie Black Bess.

THE MELANCHOLY COWBOY *

Come all you melancholy folks and listen unto me,
I will sing you about the cowboy whose heart's so light and free;
He roves all over the prairie and at night when he lays down
His heart's as gay as the flowers of May with his bed spread on the
ground.

They are a little bit rough, I must confess, the most of them at
least;
But as long as you do not cross their trail, you can live with them
in peace.
But if you do, they're sure to rule, the day you come to their land,
For they'll follow you up and shoot it out, they'll do it man to
man.

You can go to a cowboy hungry, go to him wet or dry,
And ask him for a few dollars in change and he will not deny;
He will pull out his pocketbook and hand you out a note—
Oh, they are the fellows to strike, boys, whenever you are broke.

You can go to their ranches and often stay for weeks,
And when you go to leave, boys, they'll never charge you a cent;

* From D. L. Browning, Garner, Texas.

[220]

But when you go to town, boys, you bet their money is spent.
They walk right up, they take their drinks, and they pay for every
    one.
They'll never ask your pardon, boys, for a thing that they have
    done.

They go to the ballroom, and swing the pretty girls around;
They ride their bucking broncos, and wear their broad-brimmed
    hats;
Their California saddles, their pants below their boots,
You can hear their spurs go jing-a-ling, or perhaps somebody shoots.

Come all you soft and tender feet, if you want to have some fun,
Come go among the cowboys and they'll show you how it's done;
But take the advice of me as I gave it to you before,
For if you don't, they'll order you off with an old Colt's forty-
    four.

A WILD RATTLING COWBOY *

I am a cowboy by my trade.
Joe Johnson is my name,
And 'twas a false deluded girl,
Who caused my grief and pain.

Come all you wild rattling cowboys,
Be careful how you sail.
They will take you up, whether guilty or not
Lock you up in some county jail.

* From M. P. Elder, Sulphur Springs, Texas, an old resident of Travis, Bell, and Williamson counties.

For I was a wild rattling cowboy,
Not caring how I sailed,
On Thursday night I was taken,
Locked up in Clay County jail.

They kept me there about four weeks,
I had friends I knew would not fail,
But they was so sure that I done the shooting,
They would not allow me bail.

Out of that jail-house they took me,
Bound down with irons strong,
With rattling chains all around my feet,
And handcuffs on my arms.

Back down to Lampasas they took me,
Locked up both tight and fast.
The walls were made of iron and stone,
The doors of wood and cast.

It grieved my mother to her heart
To hear of my misery,
I shook off my chains, I scaled the walls,
I gained my liberty.

My mother talked so kind to me—
She gave me good advice,
Saying, "O son, shun all bad company
And lead a sober life."

If ever I get out of this,
A solemn vow I'll take,
I'll shun all bad company,
For my poor mother's sake.

If ever I get out of this,
For my poor mother's sake
I'll shun all bad company
And every girl forsake.

THE DYING DESPERADO*

Don't pull off my boots and pull off my hat;
You've taken my gun and I s'pose you'll keep that.
I've lived a reckless life, I've fought and killed my men,
And now as I lay a-dying, I think of times that's been:
Of a gal away down in Texas by the name of Pompey Stiles—
She ain't much on the figger and don't give a damn for styles;
Her father was a hog-thief, and her brother was doin' well
Till he went liftin' cattle, was caught and sent to hell.

'Twas this way with that brother: he was liftin' more'n his load,
So he drifted off a-fightin' and fell aside the road;
He'd 'a' been a-livin' yet, too, if an accident hadn't occurred,
For one pistol hung in the scabbard and he didn't have a third.
But about that gal in Texas, as I had went to say,
She's a shore plumb good un—you don't meet 'em every day.
Could spin the longest windy, could rope the biggest steer,
And ride the wildest bronco that stands upon its ear.

At Hooty George's dance hall I killed a man one night,
Almost had been 'rested when Pomp shot out the light.
"You'd better be a-driftin'," she touched my arm and said.
"Follow the wall right out of the hall, then ride up the river bed."

* From Blair Boyd, a cow-puncher of the Rocking Chair Ranch, Texas.

Well, I hung my spurs in Shorty and he struck a steady lope
Till we had passed the schoolhouse and started up the slope.
I knew they wouldn't follow me; they knew my rep had been
That those who tried trackin' me never came back again.

Next time I see Pompey I sort of out and say:
"Come, gal, come git married. Hitch up this very day."
Of course, I knew she wouldn't—I ain't her style nohow,
For how could I support her on one old maverick cow?
But if I was wild and reckless, could Billie Trencher be
Classed in my class? No, alas, he's tougher some than me.
Since I had never killed a man but what was needin' lead,
They up and made me sheriff—to keep things straight, they said.

First thing I straightened out was old Bill Trencher's case,
Caught him stealin' kisses from Pompey Stiles's face.
Now I was jedge and jury in good old days gone by,
I shot him where he stood and left him lay to die.
Pomp sort of jumped aside and made a little frown:
"You shot too high that time. Aim a little farther down."
She took it sorta hard at first till I explained the case,
For I was sheriff then and had to beat the ace.

So in a gulch we buried Bill; for once in life he'd had his fill.
And on the stone that I had made my words stand there to never
    fade:
"O Lord, here lies one among the best, that Butt's gun has sent to
    rest,
For when he shoots he shoots for keeps and piles his victims up in
    heaps."

ANNIE BREEN*

Charles J. Finger says that he obtained this song from a blind min-strel in the streets of Fayetteville, Arkansas, and remarks: "Affect a sort of nasal tone. Remember that Annie was natural and engaging —the villain a smooth talker, very resplendent in black broadcloth and white collar, much given to dallyings. Arkansas must be pro-nounced thus: Ark-*in*-saw. Strike a high moral note. Blush, if pos-sible, at the fifth stanza, and let the blush spread and deepen until the middle of the sixth."

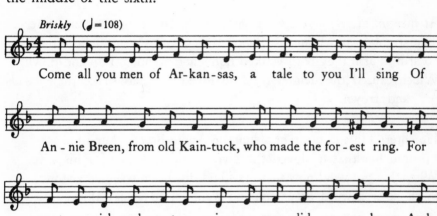

Come all you men of Ar-kan-sas, a tale to you I'll sing Of

An - nie Breen, from old Kain-tuck, who made the for - est ring. For

sweet - er girl and sweet-er voice, no man did ev - er know, And

well she loved a straight-limbed lad whose name was Tex - as Joe.

Come all you men of Arkansas, a tale to you I'll sing
Of Annie Breen, from old Kaintuck, who made the forest ring.
For sweeter girl and sweeter voice, no man did ever know,
And well she loved a straight-limbed lad whose name was Texas
      Joe.

* From p. 79, *Frontier Ballads*, by Charles J. Finger (New York: Doubleday, Page, 1927).

To meetin' she and Joey went, and oh, her eyes did shine,
To see him full of manly strength, so clear and tall and fine!
To be his wife and helping hand she wanted as her fate,
But sad the story that befell as now I will relate.

One morn when birds were singin' an' the lilacs were abloom,
There came unto the little town and there he took a room,
A evil-hearted city man who said he'd made his stake,
And then it was that the serpent in old Paradise did wake.

At meetin' after prayers were said, sweet Ann sang clear and fine.
The stranger said upon his knees, "That girl she must be mine."
So arm in arm they both walked home and wandered up and down.
Which caused the neighbors, who loved Ann, to shake their heads
    and frown.

He entered in and brought a stain on Annie Breen's fair life.
He told her that he loved the girl, would take her for his wife.
When Joe got wind how matters stood, his heart was like a stone;
With ne'er a word of parting he went off to Texas alone.

Before a year in a shallow grave lay Annie and her child,
And when the tidings reached brave Joe's ears that lad went almost
    wild.
He saddled up and cantered hard, and rode both long and fast
And in Fort Smith he found the man who'd ruined Ann at last.

Then words were spoke and shots were fired and Joe fell on the
    floor.
He said, "In spite of all that's been I love my Ann the more."
His face was white as driven snow, his breath came gasping low,
He said, "My soul is clean, and to my Maker it must go."

Before he closed his dimming eye he said, "My work's not done,"
And turning on his aching side he drew his faithful gun.
"You've done your mischief, stranger, but from life you've got to
    part."
His finger pressed the trigger and he shot him through the heart.

THE WHITE STEED OF THE PRAIRIES*

Mr. Finger says he learned this song from a "hard-case" named
Jack Anthony, who had bummed, begged, and sung ballads all over
the world.

Mount, mount for the chase! let your lassoes be strong,
Forget not sharp spurs nor tough buffalo thong;
For the quarry ye seek hath oft baffled, I ween,
Steeds swift as your own, backed by riders as keen.

Fleet steed of the prairie, in vain men prepare
For thy neck arched in beauty, the treacherous snare;
Thou wilt toss thy proud head and with nostrils stretched wide
Defy them again as thou oft hast defied.

Trained steeds of the course, urged by rowel and rein,
Have racked their strong thews in pursuit in vain;
While a bowshot in front, without straining a limb,
The wild courser careered as 'twere pastime to him.

Ye may know him at once, though a herd be in sight,
As he moves o'er the plain like a creature of light,
His mane streaming forth from his beautiful form
Like a drift of a wave that has burst in the storm.

* From p. 99, *Frontier Ballads*, by Charles J. Finger (New York: Doubleday, Page, 1927).

Not the team of the sun, as in fable portrayed,
Through the firmament rushing in glory arrayed,
Could match in wild majesty, beauty and speed,
That tireless, magnificent, snowy-white steed.

Much gold for his guerdon, promotion and fame
Wait the hunter who captures that fleet-footed game;
Let them bid for his freedom, unbridled, unshod,
He will roam till he dies these pastures of God.

And ye think on his head your base halters to fling!
So ye shall—when the eagle has lent you his wing;
But no slave of the lash that your stables contain
Can force to a gallop the steed of the plain.

His fields have no fence save the mountain and sky;
His drink the snow-capped Cordilleras supply;
'Mid the grandeur of nature sole monarch is he,
His gallant heart swells with the pride of the free.

WHEN I WAS A BRAVE COWBOY*

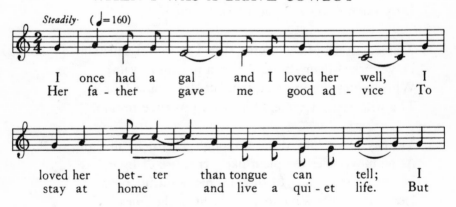

Steadily (♩=160)

I once had a gal and I loved her well, I
Her fa - ther gave me good ad - vice To

loved her bet - ter than tongue can tell; I
stay at home and live a qui - et life. But

* Words and melody from the Gant family, Austin, Texas, 1936.

[228]

told   her   that   my   love was   dear.   She
for   this   word   I   did   not   care,   This

told   me   that   she   did   not   care.
good   ad - vice   I   did   not   hear.

I once had a gal and I loved her well,
I loved her better than tongue can tell;
I told her that my love was dear.
She told me that she did not care.

Her father gave me good advice
To stay at home and live a quiet life;
But for this word I did not care,
This good advice I did not hear.

I once had a home and I loved it well;
But in those mountains I longed to dwell,
Where the coyotes yell and the panthers squall,
And the bears they climb those mountains tall.

Our bed last night was snow and sleet,
And not a moment did we sleep,
Got up next morning, the clouds hung low,
And down that trail we was forced to go.

It was on the way we told our tale;
We met the Redskins on the trail.
To keep our course we shot them down,
About they fell to the frozen ground.

[229]

We traveled, traveled many long hours,
Until we reached those camps of ours;
We started singing, we'd gained our day,
We're the brave cowboys on the western trail.

COWBOY JACK*

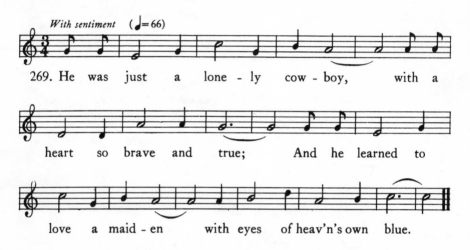

With sentiment ($\quad$ = 66)

269. He was just a lone - ly cow - boy, with a

heart so brave and true; And he learned to

love a maid - en with eyes of heav'n's own blue.

He was just a lonely cowboy, with a heart so brave and true;
And he learned to love a maiden with eyes of heaven's own blue.

They learned to love each other and had named their wedding day
When a quarrel came between them, and Jack he rode away.

He joined a band of cowboys and tried to forget her name,
But out on the lonely prairie she waits for him just the same.

One night when work was finished, just at the close of day,
Some one said, "Sing a song, Jack, just to pass the time away."

* From p. 15, *Cowboy Sings*, ed. Kenneth S. Clark (New York: Paull-Pioneer Music Co.).

When Jack began his singing, his mind, it wandered back,
For he sang the song of a maiden who waited for her Jack.

"Out on the lonely prairie, where skies are always blue,
Your sweetheart waits for you, Jack, your sweetheart waits for you."

Jack left the camp next morning, breathing his sweetheart's name:
"I'll go and ask forgiveness, for I know that I'm to blame."

But when he reached the prairie, he found a new-made mound,
And his friends they sadly told him, they'd laid his loved one down.

They said as she was dying, she breathed her sweetheart's name,
And asked them with her last breath to tell him when he came:

"Your sweetheart waits for you, Jack, your sweetheart waits for you,
Out on the lonely prairie, where skies are always blue."

YOUNG CHARLOTTIE

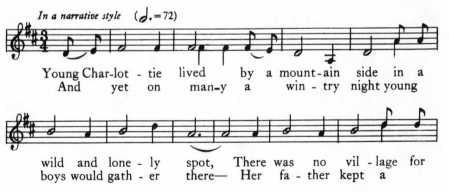

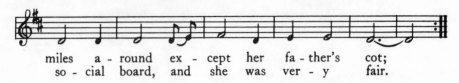

miles   a - round   ex - cept   her   fa - ther's   cot;
so - cial   board,   and   she   was   ver - y   fair.

Young Charlottie lived by a mountain side in a wild and lonely
    spot,
There was no village for miles around except her father's cot;
And yet on many a wintry night young boys would gather there—
Her father kept a social board, and she was very fair.

One New Year's Eve as the sun went down, she cast a wistful eye
Out from the window pane as a merry sleigh went by.
At a village fifteen miles away was to be a ball that night;
Although the air was piercing cold, her heart was merry and light.

At last her laughing eye lit up as a well-known voice she heard,
And dashing in front of the door her lover's sleigh appeared.
"O daughter dear," her mother said, "this blanket round you fold,
'Tis such a dreadful night abroad and you will catch your death of
    cold."

"Oh, no, oh, no!" young Charlottie cried, as she laughed like a gypsy
    queen.
"To ride in blankets muffled up, I never would be seen.
My silken coat is quite enough, you know it is lined throughout,
And there is my silken scarf to wrap my head and neck about."

Her father liked to see her dress fine as a city belle,
For she was the only child he had and he loved his daughter well.
Her bonnet and her gloves were on, she jumped into the sleigh,
And swiftly slid down the mountain side and over the hills away.

[232]

There's music in the merry bells as over the hills they go;
What a shrieking sound the runners make as they press the frozen
    snow!
All muffled up so silent, five miles at last were past
When Charlie, with few but shivering words, the silence broke at
    last.

"Such a dreadful night I never saw, my reins I can scarcely hold."
Young Charlottie then feebly said, "I am exceedingly cold."
He cracked his whip and urged his speed much faster than before,
While at least five other miles in silence had passed o'er.

Spoke Charles, "How fast the freezing ice is gathering on my
    brow!"
Young Charlottie then feebly said, "I'm growing warmer now."
So on they sped through the frosty air and the glittering cold star-
    light
Until at last the village lights and the ballroom came in sight.

They reached the door, and Charles sprang out and reached his hands
    to her.
"Why sit you there like a monument that has no power to stir?"
He called her once, he called her twice, she answered not a word;
And then he called her once again but still she never stirred.

He took her hand in his; 'twas cold and hard as any stone.
He tore her mantle from her face while cold stars on it shone.
Then quickly to the lighted hall her lifeless form he bore—
Young Charlottie's eyes were closed forever, her voice was heard no
    more.

And there he sat down by her side while bitter tears did flow,
And cried, "My own, my charming bride, you nevermore shall
    know."
He twined his arms around her neck and kissed her marble brow,
And his thoughts flew back to where she said, "I'm growing warmer
    now."

He took her back into the sleigh and quickly hurried home;
When he arrived at her father's door, oh, how her friends did
    mourn!
They mourned the loss of a daughter dear, while Charles wept over
    the gloom,
Till at last he died with the bitter grief—now they both lie in one
    tomb.

SILVER JACK

A lumberjack song adopted by the cowboys. The fight might have
occurred in a cow camp though the song first came from Michigan.

I was on the drive in Eighty
Working under Silver Jack,
Which the same is now in Jackson
And ain't soon expected back,
And there was a fellow 'mongst us
By the name of Robert Waite;
Kind of cute and smart and tonguey,
Guess he was a graduate.

He could talk on any subject
From the Bible down to Hoyle,
And his words flowed out so easy,
Just as smooth and slick as oil.

[234]

He was what they call a sceptic;
And he loved to sit and weave
Hifalutin words together
Tellin' what he didn't believe.

One day we all were sittin' round
Smokin' niggerhead tobacco
And hearing Bob expound;
Hell, he said, was all a humbug,
And he made it plain as day
That the Bible was a fable;
And we 'lowed it looked that way.
Miracles and such like
Were too rank for him to stand,
And as for him they called the Savior,
He was just a common man.

"You're a liar," some one shouted,
"And you've got to take it back."
Then everybody started—
'Twas the words of Silver Jack.
And he cracked his fists together
And he stacked his duds and cried,
" 'Twas in that thar religion
That my mother lived and died;
And though I haven't always
Used the Lord exactly right,
Yet when I hear a chump abuse him
He's got to eat his words or fight."

Now, this Bob he weren't no coward,
And he answered bold and free:
"Stack your duds and cut your capers,
For there ain't no flies on me."

[235]

And they fit for forty minutes
And the crowd would whoop and cheer
When Jack spit up a tooth or two,
Or when Bobby lost an ear.

But at last Jack got him under
And he slugged him oncet or twicet,
And straightway Bob admitted
The divinity of Christ.
But Jack kept reasoning with him
Till the poor cuss gave a yell
And 'lowed he'd been mistaken
In his views concerning hell.

Then the fierce encounter ended
And they riz up from the ground
And some one brought a bottle out
And kindly passed it round.
And we drank to Bob's religion
In a cheerful sort o' way,
But the spread of infidelity
Was checked in camp that day.

THE HELL–BOUND TRAIN *

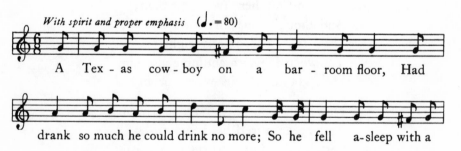

With spirit and proper emphasis (♩. = 80)

A Tex - as cow - boy on a bar - room floor, Had

drank so much he could drink no more; So he fell a-sleep with a

* Said to have been written by J. W. Pruitte, the Cowboy Preacher. Clipped from the
Fort Gibson Post, April 8, 1909.

[236]

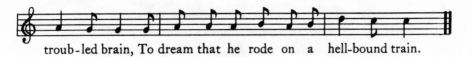

troub-led brain, To dream that he rode on a hell-bound train.

A Texas cowboy on a barroom floor,
Had drank so much he could drink no more;
So he fell asleep with a troubled brain
To dream that he rode on a hell-bound train.

The engine with murderous blood was damp,
Brilliantly lit by a brimstone lamp;
While an imp, for fuel, was shov'ling bones,
The furnace rang with a thousand groans.

The boiler was filled with lager beer,
And the devil himself was the engineer;
The passengers were a most motley crew—
Church members, atheist, Gentile, and Jew,

Rich men in broadcloth, beggars in rags,
Handsome young ladies, and withered old hags,
Yellow and black men, red, brown, and white,
All chained together—O God, what a sight!

While the train rushed on at an awful pace,
The sulphurous fumes scorched their hands and face:
Wilder and wilder the country grew,
As faster and faster the engine flew.

Louder and louder the thunder crashed
And brighter and brighter the lightning flashed;
Hotter and hotter the air became
Till the clothes were burnt from each quivering frame.

[237]

And out of the distance there arose a yell.
"Ha, ha," said the devil, "we're nearing hell!"
Then, oh, how the passengers all shrieked with pain
And begged the devil to stop the train!

But he capered about and danced for glee
And laughed and joked at their misery.
"My faithful friends, you have done the work,
And the devil never can a pay day shirk.

"You've bullied the weak, you've robbed the poor;
The starving brother you've turned from the door,
You've laid up gold where the canker rust,
And have given free vent to your beastly lust.

"You've justice scorned, and corruption sown,
And trampled the laws of nature down.
You have drunk, rioted, cheated, plundered, and lied,
And mocked at God in your hell-born pride.

"You have paid full fare, so I'll carry you through;
For it's only right you should have your due.
Why, the laborer always expects his hire,
So I'll land you safe in the lake of fire,

"Where your flesh will waste in the flames that roar,
And my imps torment you forever more."
Then the cowboy awoke with an anguished cry,
His clothes wet with sweat and his hair standing high.

Then he prayed as he never had prayed till that hour
To be saved from his sin and the demon's power.
And his prayers and his vows were not in vain;
For he never rode the hell-bound train.

V

OFF GUARD

Dancing, drinking, gambling, fighting
Are the pastimes of our gang.
"Enjoy yourself," our motto is,
"For tomorrow—you may hang!"

A COWBOY DANCE SONG*

My name is Sam, an' I don't give a damn;
A la boys, give the fiddler a dram;
Swing the girls, an' let 'em go;
Rattle yer hoofs, an' don't be slow!

    Doodle doo-de doo; doodle doo-de doo.

It's faro, monte, crackaloo,
Grip ther fins, an' trot 'em through;
Balance! swing! an' all pass by;
Grab yer pardners on the fly!

    Doodle doo-de doo; doodle doo-de doo.

Some likes girls thet's purty in the face,
An' some likes girls thet's small 'roun' the waist;
But give me the girl with a chubby fat han'
An' a dimple in her cheek like a hole in a pan.

    Doodle doo-de doo; doodle doo-de doo.

She ranges in the Live Oak branch;
The purtiest heifer at the ranch;
With hazel eyes an' golden hair—
An' try to steal 'er if you dare!

    Doodle doo-de doo; doodle doo-de doo.

* From Luther A. Lawhon, San Antonio, Texas.

Oh, I'm as happy as a king!
We'll be married in the spring;
When grass has come—you bet you! and
We'll start us up a little brand.

Doodle doo-de doo; doodle doo-de doo.

RHYMED DANCE CALLS

From W. A. Hoffarth of Missouri, who writes: "I am fond of reading *Wild West Weekly* and, picking up an old number of April 25, 1936, was interested in the article on Square Dancing by John A. Lomax, which called to mind my boyhood days in the Ozarks, in Missouri, from 1896 to 1910. We had some log-cabin dances to the music of most of the tunes Mr. Lomax lists in his article with 'Surang Hornpipe,' 'Van Wagner,' 'Fisher's Hornpipe,' 'Irish Washerwoman,' 'Arkansaw Traveler,' and music furnished by violin, second fiddle, 'bass vile,' dulcimer, guitar, and broomstick, with one beating time on the leading fiddler's instrument with a pair of steel knitting needles."

Join hands and circle to the left
Circle right back—swing your pard
And lady on left—right to pard and
Grand right and left—meet your pard
    And promenade away.

First gent swing the lady so fair,
Now the one right over there,
Now the one with the curly hair,
Now the belle of the ballroom. (*Swing!*)
(*Everybody swing!*) Promenade all.

Second gent swing the lady so sweet,
Now the one with the great big feet,
Now the one that looks so neat,
Now the belle of the ballroom,
    Promenade all.

Three or four just go through the same performance. Caller changes wording to suit the occasion.

First lady swing the gent with the two sore toes,
Now the one with the great big nose,
Now the one that wears store clothes,
Now the dude of the ballroom. (*Swing!*)
    Promenade all.

Second lady swing the gent so green,
Now the one that ate the beans,
Now the one that wears the jeans,
Now the dude of the ballroom. (*Swing!*)
    Promenade all.

Third lady swing the gent so raw,
Now the one from Arkansaw,
Now the one that says "Haw-haw!"
Now the dude of the ballroom. (*Swing!*)
    Promenade all.

Fourth lady swing the gent so blue,
Now the one that ate the glue,
Now the one that's stuck on you,
Now the dude of the ballroom. (*Swing!*)
    Promenade to seats.

THE HARRINGTON BARN DANCE*

Come all you woolly waddies,
Let's to Harrington's ranch,
The fiddlers are a-comin',
An' they're goin' to have a dance.

George has roped his old piano
An' drug it in the barn,
An' tonight we're gonna pay
The mortgage off the little farm.

Such a dance as we're having
Has never been had, yet,
Tom Kenyon is a-comin'
An' he's gonna call the sets.

Mat Miller plays the fiddle
And his brother plays the drum,
So slick up in yore war paint
An' get ready for the fun.

Jim Gilliland, the sheriff,
Will represent the Jaw.
You should see the waddies step
To the "Turkey in the Straw."

But you needn't fear that Jim
Will try to stop yore fun,
If you're decent with your licker
An' leave your shootin' iron at home.

* Sent by Williams Clements of Arkansas to the *Wild West Weekly*.

Charley Summers is a-comin',
An' them bloomin' feet o' his
Can do the old-time schottische
Like nobody's biz.

"Footer Mac" will do the Charleston,
An' the gals will come from town.
George is gonna build a new barn,
So we'll tear the old one down.

CHEYENNE

I'm a-tellin' you the truth and not lying nor joking,
I'd rather be in jail than to be heart-broken.

Refrain:
Cheyenne-a, Cheyenne, I'm a-leaving Cheyenne;
Cheyenne-a, Cheyenne, I'm a-leaving Cheyenne.

My foot's in the stirrup, my rein's in my hand,
I'm a-riding old Paint and a-leaving Cheyenne.

My foot's in the stirrup, my rein's in my hand,
Good-by, old Paint, you're a-leaving Cheyenne.

THE COWBOY'S CHRISTMAS BALL

This poem, one of the best in Larry Chittenden's *Ranch Verses,*
published by G. P. Putnam's Sons, New York, has been set to music
by the cowboys and its phraseology slightly changed, as this copy will
show, by oral transmission. I first heard it sung in New Mexico
on the Hearst (Diamond A) Ranch, and it has been sent to me from
various places—always as a song. None of those who sent in the song
knew that it was already in print. During Christmas week each year
at "Anson City," "The Cowboy's Christmas Ball" is repeated.

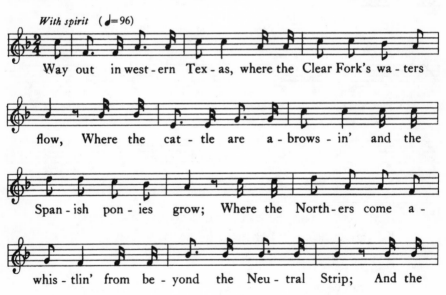

With spirit (♩=96)

Way out in west-ern Tex-as, where the Clear Fork's wa-ters

flow, Where the cat-tle are a-brows-in' and the

Span-ish pon-ies grow; Where the North-ers come a-

whis-tlin' from be-yond the Neu-tral Strip; And the

prai-rie dogs are sneez-in', as though they had the grip.

Way out in western Texas, where the Clear Fork's waters flow,
Where the cattle are a-browsin' and the Spanish ponies grow;
Where the Northers come a-whistlin' from beyond the Neutral Strip;
And the prairie dogs are sneezin', as though they had the grip;

Where the coyotes come a-howlin' round the ranches after dark,
And the mockin' birds are singin' to the lovely medder lark;
Where the 'possum and the badger and the rattlesnakes abound,
And the monstrous stars are winkin' o'er a wilderness profound;

Where lonesome, tawny prairies melt into airy streams,
While the Double Mountains slumber in heavenly kinds of dreams;
Where the antelope is grazin' and the lonely plovers call—
It was there I attended the Cowboy's Christmas Ball.

The town was Anson City, old Jones' county seat,
Where they raised Polled Angus cattle and waving whiskered
    wheat;
Where the air is soft and bammy and dry and full of health,
Where the prairies is explodin' with agricultural wealth;

Where they print the *Texas Western,* that Hec McCann supplies
With news and yarns and stories, of most amazing size;
Where Frank Smith "pulls the badger" on knowing tenderfeet,
And Democracy's triumphant and mighty hard to beat;

Where lives that good old hunter, John Milsap from Lamar,
Who used to be the sheriff "back east in Paris, sah"!

'Twas there, I say, at Anson with the lovely Widder Wall,
That I went to that reception, the Cowboy's Christmas Ball.

The boys had left the ranches and come to town in piles;
The ladies, kinder scatterin', had gathered in for miles.
And yet the place was crowded, as I remember well,
'Twas gave on this occasion at the Morning Star Hotel.

The music was a fiddle and a lively tambourine,
And a viol came imported, by the stage from Abilene.
The room was togged out gorgeous—with mistletoe and shawls,
And the candles flickered festious, around the airy walls.

The wimmen folks looked lovely—the boys looked kinder treed,
Till the leader commenced yelling, "Whoa, fellers, let's stampede,"
And the music started sighing and a-wailing through the hall
As a kind of introduction to the Cowboy's Christmas Ball.

The leader was a feller that came from Swenson's ranch—
They called him Windy Billy from Little Deadman's Branch.
His rig was kinder keerless—big spurs and high-heeled boots;
He had the reputation that comes when fellers shoots.

His voice was like the bugle upon the mountain height;
His feet were animated, and a mighty movin' sight,
When he commenced to holler, "Now, fellers, shake your pen!
Lock horns ter all them heifers and rustle them like men;

"Saloot yer lovely critters; neow swing and let 'em go;
Climb the grapevine round 'em; neow all hands do-ce-do!
You maverick, jine the round-up—jes' skip the waterfall,"
Huh! hit was getting active, the Cowboy's Christmas Ball.

[248]

The boys was tolerable skittish, the ladies powerful neat,
That old bass viol's music just got there with both feet!
That wailin', frisky fiddle, I never shall forget;
And Windy kept a-singin'—I think I hear him yet—

"Oh, X's, chase yer squirrels, and cut 'em to our side;
Spur Treadwell to the center, with Cross P Charley's bride,
Doc Hollis down the center, and twine the ladies' chain,
Van Andrews, pen the fillies in big T Diamond's train.

"All pull your freight together, neow swallow fork and change;
Big Boston, lead the trail herd through little Pitchfork's range.
Purr round yer gentle pussies, neow rope and balance all!"
Huh! Hit were gettin' active—the Cowboy's Christmas Ball.

The dust riz fast and furious; we all jes' galloped round,
Till the scenery got so giddy that T Bar Dick was downed.
We buckled to our partners and told 'em to hold on,
Then shook our hoofs like lightning until the early dawn.

Don't tell me 'bout cotillions or germans. No, sir-ee!
That whirl at Anson City jes' takes the cake with me.
I'm sick of lazy shufflin's, of them I've had my fill,
Give me a frontier breakdown backed up by Windy Bill.

McAllister ain't nowhere, when Windy leads the show;
I've seen 'em both in harness and so I ought ter know.
Oh, Bill, I shan't forget yer, and I oftentimes recall
That lively gaited sworray—the Cowboy's Christmas Ball.

THE COWBOY'S DANCE SONG*

With animation ($\quad$ = 104)

You can't ex - pect a cow - boy to ag - i - tate his

shanks In et - i - quet - tish man - ner in ar -

is - to - crat - ic ranks, When he's al - ways been ac -

cus - tomed to shake the heel and toe At the

rat - tling ranch - er dan - ces where much et - i - quette don't

go. You can bet I set them laugh - ing in

quite an ex - cit - ed way; A giv - ing of their

* By James Barton Adams. From *Songs of the Cattle Trail and Cow Camp*, by John A. Lomax (New York: Macmillan, 1919).

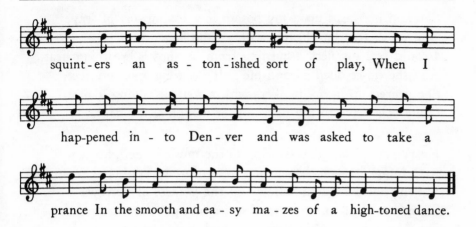

squint-ers an as - ton-ished sort of play, When I

hap-pened in - to Den - ver and was asked to take a

prance In the smooth and ea - sy ma - zes of a high-toned dance.

You can't expect a cowboy to agitate his shanks
In etiquettish manner in aristocratic ranks,
When he's always been accustomed to shake the heel and toe
At the rattling rancher dances where much etiquette don't go.
You can bet I set them laughing in quite an excited way,
A-giving of their squinters an astonished sort of play,
When I happened into Denver and was asked to take a prance
In the smooth and easy mazes of a high-toned dance.

When I got among the ladies in their frocks of snowy white,
And the dudes togged out in wrappings that were simply out of sight,
Tell you what, I was embarrassed, and somehow I couldn't keep
From feeling like a burro in a pretty flock of sheep.
Every step I made was awkward and I blushed a fiery red,
Like the principal adornment of a turkey gobbler's head.
The ladies said 'twas seldom that they had had the chance
To see an old-time puncher at a high-toned dance.

I cut me out a heifer from a bunch of pretty girls
And yanked her to the center to dance the dreamy whirls.

[251]

She laid her head upon my bosom in a loving sort of way,
And we drifted into heaven as the band began to play.
I could feel my neck a-burning from her nose's breathing heat,
And she do-ce-doed around me half the time upon my feet,
She peered up in my blinkers with a soul-dissolving glance,
Quite conducive to the pleasures of a high-toned dance.

Every nerve just got a-dancing to the music of delight
As I hugged the little sagehen uncomfortably tight;
But she never made a bellow and the glances of her eyes
Seemed to thank me for the pleasure of a genuine surprise.
She snuggled up against me in a loving sort of way,
And I hugged her all the tighter for her trustifying play—
Tell you what, the joys of heaven ain't a cussed circumstance
To the hug-a-mania pleasures of the high-toned dance.

When they struck the old cotillion on the music bill of fare,
Every bit of devil in me seemed to burst out on a tear.
I fetched a cowboy whoop and started in to rag,
And cut her with my trotters till the floor began to sag;
Swung my pardner till she got seasick and rushed for a seat;
I balanced to the next one but she dodged me slick and neat.
Tell you what, I shook the creases from my go-to-meeting pants,
When I put the cowboy trimmings on that high-toned dance.

JACK O' DIAMONDS

or

THE RABBLE SOLDIER

O Mol-lie, O Mol-lie, 'tis for your sake a-lone That I
Refrain: Jack o' Dia-monds, Jack o' Dia-monds, I know you of old; You've

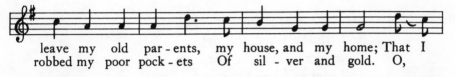

leave my old par-ents, my house, and my home; That I
robbed my poor pock-ets Of sil-ver and gold. O,

leave my old par-ents, you caused me to roam—I'm an
whis-ky, you vil-lain, You've been my down-fall, You've

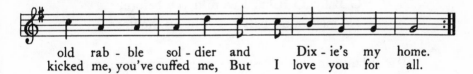

old rab-ble sol-dier and Dix-ie's my home.
kicked me, you've cuffed me, But I love you for all.

O Mollie, O Mollie, 'tis for your sake alone
That I leave my old parents, my house, and my home,
That I leave my old parents, you caused me to roam—
I'm an old rabble* soldier and Dixie's my home.

Jack o' Diamonds, Jack o' Diamonds,
I know you of old.
You've robbed my poor pockets
Of silver and gold.

* Vernacular for "rebel."

[253]

O Whisky, you villain,
You've been my downfall,
You've kicked me, you've cuffed me,
But I love you for all.

My foot's in the stirrup, my bridle's in my hand,
I'm going to leave sweet Mollie,* the fairest in the land
Her parents don't like me, they say I'm too poor,
They say I'm unworthy to enter her door.

Beefsteak when I'm hungry,
And whisky when I'm dry,
Greenbacks when I'm hard up,
And heaven when I die.
Rye whisky, rye whisky,
Rye whisky, I cry,
If I don't get rye whisky,
I surely will die.
O Baby, O Baby, I've told you before,
Do make me a pallet, I'll lie on the floor.

I will build me a big castle on yonder mountain high,
Where my true love can see me when she comes riding by,
Where my true love can see me and help me to mourn—
I'm an old rabble soldier and Dixie's my home.

I'll get up in my saddle, my quirt I'll take in hand,
I'll think of you, Mollie, when in some far distant land,
I'll think of you, Mollie, you caused me to roam—
I'm an old rabble soldier and Dixie's my home.

* Once Mollie speaks:
"My children are nungry and crying for bread,
My husband's a drunkard and I wish I was dead."

If the ocean was whisky,
And I was a duck,
I'd dive to the bottom
To get one sweet sup;
But the ocean ain't whisky,
And I ain't a duck,
So I'll round up the cattle
And then we'll get drunk.
     O Baby, O Baby, I've told you before,
     Do make me a pallet, I'll lie on the floor.

I've rambled and trambled* this wide world around,
But it's for the rabble army, dear Mollie, I'm bound;
It is to the rabble army, dear Mollie, I roam—
I'm an old rabble soldier and Dixie's my home.

I have rambled and gambled all my money away,
But it's with the rabble army, O Mollie, I must stay;
It is with the rabble army, O Mollie, I must roam—
I'm an old rabble soldier and Dixie's my home.

My foot in the stirrup, my bundle in my hand
A-courtin' fair Mollie, to marry if I can;
I'll drink and I'll gamble, my money's my own
And them that don't like me can leave me alone.

     Jack o' Diamonds, Jack o' Diamonds,
     I know you of old,
     You've robbed my poor pockets
     Of silver and gold.
     Rye whisky, rye whisky,
     Rye whisky, I cry,

* Folk etymology: traveled.

If you don't give me rye whisky
I'll lie down and die.
O Baby, O Baby, I've told you before,
Do make me a pallet, I'll lie on the floor.

THE ARIZONA BOYS AND GIRLS

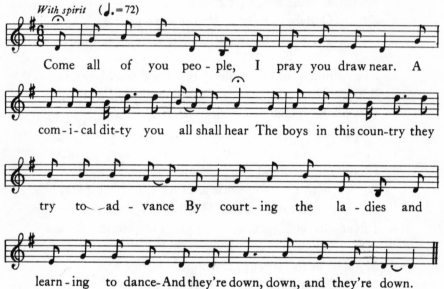

With spirit (♩.=72)

Come all of you peo-ple, I pray you draw near. A
com-i-cal dit-ty you all shall hear The boys in this coun-try they
try to ad-vance By court-ing the la-dies and
learn-ing to dance-And they're down, down, and they're down.

Come all of you people, I pray you draw near,
A comical ditty you all shall hear.
The boys in this country they try to advance,
By courting the ladies and learning to dance—
And they're down, down, and they're down.

The boys in this country they try to be plain,
Those words that you hear you may hear them again,
With twice as much added on if you can.

There's many a boy stuck up for a man—
And they're down, down, and they're down.

They will go to their parties, their whisky they'll take,
And out in the dark their bottles they'll break;
You'll hear one say, "There's a bottle around here;
So come around, boys, and we'll all take a share"—
And they're down, down, and they're down.

There is some wears shoes and some wears boots,
But there are very few that rides who don't shoot;
More than this, I'll tell you what they'll do,
They'll get them a watch and a ranger hat, too—
And they're down, down, and they're down.

They'll go in the hall with spurs on their heel,
They'll get them a partner to dance the next reel,
Saying, "How do I look in my new brown suit,
With my pants stuffed down in the top of my boot?"—
And they're down, down, and they're down.

Now I think it's quite time to leave off these lads
For here are some girls that's fully as bad;
They'll trim up their dresses and curl up their hair,
And like an old owl before the glass they'll stare—
And they're down, down, and they're down.

The girls in the country they grin like a cat,
And with giggling and laughing they don't know what
    they're at,
They think they're pretty and I tell you they're wise,
But they couldn't get married to save their two eyes—
And they're down, down, and they're down.

Their rusty old stirrups they'll brush and they'll rub,
Their old dirty boots they'll black and they'll scrub.
They'll dress themselves up; they'll look in the glass,
Saying, "Tee, hee, hee, hee! What a fine bonny lass!"
And they're down, down, and they're down.

Just let their old parents be ever so poor,
They must have a little hat with a feather before.
They will dress themselves up, put on a false hair,
And then like an owl in a glass they will stare.
And they're down, down, and they're down.

The girls of this country will give the boys a slap;
They're always a-laughin', an' they don't know what at.
But if there's any here that would take offense,
They can go to the Devil and seek recompense.
And they're down, down, and they're down.

You can tell a good girl wherever she's found;
No trimming, no lace, no nonsense around;
With a long-eared bonnet tied under her chin,
And long, shiny hair in plenty within—
And they're down, down, and they're down.

They'll go to church with their snuffbox in hand,
They'll give it a tap to make it look grand;
Perhaps there is another one or two
And they'll pass it around and it's "Madam, won't you"—
And they're down, down, and they're down.

Now, I think it's quite time for this ditty to end;
If there's any one here that it will offend,
If there's any one here that thinks it amiss,
Just come around now and give the singer a kiss—
And they're down, down, and they're down.

DON'T GROW WEARY, BOYS*

Sent to J. Frank Dobie by Dr. J. W. Hargus of Asherton, Texas, who says it was sung to the tune of the then popular "If Ever I Cease to Love." Bears a strong resemblance to "Rye Whisky."

Ducks in the mill-pond eating up moss,
Devil on the hillside kicking like a hoss.

Refrain:
Don't grow weary, boys,
Don't grow weary, boys,
For we're going to the ball.

Meat on the goose-foot, marrow on the bone,
Devil on the hillside—don't you hear him groan?

Beefsteak when I'm hungry, liquor when I'm dry,
Greenbacks when I'm hard up, and religion when I die.

I AM FUR FROM MY SWEETHEART

A sample of a ballad collector's mail, received by John B. Jones, Houston, Texas, December 12, 1909.

"Dear Friend You ask me to write of one of the songs I usto sing while we usto viset with each other here in the park. I guess I had beter give you a little history first before I write the song During the Civel War there was a regiment raised in Denver called the name Colorado first this regiment had just ben raised when the Govener of New Mexico called on Colorado for suport as the Con-

---

* From "Texas and Southwestern Lore," ed. J. Frank Dobie (*Publications of the Texas Folk-Lore Society*, Vol. VI); the information about the song from his article "Ballads and Songs of the Frontier Folk."

federate souldiers from Texas had invaded his state. In the Colorado regiment was a recrute from Denver and at the battle of Apache kenion these two forses met and they had two days fight and the Confederate side were beaten and quite a number of priseners were captured by the federals and among them was a recrute from San Antonio with the Confederates and this prisiner sang this song and the recruit from Denver learned it and I herd the old soldier from Denver sing it so I learned it and send it to you I tried to or three times to write the song and failed so I got my wife to help me and by her help I finly got pretty well. but I dount know how you will get the air to it unless you come over and let me sing it or you might wander around in the park and catch it ha-ha. Well I guess I would make a pretty bad stab at soldering now. as I have not had much drilling of any kind except at the Oddfelows hall and that is quite diferent. We all wish you a Happy Christmas and New Yer. We all are siting here by the mantel eating pecans and walnuts If you were here I might setem up out of my jug Well I must say goodby bee a good boy and get all of the schooling you can ever your friend Dolph Johns Write soon so long."

Miss Lucy she is slender, Miss Lucy she is stout,
Her face looks like the fireplace with the ashes taken out.

I'm fur from my sweetheart and she is fur from me,
And when I'll see my sweetheart, I can't say when 'twill be.

But I love her just the same, no matter where I roam,
And that there girl will wait for me whenever I come home.

I've roamed the Texas prairies, I've followed the cattle trail,
I've rid a pitching pony till the hair come off his tail.

I've been to cowboy dances, I've kissed the Texas girls,
But there ain't none what can compare with my own sweetheart's
curls.

DAN TAYLOR*

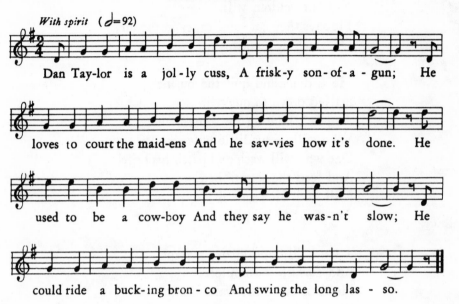

> Dan Taylor is a jolly cuss,
> A frisky son of a gun,
> He loves to court the maidens
> And he savvies how it's done.
> He used to be a cowboy
> And they say he wasn't slow,
> He could ride a bucking bronco
> And swing the long lasso.
>
> He could catch a maverick† by the head,
> Or heel him on the fly;
> He could pick up his front ones
> Whenever he chose to try.

* From Mrs. M. B. Wight, Fort Thomas, Arizona.
† Here the word is generalized to mean "cattle."

[261]

He used to ride most anything;
Now he seldom will.
He says they cut some caper in the air,
Of which he's got his fill.

He is done and quit the business,
Settled down to quiet life,
And he's hunting for some maiden
Who will be his little wife—
One who will wash and patch his britches
And feed the setting hen,
Milk old Blue and Brindy,
And tend to baby Ben.

Then he'll build a cozy cottage
And furnish it complete;
He'll decorate the walls inside
With pictures new and sweet.
He will leave off riding broncos
And be a different man;
He will do his best to please his wife
In every way he can.

Then together in double harness
They will trot along down the line
Until death shall call them over
To a bright and sunny clime.
May your joys be then completed
And your sorrows have an end
Is the fondest wish of the writer—
Your true and faithful friend.

LULU

With spirit and verve (♩=92)

If you don't quit mon-keying with my Lu - lu, I'll
My Lu - lu had a ba - by, 'Twas

tell you what I'll do, I'll carve you up with my
born on Christ-mas Day; She washed its face in

bow - ie knife And shoot you with my pis - tol,
bran - dy And called it Hen - ry

too, And shoot you with my pis - tol, too.
Clay, And called it Hen - ry Clay.

If you don't quit monkeying with my Lulu,
I'll tell you what I'll do,
I'll carve you up with my bowie knife
And shoot you with my pistol, too,
And shoot you with my pistol, too.

My Lulu had a baby,
'Twas born on Christmas Day;
She washed its face in brandy
And called it Henry Clay,
And called it Henry Clay.

[263]

You know you couldn't gamble,
You ought to stay at home
And pick up chips for your mamma,
And let the gamblers alone,
And let the gamblers alone.

I seen my Lulu in the springtime,
I seen her in the fall;
She wrote me a letter in the winter-time,
Says, "Good-by, honey"—that's all,
Says, "Good-by, honey"—that's all.

My Lulu, she's a dandy,
She stands and drinks like a man,
She calls for gin and brandy,
And she doesn't give a damn,
And she doesn't give a damn.

I ain't goin' to work on the railroad,
I ain't goin' to lie in jail,
I'm goin' down to Cheyenne town
To live with my Lulu gal,
To live with my Lulu gal.

My Lulu hugged and kissed me,
She wrung my hand and cried;
She said I was the sweetest thing
That ever lived or died,
That ever lived or died.

Lulu had twin babies,
Born on Christmas Day;
She mashed one's head with a rollin' pin,
The other one got away,
The other one got away.

[264]

WAY OUT IN IDYHO*

With the utmost verve ($\quad$.=104)

Re - mem - ber what   I   prom-ised you,   As
Fare - well,   it's moth - er   and   child,   I'm

we   set side by   side,   Be - neath that old   per -
off   for to stay a - while,   So   won't you kiss me be -

sim - mon tree,   I   said   I'd   be   your   bride.
fore   I   go,   And   call   me your   dar - ling   child?

REFRAIN

Way   out   in   I - dy - ho,   We're com-ing to   I - dy -

ho,   With a   four - horse team,   We'll   soon   be   seen,   Way

out   in   I - dy - ho.

Remember what I promised you,
As we set side by side,

* From p. 77, *Singing Cowboy*, by Margaret Larkin (New York: Knopf). This was given to Miss Larkin by Lynn Riggs of *Green Grow the Lilacs* fame.

[265]

Beneath that old persimmon tree,
I said I'd be your bride.

Way out in Idyho,
We're coming to Idyho,
With a four horse team
We'll soon be seen,
Way out in Idyho.

Farewell, it's mother and child,
I'm off for to stay awhile,
So won't you kiss me before I go?
And call me your darling child?

RAMBLING GAMBLER

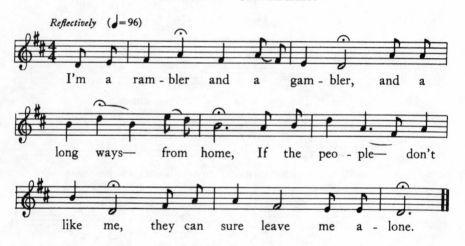

Reflectively (♩ = 96)

I'm a ram - bler and a gam - bler, and a long ways— from home, If the peo - ple— don't like me, they can sure leave me a - lone.

I'm a rambler and a gambler, and a long ways from home,
If the people don't like me, they can sure leave me alone.

Oh! it's dark and a-rainin', and the moon gives no light;
My pony won't travel a dark road at night.

Go put up your pony and give him some hay,
Come take your seat by me so long as you stay.

My pony is hungry nor he won't eat your hay;
I'll go to Wyomin', I'll graze on the way.

When you get to Wyomin' a letter you'll see,
If you get into trouble, just write and tell me.

I use' to have a little sweetheart, her age was fourteen,
She was the flower of Belton, and the rose of Saline;

Her parents were against me, and now she is the same,
If I'm on your book, love, please blot out my name.

BUCKING BRONCO

According to N. Howard Thorp (*Songs of the Cowboys*, p. 14),
this song was written by Belle Star, a notorious woman desperado
of the Indian Territory.

My love is a rider and broncos he breaks,
But he's given up riding and all for my sake;
For he found him a horse and it suited him so
He vowed he'd ne'er ride any other bronco.

My love has a gun, and that gun he can use,
But he's quit his gun fighting as well as his booze;
And he's sold him his saddle, his spurs, and his rope,
And there's no more cow-punching, and that's what I hope.

The first time I met him, 'twas early one spring,
Riding a bronco, a high-headed thing.

He tipped me a wink as he gayly did go;
For he wished me to look at his bucking bronco.

The next time I saw him 'twas late in the fall,
Swinging the girls at Tomlinson's ball.
He laughed and he talked as we danced to and fro,
Promised never to ride on another bronco.

He made me some presents, among them a ring;
The return that I made him was a far better thing:
'Twas a young maiden's heart, I'd have you all know;
He's won it by riding his bucking bronco.

My love has a gun that has gone to the bad,
Which makes poor old Jimmy feel pretty damn sad;
For the gun it shoots high and the gun it shoots low,
And it wabbles about like a bucking bronco.

Now all you young maidens, where'er you reside,
Beware of the cowboy who swings the rawhide;
He'll court you and pet you and leave you and go
In the spring up the trail on his bucking bronco.

THE LOVESICK COWBOY*

I am a bold cowboy, from Midland I came,
But my virtue's departed, I'm covered with shame;
The cold darts of Cupid have wrought me much grief,
My heart's burst asunder, I can find no relief.

I am a bold cowboy, on the green prairies roam,
My name is engraved on the sand hills alone;

* Sent by D. L. Browning, Garner, Texas, who learned it from its composer Charles A.
Bobston, Midland, Texas.

In the town of Odessa I am very well known
As a dashing young cowboy, and Midland's my home.

But I will tell you my troubles without further delay,
Of a sweet little lassie who my heart stole away;
She was a good woman's daughter upon the north side,
And I always intended to make her my bride.

But one Sabbath morning a letter I received,
She said from her promise she long had deceived;
She would marry another, she long had delayed,
And the next time I met her she would no more be a maid.

Come all you young cowboys, I'm tellin' you true,
Don't depend on a woman—you're beat if you do;
And when you meet one with bright golden hair,
Just think of this cowboy that will die in despair.

Kind friends, take warning and heed what I say,
For the message of death is calling today;
How soon you will follow there is no one can tell;
I ask God to help you and bid you farewell.

THE GOL–DARNED WHEEL

Once popular along the Rio Grande. The unfortunate bicycle was
of the very tall front wheel variety, which preceded the safety type.
W. Bogel, a student at the Agricultural and Mechanical College of
Texas, first sang this song to me in 1908.

Vigorously ($\downarrow$=144)

323 I can take the wild-est bron-co in the tough old wool-ly West.

I can take the wildest bronco in the tough old woolly West;
I can ride him, I can break him, let him do his level best.

I can handle any cattle ever wore a coat of hair,
And I've had a lively tussle with a tarnal grizzly bear.

I can rope and throw the longhorn of the wildest Texas brand,
And in Indian disagreements I can play a leading hand,

But at last I got my master and he surely made me squeal
When the boys got me astraddle of that gol-darned wheel.

It was at the Eagle Ranch, on the Brazos,
When I first found that darned contrivance that upset me in the
    dust.

A tenderfoot had brought it, he was wheeling all the way
From the sunrise end of freedom out to San Francisco Bay.

He tied up at the ranch for to get outside a meal,
Never thinking we would monkey with his gol-darned wheel.

Arizona Jim begun it when he said to Jack McGill
There was fellows forced to limit bragging on their riding skill,

And he'd venture the admission the same fellow that he meant
Was a very handy cutter far as riding broncos went;

But he would find that he was bucking 'gainst a different kind of
    deal
If he threw his leather leggins 'gainst a gol-darned wheel.

Such a slam against my talent made me hotter than a mink,
And I swore that I would ride him for amusement or for chink.

And it was nothing but a plaything for the kids and such about,
And they'd have their ideas shattered if they'd lead the critter out.

They held it while I mounted and gave the word to go;
The shove they gave to start me warn't unreasonably slow.

But I never spilled a cuss word and I never spilled a squeal—
I was building reputation on that gol-darned wheel.

Holy Moses and the Prophets, how we split the Texas air,
And the wind it made whip-crackers of my same old canthy hair,

And I sorta comprehended as down the hill we went
There was bound to be a smash-up that I couldn't well prevent.

Oh, how them punchers bawled, "Stay with her, Uncle Bill!
Stick your spurs in her, you sucker! Turn her muzzle up the hills!"

But I never made an answer, I just let the cusses squeal,
I was finding reputation on that gol-darned wheel.

The grade was mighty sloping from the ranch down to the creek
And I went a-galliflutin' like a crazy lightning streak—

Went whizzing and a-darting first this way and then that,
The darned contrivance sort o' wabbling like the flying of a bat.

I pulled upon the handles, but I couldn't check it up;
And I yanked and sawed and hollowed but the darned thing wouldn't
    stop.

Then a sort of a meachin' in my brain began to steal,
That the devil held a mortgage on that gol-darned wheel.

I've a sort of dim and hazy remembrance of the stop,
With the world a-goin' round and the stars all tangled up;

Then there came an intermission that lasted till I found
I was lying at the ranch with the boys all gathered round,

And a doctor was a-sewing on the skin where it was ripped,
And old Arizona whispered, "Well, old boy, I guess you're whipped,"

And I told him I was busted from sombrero down to heel,
And he grinned and said, "You ought to see that gol-darned wheel."

THE COWBOY AT CHURCH

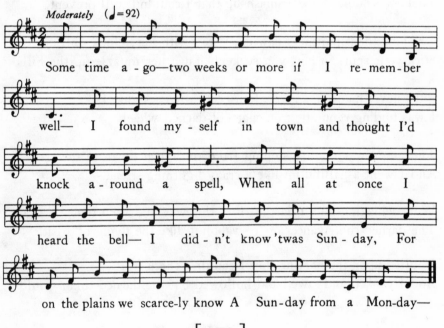

Some time a-go—two weeks or more if I re-mem-ber

well— I found my-self in town and thought I'd

knock a-round a spell, When all at once I

heard the bell— I did-n't know 'twas Sun-day, For

on the plains we scarce-ly know A Sun-day from a Mon-day—

Some time ago—two weeks or more
If I remember well—
I found myself in town and thought
I'd knock around a spell,
When all at once I heard the bell—
I didn't know 'twas Sunday,
For on the plains we scarcely know
A Sunday from a Monday—

A-calling all the people
From the highways and the hedges,
And all the reckless throng
That tread ruin's ragged edges,
To come and hear the pastor tell
Salvation's touching story,
And how the new road misses hell
And leads you straight to glory.

I started by the chapel door,
But something urged me in,
And told me not to spend God's day
In revelry and sin.
I don't go much on sentiment,
But tears came in my eyes.
It seemed just like my mother's voice
Was speaking from the skies.

I thought how often she had gone
With little Sis and me
To church, when I was but a lad
Way back in Tennessee.
It never once occurred to me
About not being dressed

[273]

In Sunday rig, but carelessly
I went in with the rest.

You should have seen the smiles and shrugs
As I went walking in,
As though they thought my leggins
Worse than any kind of sin;
Although the honest parson,
In his vestry garb arrayed
Was dressed the same as I was—
In the trappings of his trade.

The good man prayed for all the world
And all its motley crew,
For pagan, Hindu, sinners, Turk,
And unbelieving Jew—
Though the congregation doubtless thought
That the cowboys as a race
Were a kind of moral outlaw
With no good claim to grace.

Is it very strange that cowboys are
A rough and reckless crew
When their garb forbids their doing right
As Christian people do?
That they frequent scenes of revelry
Where death is bought and sold,
Where at least they get a welcome
Though it's prompted by their gold?

Stranger, did it ever strike you—
When the winter days are gone
And the mortal grass is springing up
To meet the judgment sun,

[274]

And we 'tend mighty round-ups
Where, according to the Word,
The angel cowboy of the Lord
Will cut the human herd—

That a heap of stock that's lowing now
Around the Master's pen
And feeding at his fodder stock
Will have the brand picked then?
And brands that, when the hair was long
Looked like the letter C,
Will prove to be the devil's,
And the brand the letter D;

While many a long-horned coaster—
I mean, just so to speak—
That hasn't had the advantage
Of the range and gospel creek
Will get to crop the grasses
In the pasture of the Lord,
If the letter C showed up
Beneath the devil's checkerboard.

THE JOLLY COWBOY *

My   lov - er   he   is   a   cow - boy,   he's
"When   ear - ly   dawn   is   break - ing   and

* From eight fragments found in Arizona and Texas.

brave and kind and true, He rides a Span - ish po - ny, he
we are far a - way, We fall in - to our sad - dles, we

throws a las - so, too; And when he comes to see me our
round-up all the day; We rope, we brand, we ear-mark— I

vows we do re - deem, He throws his arms a -
tell you we are smart; And when the herd is

REFRAIN

round me and thus be - gins to sing: "Ho, I
read - y, for Kan - sas then we start."

am a jol - ly cow - boy, from Tex - as now I hail, Give

me my quirt and po - ny, I'm read - y for the trail; I

love the roll - ing prai - ries, they're free from care and strife, Be -

hind a herd of long - horns I'll jour - ney all my life."

My lover, he is a cowboy, he's brave and kind and true,
He rides a Spanish pony, he throws a lasso, too;
And when he comes to see me our vows we do redeem,
He throws his arms around me and thus begins to sing:

"Ho, I am a jolly cowboy, from Texas now I hail,
Give me my quirt and pony, I'm ready for the trail;
I love the rolling prairies, they're free from care and strife,
Behind a herd of longhorns I'll journey all my life.

"When early dawn is breaking and we are far away,
We fall into our saddles, we round-up all the day;
We rope, we brand, we earmark—I tell you we are smart;
And when the herd is ready, for Kansas then we start.

"Oh, I am a Texas cowboy, as brave as I can be,
On my little Spanish pony I roam the wide prairie.
My trusty little pony is my companion true,
O'er creeks and hills and rivers he's sure to pull me through.

"When threatening clouds do gather and herded lightnings flash,
And heavy rain drops splatter, and rolling thunders crash,
What keeps the herd from running, stampeding far and wide?
The cowboy's long, low whistle and singing by their side.

"When in Kansas City our boss he pays us up,
We loaf around the city and take a parting cup;
We bid farewell to city life, from noisy crowds we come,
Range back to dear old Texas, the cowboy's native home."

Oh, he is coming back to marry the only girl he loves,
He says I am his darling, I am his own true love;
Some day we two will marry and then no more he'll roam,
But settle down with Mary in a cozy cottage home.

[277]

"Ho, I'm a jolly cowboy, from Texas now I hail,
Give me my bond to Mary, I'll quit the Lone Star trail.
I love the rolling prairies, they're free from care and strife,
But I'll quit the herd of longhorns for the sake of my little wife."

OLD ROSIN, THE BEAU

This must have been a very popular song throughout the middle of the nineteenth century, for its melody was used for no fewer than four political songs between 1840 and 1875. The origin of "Old Rosin" is not clear, but it must have been English or Scottish or Irish, and it probably dates from the opening of the century.

Curiously enough, the name of the hero was generally given as "Rosin, the Bow," and it is quite possible that this was considered a descriptive title for a fiddler or some other type of minstrel. But the authentic spelling is unquestionably "Beau," and there is still nothing to prove that old Rosin was anything more than popular ladies' man, with alcoholic tendencies.

Here is a correct version of the original, so far as the editor knows.

I live for the good of my nation,
And my sons are all growing low,
But I hope the next generation
All resemble old Rosin, the beau.
I've traveled this country all over,
And now to the next I will go;
For I know that good quarters await me
To welcome old Rosin, the beau.

In the gay round of pleasure I've traveled,
Nor will I behind leave a foe;

And when my companions are jovial,
They'll drink to old Rosin, the beau.
But my life is now drawn to a closing,
And all at last will be so:
So we'll take a full bumper at parting,
To the name of old Rosin, the beau.

When I'm dead and laid out on the counter,
The people all making the show,
Just sprinkle plain whisky and water
On the corpse of old Rosin, the beau.
I'll have to be buried, I reckon,
And the ladies will all want to know,
And they'll lift up the lid of my coffin,
Saying, "Here lies old Rosin, the beau."

Oh! when to my grave I am going,
The children will all want to go;
They'll run to the doors and the windows,
Saying, "There goes old Rosin, the beau."
Then pick me out six trusty fellows
And let them all stand in a row,
And dig a big hole in the circle
And in it toss Rosin, the beau.

Then shape me out two little donochs,*
Place one at my head and my toe,
And do not forget to scratch on it
The name of old Rosin, the beau.
Then let those six trusty good fellows,
Oh! let them all stand in a row,
And take down that big-bellied bottle
And drink to old Rosin, the beau.

* A Scotch word meaning "drinking mugs."

[279]

THE RANGE RIDERS*

Come all you range riders and listen to me,
I will relate you a story of the saddest degree,
I will relate you a story of the deepest distress—
I love my poor Lulu, boys, of all the girls the best.

When you are out riding, boys, upon the highway,
Meet a fair damsel, a lady so gay,
With her red, rosy cheeks and her sparkling dark eyes,
Just think of my Lulu, boys, and your bosoms will rise.

While you live single, boys, you are just in your prime;
You have no wife to scold, you have nothing to bother your minds;
You can roam this world over and do just as you will,
Hug and kiss the pretty girls and be your own still.

But when you get married, boys, you are done with this life,
You have sold your sweet comfort for to gain you a wife;
Your wife she will scold you, and the children will cry,
It will make those fair faces look withered and dry.

You can scarcely step aside, boys, to speak to a friend
But your wife is at your elbow saying "What do you mean?"
With her nose turned upon you it will look like sad news—
I advise you by experience that life to refuse.

Come fill up your bottles, boys, drink bourbon around;
Here is luck to the single wherever they are found.
Here is luck to the single, and I wish them success,
Likewise to the married ones, I wish them no less.

* From Mrs. M. B. Wight, Fort Thomas, Ariz.

I have one more request to make, boys, before we part.
Never place your affection on a charming sweetheart.
She is dancing before you your affections to gain;
Just turn your back on them with scorn and disdain.

THE COWBOY'S LIFE*

The bawl of a steer,
To a cowboy's ear,
Is music of sweetest strain;
And the yelping notes
Of the gray coyotes
To him are a glad refrain.

And his jolly songs
Speed him along,
As he thinks of the little gal
With golden hair
Who is waiting there
At the bars of the home corral.

For a kingly crown
In the noisy town
His saddle he wouldn't change;
No life so free
As the life we see
Way out on the Yaso range.

His eyes are bright
And his heart as light
As the smoke of his cigarette;

* Attributed to James Barton Adams.

[281]

There's never a care
For his soul to bear,
No trouble to make him fret

The rapid beat
Of his bronco's feet
On the sod as he speeds along,
Keeps living time
To the ringing rhyme
Of his rollicking cowboy song.

Hike it, cowboys,
For the range away
On the back of a bronc' of steel,
With a careless flirt
Of the rawhide quirt
And a dig of a roweled heel!

The winds may blow
And the thunder growl
Or the breezes may safely moan;
A cowboy's life
Is a royal life,
His saddle his kingly throne.

Saddle up, boys,
For the work is play
When love's in the cowboy's eyes—
When his heart is light
As the clouds of white
That swim in the summer skies.

THE STATE OF ARKANSAS

Freely, with great emotion (♩ = 96)

My name is Stan - ford Barnes, I come from No - ble-ville town; I've trav-eled this wide world o - ver, I've trav-eled this wide world round. I've met with ups and downs of life, but bet - ter days I've saw; But I've nev - er knew what mis - 'ry were till I came to Ar - kan - sas.

My name is Stanford Barnes, I come from Nobleville Town;
I've traveled this wide world over, I've traveled this wide world
    round;
I've met with ups and downs of life, but better days I've saw;
But I've never knew what mis'ry were till I came to old Arkansas.

I landed in St. Louis with ten dollars and no more;
I read the daily papers till both my eyes were sore;

I read the evening papers till at last I saw
Ten thousand men were wanted in the state of Arkansas.

I wiped my eyes with great surprise when I read this grateful news,
And straightway off I started to see the agent, Billy Hughes.
I handed him five dollars though it gave my heart a shock;
I was soon on the railway bound for the city of Little Rock.

I started off one morning at a quarter after five,
I started from St. Louis half dead and half alive;
I bought me a quart of whisky my misery to thaw;
I got as drunk as a biled owl when I left for old Arkansas.

I landed in Fort Smith one sultry Sunday afternoon;
It was in the month of May, the early month of June,
Up stepped a walking skeleton with a long and lantern jaw,
Invited me to his hotel, "the best in Arkansas."

There met me at the depot this seedy-looking chap,
With a ragged coat and britches and an old and greasy cap.
Says he, "Good morning, gentlemen, the morning's rather raw,
On yonder hill stands my hotel, the best in Arkansas."

I started off next morning to catch the morning train;
He says to me: "You'd better work. I have some land to drain.
I'll pay you fifty cents a day, your board, washing and all—
You'll find yourself a different man when you leave old Arkansas."

I met with good connections and started for the camp,
Where every accommodation was fitted for the tramp;
I slept beside the fire without tent or bed or straw,
As I worked upon the railroad in the state of Arkansas.

I worked six weeks for the son-of-a-gun, Jesse Howard was his
    name,
He was six feet seven in his stocking feet and taller than any crane.
His hair hung down in strings over his long and lantern jaw,
He was the photograph of all the gents who live in Arkansas.

He fed me on corn-dodgers as hard as any rock,
Until my teeth began to loosen and my knees began to knock;
I got so thin on sass'fras tea I could hide behind a straw,
And indeed I was a different man when I left old Arkansas.

I started out next morning at a quarter after five;
I staggered into a saloon, half dead and half alive;
I called for liquor merrily, I called for whisky raw;
I jumped the train for Chicago and good-by to Arkansas.

Farewell to swamp angels, canebrakes and chills;
Farewell to sage and sass'fras, and corn-dodger pills;
If I ever see this land again, I'll give to you my paw,
It will be through a telescope from here to Arkansas.*

* In one version the last two lines of the last stanza are:

    I'll hit the Indian Nation and marry me a squaw,
    And settle down forever by the state of Arkansas.

VI

SON OF A GUN*

Out on a ranch way out West
Cowboys—and they never rest
Till Saturday night comes rolling around
And they get their checks and head for town.

Foot in the stirrup, the other on the ground
The cowboy is smiling 'cause he's going to town;
He's got a girl just five feet one;
She's just as sweet as a sugar plum.

He rode right into the middle of the town,
He dropped his reins and hit the ground;
A shot rang out; he dropped down flat;
Another shot got him through the top of the hat.

He whipped out his gun, and shot so fast
That them cattle thieves just couldn't last;
He chased them down to the corner saloon,
And they shot it out to the light of the moon.

He walked up to the bar, took a drink on the house;
Them gun-toting rounders were as quiet as a mouse
A rap at the door and he turned around;
There stood his sweet, the belle of the town.

He put her on the horse by his side
And it wasn't very long till she was his bride;
And now they live in a sweet bungalow
And they're more happy than you'll ever know.†

* Son of a gun is a famous cow-camp hash or stew.
† From *Songs Sung in the Southern Appalachians*, Mellinger E. Henry (London: Mitre Press, 1934).

TRAIL END*

There was blood on the saddle,
And blood all around,
And a great, big puddle
Of blood on the ground.

A cowboy lay in it,
All covered with gore,
And he never will ride
Any broncos no more.

O pity the cowboy,
All bloody and red,
For the bronco fell on him,
And mashed in his head.

There was blood on the saddle,
And blood all around,
And a great, big puddle
Of blood on the ground.

* Written by Everett Chatham, Taos, N.M., now living at Palm Springs, Calif, according to "Tex" Ritter of Hollywood, Calif.

ONCE YOU GIT THE HABIT

A song current in Arizona, probably written by Berton Braley. Cowboys and miners often take verses that please them and fit them to music.

I've beat my way wherever any winds have blown,
I've bummed along from Portland down to San Antone,
From Sandy Hook to Frisco, over gulch and hill;
For once you git the habit, why, you can't keep still.

I settles down quite frequent and I says, says I,
"I'll never wander further till I comes to die."
But the wind it sorta chuckles, "Why, o' course you will,"
And sure enough I does it 'cause I can't keep still.

I've seed a lot o' places where I'd like to stay,
But I gets a-feelin' restless and I'm on my way.
I was never meant for settin' on my own door sill,
And once you git the habit, why, you can't keep still.

I've been in rich men's houses and I've been in jail,
But when it's time for leavin', I jes' hits the trail;
I'm a human bird of passage, and the song I trill
Is, "Once you git the habit, why, you can't keep still."

The sun is sorta coaxin' and the road is clear,
And the wind is singin' ballads that I got to hear.
It ain't no use to argue when you feel the thrill;
For once you git the habit, why, you can't keep still.

POOR LONESOME COWBOY

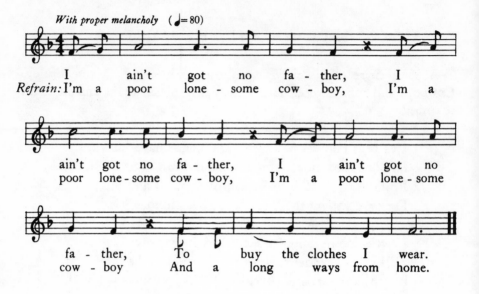

With proper melancholy (♩ = 80)

I ain't got no fa - ther, I
Refrain: I'm a poor lone - some cow - boy, I'm a

ain't got no fa - ther, I ain't got no
poor lone - some cow - boy, I'm a poor lone - some

fa - ther, To buy the clothes I wear.
cow - boy And a long ways from home.

I ain't got no father,
I ain't got no father,
I ain't got no father
To buy the clothes I wear.

> I'm a poor, lonesome cowboy,
> I'm a poor, lonesome cowboy,
> I'm a poor, lonesome cowboy
> And a long ways from home.

I ain't got no mother,
I ain't got no mother,
I ain't got no mother
To mend the clothes I wear.

I ain't got no sister,
I ain't got no sister,

I ain't got no sister
To go and play with me.

I ain't got no brother,
I ain't got no brother,
I ain't got no brother
To drive the steers with me.

I ain't got no sweetheart,
I ain't got no sweetheart,
I ain't got no sweetheart
To sit and talk with me.

I'm a poor, lonesome cowboy,
I'm a poor, lonesome cowboy,
I'm a poor, lonesome cowboy
And a long ways from home.

THE TEXAS COWBOYS*

It's of those Texas cowboys a story I'll tell,
No name I will mention, in Texas they do dwell;
Go find them where you will, they are all so very brave,
And when in good society they seldom misbehave.

When the fall work is all over in the line camp they'll be found,
For they have to ride those lonesome lines the long winter round;
They prove loyal to a comrade no matter what's to do,
And when in love with a fair one they seldom prove untrue.

But springtime comes at last and finds them glad and gay,
They ride out on the round-up about the first of May;
About the first of August they start up the trail,
They have to stay with the cattle then no matter rain or hail.

* Tom Hight's Scrap Book.

[291]

But when they get to the shipping point then they receive their
     tens,
Straightway to the barroom and gently blow them in;
It's the height of their ambition, so I've been truly told,
To ride good horses and saddles and spend the silver and gold.

Those last two things I've mentioned, it is their heart's desire,
And when they leave the shipping points their eyes like balls of
     fire.
It's of those fighting cattle they seem to have no fear,
A-riding bucking broncos oft is their heart's desire.

They will ride into the branding pen, a rope within their hands;
They will catch them by each forefoot and bring them to the sands;
It's all together in practice, with a little bit of sleight,
A-roping Texas cattle, it is their heart's delight.

But now comes the rising generation to take the cowboy's place,
Likewise the corn-fed granger with his bold and rheeky face,
It's on those plains of Texas, a lone buffalo hunter does stand,
To tell the fate of the cowboy that rode at his right hand.

THE BLACK TAIL RANGE*

I am a rov - ing cow - boy off
I start - ed o - ver to the plains in

* From p. 139, *Singing Cowboy*, by Margaret Larkin (New York: Knopf).

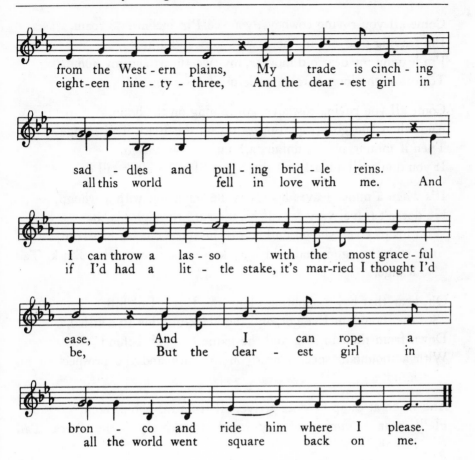

from the West-ern plains, My trade is cinch-ing
eight-een nine-ty-three, And the dear-est girl in

sad - dles and pull-ing brid-le reins.
all this world fell in love with me. And

I can throw a las-so with the most grace-ful
if I'd had a lit-tle stake, it's mar-ried I thought I'd

ease, And I can rope a
be, But the dear - est girl in

bron - co and ride him where I please.
all the world went square back on me.

I am a roving cowboy off from the Western plains,
My trade is cinching saddles and pulling bridle reins.
I can throw a lasso with the most graceful ease,
And I can rope a bronco and ride him where I please.

I started over to the plains in eighteen ninety-three,
And the dearest girl in all this world fell in love with me.
And if I'd had a little stake, it's married I thought I'd be,
But the dearest girl in all the world went square back on me.

Come all you roving cowboys, you see I'm inclined to roam,
I'm leaving dear old mother, two sisters and a home,
I'm leaving my dear old mother, my sweetheart and my home,
To follow the long-horned cattle until I am too old.

Come all you roving cowboys, got mining on the brain,
And when you go prospecting cattle on the Black Tail Range,
Then if mining proves unfair, a-hunting you can go,
If you don't kill a black-tail sheep, you'll kill a black-tail doe.

It's when a miner leaves his claim, he starts out with a whoop,
He doesn't travel very far till his toe runs through his boot.
With his pick and shovel on his back he starts out for his claim,
And with his gun and old case-knife, he scours the Black Tail
    Range.

Oh, hear that boy a-shouting along the Black Tail hill,
"See the mountain I've got, and the black-tail doe I've killed."
Down from the rim-rock and the game he's left behind
With a mountain sheep's head on his back and the prospect in his
    mind.

And when at camp he does arrive, all from his noble claim,
He'll hear a sample of my mind, the chief of the Black Tail
    Range.

CYCLONE BLUES*

I uster own the Double D;
I'm punchin' steers today,
Because a cyclone comes along
And blows my ranch away;

* From p. 90, *Songs Sung in the Southern Appalachians*, by Mellinger E. Henry (London:
Mitre Press, 1934). (Obtained from Dr. D. S. Gage, Fulton, Missouri, who had it from
Prof. Artus M. Moser, Lincoln Memorial University, Harrogate, Tenn., 1932. He received it
from Griff Crawford.)

It struck the first of April,
An' as it's goin' hence,
It takes my barns and 'dobes
An' a mile er two of fence.

It takes the steers, I'm sayin',
An' my cows an' hawses, too,
It never leaves me nothin'
But the mortgage, which is due;
An' that's the why I'm punchin'
On the Lazy B today,
A-payin' fer the chattels
What the cyclone blowed away.

BOB STANFORD*

Bob Stanford, he's a Texas boy,
He lives down on the flat;
His trade is running a well-drill,
But he's none the worse for that.

He is neither rich nor handsome,
But, unlike the city dude,
His manners they are pleasant
Instead of flip and rude.

His people live in Texas,
That is his native home,
But like many other Western lads
He drifted off from home.

* From Mrs. M. B. Wight, Fort Thomas, Arizona.

[295]

He came out to New Mexico
A fortune for to make,
He punched the bottom out of the earth
And never made a stake.

So he came to Arizona
And again set up his drill
To punch a hole for water,
And he's punching at it still.

He says he is determined
To make the business stick
Or spend that derned old well machine
And all he can get on tick.

I hope he is successful
And I'll help him if I can,
For I admire pluck and ambition
In an honest workingman.

So keep on going down,
Punch the bottom out, or try.
There is nothing in a hole in the ground
That continues being dry.

THE COWBOY UP TO DATE*

Take a common little bronco
With a saddle and a rope,
And a bandanna handkerchief
And a bottle full of "dope";

* By Charles F. Thomas, Jr.

A pair of high-heeled riding boots
And a pair of chaps to match;
Take revolver and a holster
With some fellow you can catch;

Get a sombrero for his head,
Teach him how to cuss and swear;
Oh, yes, give him a pair of spurs
And then ruffle up his hair.

Don't forget some slang expressions;
Tell him how to "fan the breeze,"
Just tell him where to hang his quirt,
How to kick his horse's knees.

Lead up your horse and saddle him,
Yes, put on a curb bit, too;
Hang some trappings on the saddle
And a buckskin strap or two.

Hang the rope by the saddle horn,
Pull on chaps and boots with vim,
Tie the kerchief around his neck—
These make a cowboy out of him.

Fasten the holster around his waist,
Tie sombrero on his head,
Now just set him in the saddle—
You've a cowboy, so 'tis said.

Howe'er on earth it skipped my mind,
I never shall quite understand;
Your cowboy is never complete
Without a cigarette in his hand.

RED RIVER VALLEY*

With sentiment (♩ = 84)

From this val - ley they say you are go - ing, I shall
I've been think - ing a long time, my dar - ling, Of the

miss your sweet face and your smile; Be - cause you are wea - ry and
sweet words you nev - er would say; Now a - las must my fond hopes all

tired, You are chang - ing your range for a while.
van - ish? For they say you are go - ing a - way.

REFRAIN

Then come sit here a-while e'er you leave us, Do not

has - ten to bid us a - dieu, Just re - mem - ber the Red Riv - er

Val - ley And the cow - boy who loves you so true.

From this valley they say you are going,
I shall miss your sweet face and your smile;
Because you are weary and tired,
You are changing your range for a while.

* Words from Patt Patterson's *Songs of the Round-Up Rangers*. Tune from *Pioneer Songs*, compiled by the Daughters of Utah Pioneers; arranged by Alfred M. Darham.

[298]

I've been thinking a long time, my darling,
Of the sweet words you never would say;
Now, alas, must my fond hopes all vanish?
For they say you are going away.

Refrain:
>   Then come sit here awhile e'er you leave us,
>   Do not hasten to bid us adieu,
>   Just remember the Red River Valley
>   And the cowboy who loves you so true.

I have promised you, darling, that never
Will words from my lips cause you pain;
And my life it will be yours forever,
If you only will love me again.
Must the past with its joys all be blighted
By the future of sorrow and pain?
Must the vows that were spoken be slighted?
Don't you think you could love me again?

There never could be such a longing
In the heart of a poor cowboy's breast,
As dwells in the heart you are breaking,
As I wait in my home in the West.
Do you think of the valley you're leaving?
Oh, how lonely and dreary it'll be!
Do you think of the kind hearts you're hurting,
And the pain you are causing to me?

>   Then come sit here awhile e'er you leave us,
>   Do not hasten to bid us adieu;
>   Just remember the Red River Valley
>   And the cowboy who loves you so true.

BURY ME OUT ON THE PRAIRIE*

Now, I've got no use for the wom - en; A
true one may sel - dom be found. They use a
man for his mon - ey; When it's gone they turn him
down. They're all a - like at the bot - tom;
Sel - fish and grasp - ing for all. They'll stay with a
man while he's win - ning, And laugh in his face at his fall.

Now, I've got no use for the women,
A true one may seldom be found.
They use a man for his money;
When it's gone they turn him down.

* From p. 42, *Cowboy Sings*, ed. by Kenneth Clark (New York: Paull-Pioneer Music Corp.).

They're all alike at the bottom;
Selfish and grasping for all,
They'll stay with a man while he's winning,
And laugh in his face at his fall.

My pal was an honest puncher,
Honest and upright and true,
But he turned to a hard-shooting gunman,
On account of a girl named Lou.
He fell in with evil companions,
The kind that are better off dead;
When a gambler insulted her picture,
He filled him full of lead.

All through the long night they trailed him,
Through mesquite and thick chaparral,
And I couldn't help think of that woman,
As I saw him pitch and fall.
If she'd been the pal that she should have,
He might have been raising a son,
Instead of out there on the prairie,
To die by a ranger's gun.

Death's sharp sting did not trouble,
His chances for life were too slim;
But where they are putting his body
Was all that worried him.
He lifted his head on his elbow;
The blood from his wounds flowed red;
He gazed at his pals grouped about him,
As he whispered to them and said:

"Oh, bury me out on the prairie,
Where the coyotes may howl o'er my grave.

Bury me out on the prairie,
But from them my bones please save.
Wrap me up in my blankets
And bury me deep in the ground,
Cover me over with boulders,
Of granite gray and round."

So we buried him out on the prairie,
Where the coyotes can howl o'er his grave,
And his soul is now a-resting,
From the unkind cut she gave;
And many another young puncher,
As he rides past that pile of stone,
Recalls some similar woman,
And thinks of his mouldering bones.

GREAT–GRANDDAD*

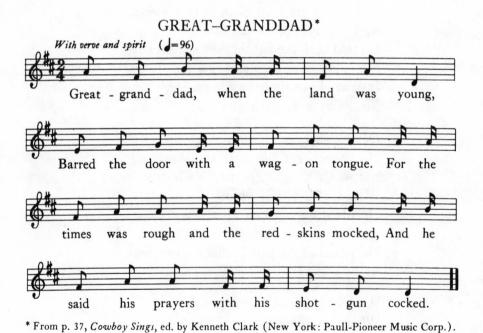

With verve and spirit (♩ = 96)

Great - grand - dad, when the land was young,

Barred the door with a wag - on tongue. For the

times was rough and the red - skins mocked, And he

said his prayers with his shot - gun cocked.

* From p. 37, *Cowboy Sings*, ed. by Kenneth Clark (New York: Paull-Pioneer Music Corp.).

Great-granddad, when the land was young,
Barred the door with a wagon tongue,
For the times was rough and the redskins mocked,
And he said his prayers with his shotgun cocked.

He was a citizen tough and grim.
Danger was duck soup to him.
He ate corn pone and bacon fat.
Great-grandson would starve on that.

Great-granddad was a busy man;
Cooked his grub in a frying pan.
He picked his teeth with his hunting knife,
He wore the same suit all of his life.

Twenty-one children came to bless
The old man's home in the wilderness.
But great-granddad didn't lose heart,
The boys hunted rabbits and they ketched right smart.

Twenty-one boys and how they grew,
Tall and strong on the bacon, too.
Slept on the floor with the dogs and cats,
And hunted in the woods with their coonskin caps.

Twenty-one boys and not one of them bad;
They never got fresh with their great-granddad.
If they had, he'd have been right glad
To tan their hides with a hickory gad.

He raised them rough, but he raised them well.
When their feet took hold on the road to hell,
He straightened them out with an iron ramrod,
And filled them full of the fear of God.

They grew strong in heart and hand,
Firm foundation of our land.
Twenty-one boys and a great-grandson,
He has a terrible time with that one.

THE LAVENDER COWBOY*

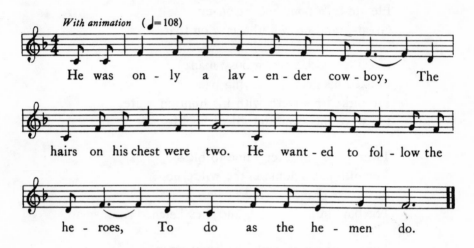

With animation (♩=108)

He was on-ly a lav-en-der cow-boy, The
hairs on his chest were two. He want-ed to fol-low the
he-roes, To do as the he-men do.

He was only a lavender cowboy,
   The hairs on his chest were two.
He wanted to follow the heroes
   To do as the he-men do.

But he was inwardly troubled
   By dreams that gave no rest:
When he heard of heroes in action
   He wanted more hairs on his chest.

Herpicide and many hair tonics
   He rubbed in morning and night,

* Sent by Barbara Bell, Minneapolis, Minn., 1937, who says that the song was found in
Wyoming, 1935, by E. Kemmer of St. Paul, Minn.

But when he looked into the mirror,
No new hairs grew in sight.

He battled for Red Nellie's honor
And cleaned out a hold-up nest.
He died with his six-gun a-smokin'
But only two hairs on his chest!

THE WANDERING COWBOY*

I am a wandering cowboy, from ranch to ranch I roam,
At every ranch when welcome I make myself at home,
Two years I worked for the Double L, one for the O Bar O,
Then drifted west from Texas to the plains of Mexico.

There I met up with a rancher who was looking for a hand,
When springtime greened the valleys I was burnin' the Bar S
    brand;
I worked on through the summer, then early in the fall
Over the distant ranges came the old, old call.

So I drifted to Arizona to work for Uncle Bob,
A-tailin' for the weak ones on a winter's feedin' job,
But the ranch camp grew too lonely with never a rest or change,
So I saddled up one mornin' and struck for a distant range.

One night in old Wyoming when the stars hung bright and low,
I lay in my tarp a-dreamin' of the far-off home rancho.
Where the cottonwood leaves are whisperin' in the evenin' soft and
    low,
'Tis there my heart's a-turnin' and homeward I must go.

* From p. 54, Patt Patterson's *Songs of the Round-Up Rangers* (copyright George T. Worth
& Co., 112 W. 44th St., New York City).

It's now I'm tired of rambling, no longer will I roam,
When my pony I've unsaddled in the old corral at home;
I've been a wandering cowboy, from ranch to ranch did roam,
But now my pony's grazin' at the rancho I call home.

THE DRY-LANDERS*

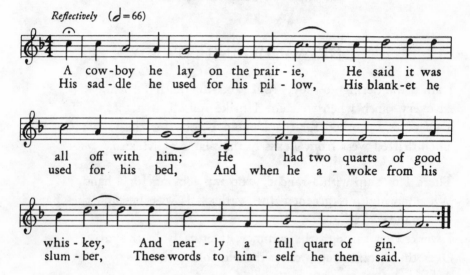

A cowboy he lay on the prairie, he said it was all off with him;
He had two quarts of good whisky and nearly a full quart of gin.
His saddle he used for his pillow, his blanket he used for his bed,
And when he awoke from his slumber, these words to himself he then
    said:

"I've been all my life in the saddle, all I know is to rope an old
    cow,
I never could work on a sheep-ranch, be damned if I'll follow a
    plow.

* From p. 15, Patt Patterson's *Songs of the Round-Up Rangers* (copyright George T. Worth
& Co., 112 W. 44th St., New York City).

There's no other job I can handle, there's no other job I'd enjoy,
Away from my spurs and my saddle, just a wild and woolly cowboy.

"Then here's wishing you luck, you dry-landers, who've settled this
country at last,
And we hope you succeed in the future as the cowboys have did in
the past.
You have come to this wonderful country, yes, you fenced in the range
from our herds,
We have fed you and drug in your firewood, but the word 'Thanks'
has never been heard.

"Then here too let me again warn you, don't steal from the ranches
close by,
Or some day you'll wake up in heaven and not on your homestead
close by.
Then too if you wish for to prosper, don't sleep in your homesteads
all day,
But hit to your toil in the mornin' or you'll soon be driftin' away.

LONE DRIFTIN' RIDERS*

If you'll come gather round me, I'll sing you a song,
Of a lone driftin' rider just rollin' along;
His spurs they are set and he's driftin' on high,
He'll quit punchin' cattle when his time comes to die.

You ask me, fair lady, who was that passin' by?
It's a lone driftin' rider just rollin' on high.
They call him Red Conklin, he's named that for short,
And at drinkin' rye whisky, he's good for a quart.

* From p. 30, Patt Patterson's *Songs of the Round-Up Rangers* (copyright George T. Worth
& Co., 112 W. 44th St., New York City).

He married Dolores from old Mexico
And turned to dry-farming, but the durned crops wouldn't grow;
He rode off one mornin' and left Dolores flat,
And said, "I'm a cowboy, I've had enough of that."

There is young Skeeter Bill, he's known far and wide,
He courted poor Sally to make her his bride;
But the call of the trail herds rang sweet in his ears,
So he rode off that spring and left Sally in tears.

There's Tom Ward and Murphy, two durn good cowhands,
Who rode into Elko from off Ely-lands,
They stopped at Ma Simmons' and promised to pay
For board and night's lodging, but left at break of day.

So, girls, all come listen and don't ask me why.
Beware of the cowboys that go driftin' by,
They'll love and caress you, they'll win you somehow,
Then ride off and leave you if you ever cry.

Let this be a warnin' to you all far and wide,
Never fall for the cowboy who throws the rawhide,
Just think of them kindly when you see them pass by,
They're the lone driftin' riders just rollin' on high.

THE SANTA FE TRAIL*

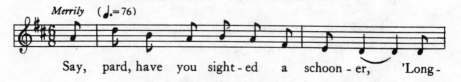

Say, pard, have you sight-ed a schoon-er, 'Long-

* From p. 52, *Songs of the Round-Up*, by Sterling Sherwin and F. Henri Klickmann (copyright, 1934, Robbins Music Corp., 799 Seventh Ave., New York City; all rights reserved including those of public performance for profit.)

[308]

side of the San-ta Fe Trail? They made it here Mon-day or

soon-er, They had a wa-ter keg tied to their tail. There was

dad-dy and ma on the mule seat And, some-where a-long by the

way, Was a tow-head-ed gal on a pin-to Just a-

REFRAIN

jan-glin' for old San-ta Fe. Yo-ho-ho, yo-

ho! Just a-jan-glin' for old San-ta Fe. Yo-ho-

ho, yo-ho! Just a-jan-glin' for old San-ta Fe.

Say, pard, have you sighted a schooner,
'Longside of the Santa Fe Trail?
They made it here Monday or sooner;
They had a water keg tied to their tail.

There was daddy and ma on the mule seat
And, somewhere along by the way,
Was a tow-headed gal on a pinto
Just a-janglin' for old Santa Fe.

Chorus:

Yo-ho-ho, yo-ho!
Just a-janglin' for old Santa Fe.
Yo-ho-ho, yo-ho!
Just a-janglin' for old Santa Fe.

I seen her ride down the arroyo,
Way back on the Arkansaw sands;
She had smiles like an acre of sunflowers
And a quirt in her little brown hand.
She mounted her pinto so airy,
She rode like she carried the mail;
And her eyes ne'er set fire to the prairie,
'Longside of the Santa Fe Trail.

Yo-ho-ho, yo-ho!
Just alongside the old Santa Fe.
Yo-ho-ho, yo-ho!
Just alongside the old Santa Fe.

I know a gal down on the border,
That I'd ride to El Paso to sight.
I'm acquainted with high-flyin' orders
And sometimes kiss some gals good night.
But, Lord, they're all ruffles an' beadin',
And drink fancy tea by the pail;
I'm not used to that sort of stampedin'
'Longside of the Santa Fe Trail.

I don't know her name on the prairie;
When you're huntin' one gal it's some wide;
And it's shorter from hell to Helarie,
Than it is on that old Santa Fe ride.
So I'll try to make Plummer's by sundown,
Where a camp can be made on the swale;
Then I'll come on that girl with her pinto,
She'll be camped by the Santa Fe Trail.

THE COWBOY AND HIS LOVE*

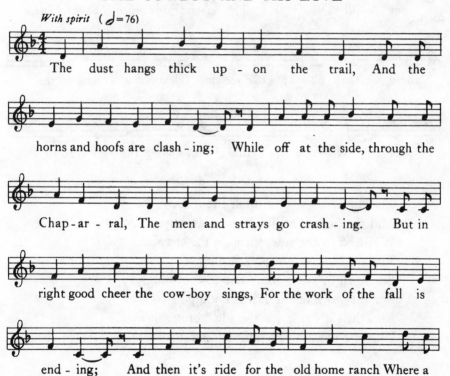

With spirit (♩ = 76)

The dust hangs thick up - on the trail, And the

horns and hoofs are clash - ing; While off at the side, through the

Chap - ar - ral, The men and strays go crash - ing. But in

right good cheer the cow-boy sings, For the work of the fall is

end - ing; And then it's ride for the old home ranch Where a

* By John Milton Hagen. From p. 10, *Songs of the Saddle* (compiled and ed. by F. Henri Klickmann and Sterling Sherwin; published and copyrighted by Sam Fox Publishing Co., Cleveland, New York, Chicago, Los Angeles, London, Paris, Berlin, and Melbourne).

[311]

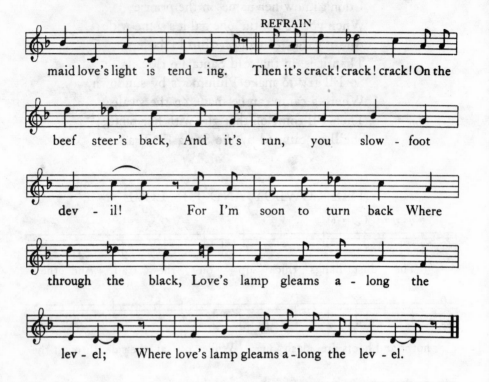

REFRAIN

maid love's light is tend-ing. Then it's crack! crack! crack! On the beef steer's back, And it's run, you slow - foot dev - il! For I'm soon to turn back Where through the black, Love's lamp gleams a - long the lev - el; Where love's lamp gleams a - long the lev - el.

The dust hangs thick upon the trail,
And the horns and hoofs are clashing;
While off at the side, through the chaparral,
The men and strays go crashing.
But in right good cheer the cowboy sings,
For the work of the fall is ending.
And then it's ride for the old home ranch
Where a maid love's light is tending.

Refrain:

Then it's crack! crack! crack! on the beef steer's back,
And it's run, you slow-foot devil!

For I'm soon to turn back where, through the black,
Love's lamp gleams along the level;
Where love's lamp gleams along the level.

He's trailed them far o'er the trackless range,
Has this knight of the saddle leather;
He has risked his young life in the mad stampede
And breasted all kinds of weather.
But now the end of the trail is in sight,
And the hours on wings are sliding:
For it's back to the home and the only girl,
Where the foreman okays the option.

THE LLANO ESTACADO

"A song that in the early days was a great favorite among the men of the ranches deals with the heartlessness of a belle of the border who sent her lover away on a mission which resulted in his death, while she danced away the hours with no thought of his possible fate. Llano Estacado, or Staked Plains, was a desert region at the time the song was written, but it is now one of the most productive parts of Texas. The gallant hero of the song would not now have to ride far to get water."—*San Antonio Express*, May 30, 1909.

"If I may trust your love," she cried,
"And you would have me for a bride,
Ride over yonder plain and bring
Your flask full from the Mustang Spring,
Fly, just as the western eagles wing
    O'er the Llano Estacado."

He heard and bowed without a word;
His gallant steed he slightly spurred;

He turned his face, and rode away,
And vanished with the parting day
    O'er the Llano Estacado.

Night came on and found him riding on;
Day came and still he rode alone.
He spared not spur, he drew no rein,
Across the broad, unchanging plain.
Till he the Mustang Spring might gain,
    On the Llano Estacado.

A little rest, a little draught,
Hot from his hand and quickly quaffed,
His flask was filled and then he turned,
Once more his steed the maguey spurned,
Once more the sky above him burned
    On the Llano Estacado.

How hot the quivering landscape glowed!
His brain seemed boiling as he rode.
Was it a dream, a drunken one,
Or was he really riding on?
Was that a skull that gleamed and shone
    On the Llano Estacado?

"Brave steed of mine, brave steed," he cried,
"So often true, so often tried,
Bear up a little longer yet!"
His mouth was black with blood and sweat.
Heaven! how he longed his lips to wet,
    On the Llano Estacado.

And still within his breast he held
The precious flask so lately filled.

Oh, for a drink! but well he knew,
If empty it should meet her view,
Her scorn; but still his longing grew
    On the Llano Estacado.

His horse went down. He wandered on,
Giddy, blind, beaten and alone.
While upon your enshrouded couch you lie,
Oh, think how hard it is to die
Beneath the cruel, unclouded sky
    On the Llano Estacado.

At last he staggered, stumbled, fell—
His day was done, he knew full well—
And raising to his lips the flask,
The end, the object of his task,
Drank to her—more, she could not ask—
    Ah! the Llano Estacado.

That night, at the presidio
Beneath the torchlight's wavy glow,
She danced and never thought of him;
The victim of a woman's whim,
Lying with face upturned and grim
    On the Llano Estacado.

SPEAKING OF COWBOY'S HOME*

Sky is his ceiling, grass is his bed,
Saddle is the pillow for cowboy's head;
Way out West where antelope roam,
Coyote howls round cowboy's home.

* From manuscript sent to me by J. M. Grigsby, Comanche, Texas, 1911.

[315]

Valleys all checkered with cattle trails,
Feed old Blue Dog in Mexican morral.*
Miner digs for hidden gold,
Life of cowboys has never been told.†

When I was riding the lonesome line,
Those pleasant thoughts came to my mind;
When we get through to old Fort Worth,
Oh, won't we have a high old time!
The life of the cowboy was a reckless one,
He would always acknowledge his faith in God,
Often pondering in his wandering mind
If he'd be cut out with the good when he crossed the line.

When I left home my mother said:
"My son, you are young and easy led;
When you get out on the cattle range,
You are apt to see many strange things."
Those words from mother all came true;
It was love she had for her wandering boy.

On a mother's advice you can depend,
And when she's gone you've lost your best friend.

Come all you old cowboys wherever you go,
Your mother's words you should not ignore;
When you get down all out and in,
It's then you will find that she's your best friend.

* Nose feed bag.
† Another fragment runs:
> Sky is his ceiling, grass is his bed,
> Saddle is the pillow for the cowboy's head;
> Way out West where the antelope roam,
> And the coyotes howl round the cowboy's home;
> Where the miner digs for the golden veins,
> And the cowboy rides o'er the silent plains;
> Where the prairies are covered with chaparral frail,
> And the valleys are checkered with the cattle trails;
> Where the eagles scream and the catamounts squall,
> The cowboy's home is the best of all.

HELL IN TEXAS*

The text of "Hell in Texas," as printed in *Cowboy Songs,* came from the proprietor of the Buckhorn Saloon in San Antonio, Texas, a famous resort for the thirsty. When he handed me the printed broadside in 1909, the proprietor of the Buckhorn told me that he had given away more than 100,000 printed copies. John R. Steele of the United States Signal Corps, stationed at Brownsville in early frontier days, is said to have written the song.

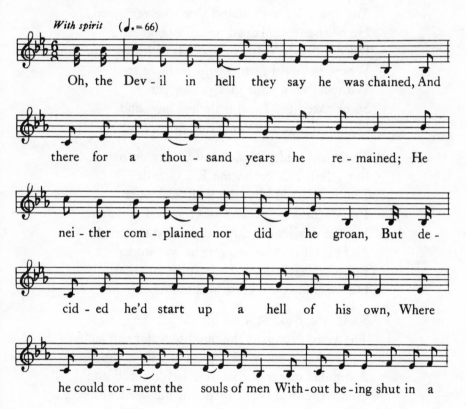

Oh, the Dev-il in hell they say he was chained, And
there for a thou-sand years he re-mained; He
nei-ther com-plained nor did he groan, But de-
cid-ed he'd start up a hell of his own, Where
he could tor-ment the souls of men With-out be-ing shut in a

* For the history of this song see *American Ballads and Folk Songs,* pp. 397-401 (New York: Macmillan, 1934).

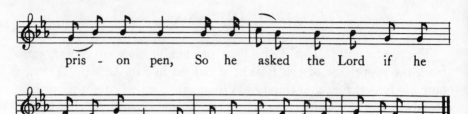

pris - on pen, So he asked the Lord if he

had an - y sand Left o - ver from mak - ing this great land.

Oh, the devil in hell they say he was chained,
And there for a thousand years he remained;
He neither complained nor did he groan,
But decided he'd start up a hell of his own,
Where he could torment the souls of men
Without being shut in a prison pen.
So he asked the Lord if he had any sand
Left over from making this great land.

The Lord said, "Yes, I had plenty on hand,
But I left it down on the Rio Grande;
The fact is, old boy, the stuff is so poor
I don't think you could use it in hell any more."
But the devil went down to look at the truck,
And said if it came as a gift he was stuck;
For after examining it carefully and well
He concluded the place was too dry for hell.

So, in order to get it off his hands,
The Lord promised the devil to water the lands;
For he had some water, or rather some dregs,
A regular cathartic that smelled like bad eggs.
Hence the deal was closed and the deed was given
And the Lord went back to his home in heaven.
And the devil then said, "I have all that is needed
To make a good hell," and hence he succeeded.

He began to put thorns in all of the trees,
And mixed up the sand with millions of fleas;
And scattered tarantulas along all the roads;
Put thorns on the cactus and horns on the toads.
He lengthened the horns of the Texas steers,
And put an addition on the rabbit's ears;
He put a little devil in the bronco steed,
And poisoned the feet of the centipede.

The rattlesnake bites you, the scorpion stings,
The mosquito delights you with buzzing wings;
The sand-burrs prevail and so do the ants,
And those who sit down need half-soles on their pants.
The devil then said that throughout the land
He'd managed to keep up the devil's own brand,
And all would be mavericks unless they bore
The marks of scratches and bites and thorns by the score

The heat in the summer is a hundred and ten,
Too hot for the devil and too hot for men.
The wild boar roams through the black chaparral—
It's a hell of a place he has for a hell.
The red pepper grows on the banks of the brook;
The Mexicans use it in all that they cook.
Just dine with a Greaser and then you will shout,
"I've hell on the inside as well as the out!"

NEW NATIONAL ANTHEM

My country, 'tis of thee,
Land where things used to be
So cheap, we croak.

Land of the mavericks,
Land of the puncher's tricks,
Thy culture-inroad pricks
The hide of this peeler-bloke.

Some of the punchers swear
That what they eat and wear
Takes all their calves.
Others vow that they
Eat only once a day
Jerked beef and prairie hay
Washed down with tallow salve.

These salty-dogs* but crave
To pull them out the grave
Just one Kiowa spur.
They know they still will dine
On flesh and beef the time;
But give us, Lord divine,
One "hen-fruit stir."†

Our father's land, with thee,
Best trails of liberty,
We chose to stop.
We don't exactly like
So soon to henceward hike,
But hell, we'll take the pike
If this don't stop.

* A buckaroo; a high-loping cowboy.
† Pancake.

I'D LIKE TO BE IN TEXAS WHEN THEY ROUND–UP
IN THE SPRING*

In narrative style, with enthusiasm (♩=96)

In the lob-by of a big ho-tel, in New York town one day, Sat a
bunch of fel-lows tell-ing yarns to pass the time a-way. They
told the plac-es where they'd been and diff-'rent sights they'd seen; Some of
them pre-ferred Chi-ca-go town, and oth-ers New Or-leans. In a
corn-er in an old-arm chair sat a man whose hair was grey; He
lis-tened to them ea-ger-ly, to what they had to say. They

* From "Texas and Southwestern Lore" (*Publications of the Texas Folk-Lore Society*, Vol. VI). Editor J. Frank Dobie in an article "Ballads and Songs of the Frontier Folk" says that he found two lines in an unpublished play of Mr. Andy Adams. When he requested the full version, Mr. Adams sent him two stanzas and the chorus, which he had obtained fifteen years previously from W. E. Hawks, a ranchman now living in Burlington, Vt. However, he claimed to be responsible for most of the second stanza. Later Mr. Dobie obtained from Lon Fishback, who was singing and selling the song in a Fort Worth hotel lobby, a printed copy of two stanzas and chorus. The third stanza is the one composed by Mr. Adams.

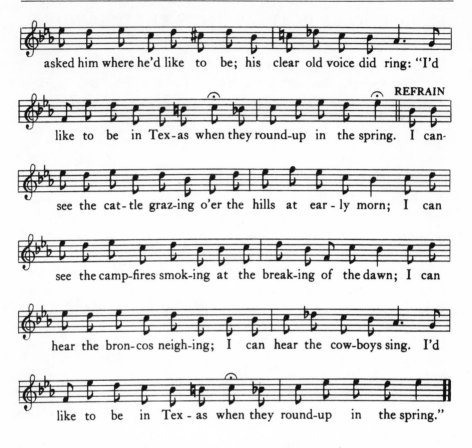

asked him where he'd like to be; his clear old voice did ring: "I'd

REFRAIN

like to be in Tex-as when they round-up in the spring. I can-

see the cat-tle graz-ing o'er the hills at ear-ly morn; I can

see the camp-fires smok-ing at the break-ing of the dawn; I can

hear the bron-cos neigh-ing; I can hear the cow-boys sing. I'd

like to be in Tex-as when they round-up in the spring."

In the lobby of a big hotel, in New York town one day,
Sat a bunch of fellows telling yarns to pass the time away.
They told the places where they'd been and diff'rent sights they'd
    seen;
Some of them preferred Chicago town and others New Orleans.
In a corner in an old armchair sat a man whose hair was grey;
He listened to them eagerly, to what they had to say.
They asked him where he'd like to be; his clear old voice did
    ring:
"I'd like to be in Texas when they round-up in the spring."

Refrain:

"I can see the cattle grazing o'er the hills at early morn;
I can see the campfires smoking at the breaking of the dawn;
I can hear the broncos neighing; I can hear the cowboys sing.
I'd like to be in Texas when they round-up in the spring."

They all sat still and listened to each word he had to say;
They knew the old man sitting there had once been young and gay.
They asked him for a story of his life upon the plains.
He slowly then removed his hat and quietly thus began:
"I've seen them stampede o'er the hills until you'd think they'd never
    stop;
I've seen them run for miles and miles until their leaders drop.
I was a foreman on a cow ranch—the calling of a king.
I'd like to be in Texas when they round-up in the spring.

"There's a grave in sunny Texas where Mollie Deming sleeps,
'Mid a grove of mossy live oaks that constant vigil keeps.
In my heart's a recollection of a long, long bygone day
When we rode the range together like truant kids astray.
Her gentle spirit calls me in the watches of the night,
And I hear her laughter freshening the dew of early light.
Yes, I was foreman of that cow ranch—the calling of a king,
And I'd like to be in Texas when they round-up in the spring."

I WANTED TO DIE IN THE DESERT*

Professor Runzler makes the following comment: "This poem was
found among the possessions of a 'desert rat' who committed suicide
in a cheap hotel in San Francisco. The man concerned was a certain
John Bauhm, a prospector."

* Sent to me by W. T. Runzler, Department of Modern Languages, University of Utah,
March 12, 1919.

[323]

I wanted to die in the desert,
I planned it for twenty year;
Alone with my God and my conscience,
And not a sky-pilot near.

I meant what I said when I doped it,
For it threw a spell over me.
Its mesas, its sand, and its deadness—
It was the place I wanted to be.

I've hoofed with my jack all over it;
I've stood on the brink of hell;
I wooed it, I coaxed it, I fought it,
And was caught in its deadly spell.

I said when I croaked that I'd go
To the desert to find my hole,
With snakes and toads to watch over me,
And my headstone a yucca pole.

But the death I've cheated so often
Has pulled its freight into town,
And I can't get back to the desert;
I'm broke—not a penny—I'm down.

Life is a burden and not worth the while;
So I'll play the ace up my sleeve.
It's poison—quick stuff—and Saint Peter;
Adiós to the world I leave.

Just throw my old hide in the cactus,
Out where the desert wind moans;
For I wanted to die in the desert,
Where the buzzards would peck at my bones.

THE LAST LONGHORN*

An ancient long-horned bovine
Lay dying by the river;
There was lack of vegetation
And the cold winds made him shiver;
A cowboy sat beside him
With sadness in his face,
To see his final passing—
This last of a noble race,

The ancient eunuch struggled
And raised his shaking head,
Sayin', "I care not to linger
When all my friends are dead.
These Jerseys and these Holsteins,
They are no friends of mine;
They belong to the nobility
Who live across the brine.

"Tell the Durhams and the Herefords
When they come a-grazing round,
And see me lying stark and stiff
Upon the frozen ground,
I don't want them to bellow,
When they see that I am dead,
For I was born in Texas
Near the river that is Red.

"Tell the coyotes, when they come at night
A-hunting for their prey,
They might as well go further,
For they'll find it will not pay.

* Said to have been written by Judge R. W. Hall, Amarillo, Texas.

If they attempt to eat me,
They very soon will see
That my bones and hide are petrified—
They'll find no beef on me.

"I remember back in the seventies,
Full many summers past,
There was grass and water plenty,
But it was too good to last.
I little dreamed what would happen
Some twenty summers hence,
When the nester came with his wife, his kids,
His dogs, and his barbed-wire fence."

His voice sank to a murmur,
His breath was short and quick;
The cowboy tried to skin him
When he saw he couldn't kick;
He rubbed his knife upon his boot
Until he made it shine,
But he never skinned old longhorn,
Caze he couldn't cut his rine.

And the cowboy riz up sadly
And mounted his cayuse,
Saying, "The time has come when longhorns
And their cowboys are no use!"
And while gazing sadly backward
Upon the dead bovine,
His bronc' stepped in a dog-hole
And fell and broke his spine.

The cowboys and the longhorns
Who partnered in Eighty-four

Have gone to their last round-up
Over on the other shore;
They answered well their purpose,
But their glory must fade and go,
Because men say there's better things
In the modern cattle show.

TO MIDNIGHT

An Epitaph

On the range near Johnston City, Colorado, is buried Midnight, an outlaw show horse, never ridden except one time.

Under this sod lies a great bucking hoss;
There never lived a cowboy he couldn't toss.
His name was Midnight, his coat was black as coal,
If there is a hoss-heaven, please, God, rest his soul.

THE GREAT ROUND-UP*

When I think of the last great round-up
On the eve of eternity's dawn,
I think of the past of the cowboys
Who have been with us here and are gone.
And I wonder if any will greet me
On the sands of the evergreen shore
With a hearty, "God bless you, old fellow,"
That I've met with so often before.

* From Mrs. Z. Hamilton, Baird, Texas, as a newspaper clipping.

I think of the big-hearted fellows
Who will divide with you blanket and bread,
With a piece of stray beef well roasted,
And charge for it never a red.
I often look upward and wonder
If the green fields will seem half so fair,
If any the wrong trail have taken
And fail to "be in" over there.

For the trail that leads down to perdition
Is paved all the way with good deeds,
But in the great round-up of ages,
Dear boys, this won't answer your needs.
But the way to the green pastures, though narrow,
Leads straight to the home in the sky,
And Jesus will give you the passports
To the land of the sweet by-and-by.

For the Savior has taken the contract
To deliver all those who believe,
At the headquarters ranch of his Father,
In the great range where none can deceive.
The Inspector will stand at the gateway
And the herd, one by one, will go by—
The round-up by the angels in judgment
Must pass 'neath his all-seeing eye.

No maverick or slick will be tallied
In the great book of life in his home,
For he knows all the brands and the earmarks
That down through the ages have come.
But, along with the tailings and sleepers,
The strays must turn from the gate;

No road brand to gain them admission,
But the awful sad cry "Too late."

Yet I trust in the last great round-up
When the rider shall cut the big herd,
That the cowboys shall be represented
In the earmark and brand of the Lord,
To be shipped to the bright, mystic regions
Over there in green pastures to lie,
And led by the crystal still waters
In that home of the sweet by-and-by.

THE COWMAN'S PRAYER

Now, O Lord, please lend me thine ear, The prayer of a cat-tle-man to hear, No doubt the pray-er may seem strange, But I want you to bless our cat-tle range.

Now, O Lord, please lend me thine ear,
The prayer of a cattleman to hear;
No doubt the prayer may seem strange,
But I want you to bless our cattle range.

Bless the round-ups year by year,
And don't forget the growing steer;
Water the lands with brooks and rills
For my cattle that roam on a thousand hills.

Prairie fires, won't you please stop?
Let thunder roll and water drop.
It frightens me to see the smoke;
Unless it's stopped, I'll go dead broke.

As you, O Lord, my herd behold,
It represents a sack of gold;
I think at least five cents a pound
Will be the price of beef the year around.

One thing more and then I'm through:
Instead of one calf, give my cows two.
I may pray different from other men
But I've had my say, and now, Amen.

ROUNDED UP IN GLORY*

With ardent sentiment (♩ = 72)

I've been think-ing to-day, As my thoughts be-gan to stray, Of your

*Sent by C. C. Staley, Comanche, Texas. The music of this song was composed by Oscar J.
Fox of San Antonio, Texas, and has added to his reputation as a writer of popular tunes.
Copyright, 1923, by Carl Fischer, Inc., New York.

mem - o - ry to me worth more than gold. As you

ride a-cross the plain, 'Mid the sun-shine and the rain—You'll be

REFRAIN

round-ed up in glo-ry by - and - by. You will be

round-ed up in glo-ry by - and - by, You will be

round-ed up in glo-ry by - and - by, When the

mill-ing time is o'er, And you will stam-pede no more, When He

rounds you up with - in the Mas - ter's fold.

I've been thinking today,
As my thoughts began to stray,
Of your memory to me worth more than gold.
As you ride across the plain,
'Mid the sunshine and the rain—
You'll be rounded up in glory by-and-by.

[331]

Chorus:

You'll be rounded up in glory by-and-by,
You'll be rounded up in glory by-and-by,
When the milling time is o'er
And you will stampede no more,
When He rounds you up within the Master's fold.

As you ride across the plain
With the cowboys that have fame,
And the storms and the lightning flash by;
We shall meet to part no more
Upon the golden shore
When he rounds us up in glory by-and-by.

May we lift our voices high
To that sweet by-and-by,
And be known by the brand of the Lord;
For his property we are,
And he will know us from afar
When he rounds us up in glory by-and-by.

VII

WAY OUT WEST

'Twas good to live when all the range,
Without no fence and fuss,
Belonged in partnership with God,
The Government, and us.

With sky-line bounds from east to west,
With room to go and come,
I liked my fellow man best
When he was scattered some.

When my old soul hunts range and rest
Beyond the last divide,
Just plant me on some strip of West
That's sunny, lone and wide.

Let cattle rub my headstone round,
And coyotes wail their kin,
Let hosses come and paw the mound,
But don't you fence it in.

From *A Lone Star Cowboy*, by Charles A. Siringo.

Take me back to old Montana
    Where there's plenty room and air;
Where there's cottonwood an' pine trees,
    Bitter-root an' prickly-pear;
Where there ain't no pomp nor glitter,
    Where a shillin's called a "bit";
Where at night the magpies twitter,
    Where the Injun fights were fit.

Take me where land is plenty,
    Where there's rattlesnakes and ticks;
Where a stack of "whites" costs twenty,
    Where they don't sell gilded bricks;
Where the old Missouri River
    An' the muddy Yellowstone
Make green patches in the Bad Lands
    Where old Sittin' Bull was known.

Take me where there ain't no subways
    Nor no forty-story shacks;
Where they shy at automobiles,
    Dudes, plug-hats an' three-rail tracks;
Where the old sun-tanned prospector
    Dreams of wealth an' pans his dirt;
Where the sleepy night-herd puncher
    Sings to steers and plies his quirt.

Take me where there's diamond hitches,
    Ropes an' brands an' ca'tridge belts;
Where the boys wear chaps fer britches,
    Flannel shirts an' Stetson felts,
Land of alkali an' cattle,
    Land of sagebrush an' of gold!
Take me back to dear Montana,
    Let me die there when I'm old.

THE BUFFALO SKINNERS*

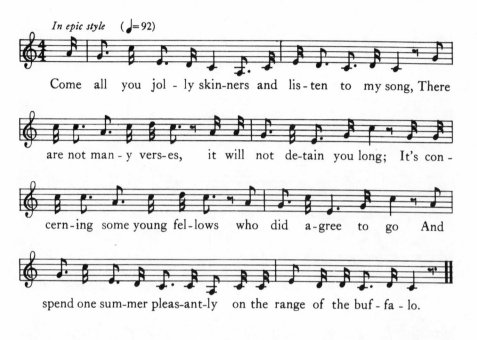

In epic style (♩=92)

Come all you jol - ly skin-ners and lis - ten to my song, There are not man - y vers-es, it will not de-tain you long; It's con - cern-ing some young fel-lows who did a-gree to go And spend one sum-mer pleas-ant-ly on the range of the buf - fa - lo.

'Twas in the town of Jacks-bo-ro in the spring of Sev'n-ty-three, A

NOTE.—The importance of this ballad has been emphasized by John Lomax, Carl Sandburg, Virgil Thomson, G. L. Kittredge, and others. It seemed fitting, therefore, to write out in full at least three stanzas, thus lessening any difficulty the singer may have in adapting the varying number of syllables to the square-cut tune.—E. N. W.
* "Song made by Buffalo Jack," writes J. E. McCauley, Seymour, Texas; "I don't know the author or how it come to be wrote, or anything of that kind, but they must have been somebody of that name for a starter." Cf. Shoemaker, *North Pennsylvania Minstrelsy*, pp. 76-78; Gray, *Songs and Ballads of Maine*, pp. 37-38; *Adventure*, Oct. 20, 1924, p. 191. These contain a miner's song, a lumber chantey, and a railroad song that seem to be forerunners of "The Buffalo Skinners."

man by the name of Cre-go   came step-ping up   to me,   Say-ing

"How do you do, young fel-low,   and how would you like to go   And

spend one sum-mer pleas-ant- ly   on the range of the buf - fa - lo?"

"It's me be-ing out of employment," this to Cre-go   I did say, "This

go-ing out on the buf-fa - lo range   de-pends up-on   the pay,   But

if you will pay good wag - es   and trans-por-ta - tion, too,   I

think, sir,   I   will go with you to the range of the buf - fa - lo.

Come all you jolly skinners and listen to my song,
There are not many verses, it will not detain you long;
It's concerning some young fellows who did agree to go
And spend one summer pleasantly on the range of the buffalo.

'Twas in the town of Jacksboro in the spring of Sev'nty-three,
A man by the name of Crego came stepping up to me,

Saying, "How do you do, young fellow, and how would you like
    to go
And spend one summer pleasantly on the range of the buffalo?"

"It's me being out of employment," this to Crego I did say,
"This going out on the buffalo range depends upon the pay.
But if you will pay good wages and transportation, too,
I think, sir, I will go with you to the range of the buffalo."

"Yes, I will pay good wages, give transportation too,
Provided you will go with me and stay the summer through;
But if you should grow homesick, come back to Jacksboro,
I won't pay transportation from the range of the buffalo."

It's now our outfit was complete—seven able-bodied men,[*]
With navy six and needle gun—our troubles did begin;
Our way it was a pleasant one, the route we had to go,
Until we crossed Pease River on the range of the buffalo.

It's now we've crossed Pease River, our troubles have begun.
The first damned tail I went to rip, Christ! how I cut my thumb!
While skinning the damned old stinkers our lives they had no
    show,
For the Indians watched to pick us off while skinning the buffalo.

He fed us on such sorry chuck I wished myself most dead,
It was old jerked beef, croton coffee, and sour bread.
Pease River's as salty as hell fire, the water I could never go—
O God! I wished I had never come to the range of the buffalo.

Our meat it was buffalo hump and iron wedge bread,
And all we had to sleep on was a buffalo robe for a bed;

* "Two to kill, four to skin, and one to cook."

The fleas and graybacks worked on us, O boys, it was not slow,
I'll tell you there's no worse hell on earth than the range of the
    buffalo.

Our hearts were cased with buffalo hocks, our souls were cased with
    steel,
And the hardships of that summer would nearly make us reel.
While skinning the damned old stinkers our lives they had no
    show,
For the Indians waited to pick us off on the hills of Mexico.

The season being near over, old Crego he did say
The crowd had been extravagant, was in debt to him that day.
We coaxed him and we begged him and still it was no go—
We left old Crego's bones to bleach on the range of the buffalo.

Oh, it's now we've crossed Pease River and homeward we are
    bound,
No more in that hell-fired country shall ever we be found.
Go home to our wives and sweethearts, tell others not to go,
For God's forsaken the buffalo range and the damned old buffalo.

THE TEXIAN BOYS

The author learned "The Texian Boys" from J. D. Mitchell of
Victoria, Texas, who says proudly: "I learned this song in '68 when
the beef trail was between Texas and the Mississippi River. The old
Acadian who taught it to me said he learned it from his 'pap,' and his
father told him it originated in the days of the Texas Republic. I
descended from one of Austin's first three hundred. I am all Texian."*

* With Mr. Mitchell's version are combined some stanzas from *The American Songbag* (Carl
Sandburg).

[338]

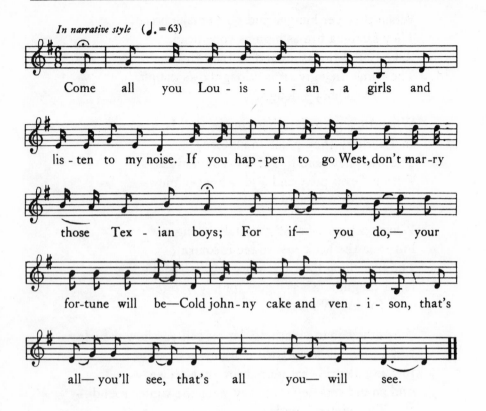

In narrative style (♩. = 63)

Come all you Lou - is - i - an - a girls and
lis - ten to my noise. If you hap - pen to go West, don't mar - ry
those Tex - ian boys; For if— you do,— your
for - tune will be—Cold john - ny cake and ven - i - son, that's
all— you'll see, that's all you— will see.

Come all you Louisiana girls and listen to my noise.
If you happen to go West, don't marry those Texian boys;
For if you do, your fortune will be
Cold johnnycake and venison, that's all you'll see—
    That's all you will see.

They live in a hut with a hewed-log wall,
But it ain't got any windows at all;
With a clapboard roof and a puncheon floor,
And that's the way all Texas o'er—
    All Texas o'er.

[339]

When they get hungry and go to make bread,
They kindle a fire as high as your head,
Rake round the ashes and in they throw—
The name they give it is "doughboy's dough."
 "Doughboy's dough."

When they go to farming you needn't be alarmed,
In February they plant their corn,
The way they tend it, I'll tell you now,
With a Texas pony and a grasshopper plow—
 A grasshopper plow.

When they go a-fishin' they take along a worm,
Put it on the hook just to see it squirm,
The first thing they say when they get a bite
Is, "I caught a fish as big as Johnny White—
 Johnny White."

When they go to preaching, let me tell you how they dress;
Just an old black shirt without any vest,
Just an old straw hat more brim than crown,
And an old sock leg that they wear the winter round—
 The winter round.

When they go a-courting I'll tell you what they ride,
An old pack saddle all covered with hide,
An old hair girth made out of a rope,
Astraddle of a horse that can't fetch a lope—
 Can't fetch a lope.

When they go a-courtin' here's what they wear,
An old leather coat all picked and bare,
An old brown hat with the brim torn down,
And a pair of dirty socks they've worn the winter round—
 The winter round.

When he comes in, the first thing you hear
Is, "Madam, your daddy has killed a deer."
And the next thing he says when he sits down
Is, "Madam, the johnnycake is too damned brown—
    Is too damned brown."

For your wedding supper there'll be beef and cornbread;
There it is to eat when the ceremony's said.
And when you go to milk you'll milk into a gourd,
And set it in the corner and cover it with a board.
For that's the way with the Texians—
    With the Texians.

They will take you out on a live-oak hill
And there they will leave you much against your will.
They will leave you on the prairie, starve you on the plains.
For that's the way with the Texians—
    With the Texians.

*   *   *   *   *

Hello, girls, listen to my voice,
Don't you ever marry no good-for-nothing boys,
If you do, your doom will be,
Hoecake, hominy, and sassafras tea—
    And sassafras tea.

Young boys walking down the street,
Young girls think they look mighty sweet.
Hands in their pockets, not a dime can they find,
Oh, how tickled, poor girls mine—
    Poor girls mine!

When a young man falls in love,
First it's honey and then turtledove,

[341]

After he's married no such thing,
"Get up and get my breakfast, you good-for-nothing thing—
    Good-for-nothing thing!"

Brandy is brandy any way you mix it,
A Texian is a Texian any way you fix it.
When good folks are all gone to bed
The devil is a-working in a Texian's head—
    In a Texian's head.

THE LONE BUFFALO HUNTER

It's of those Texas cowboys a story I'll tell;
No name I will mention though in Texas they do dwell.
Go find them where you will, they are all so very brave,
And when in good society they seldom misbehave.

When the fall work is all over, in the line-camp they'll be found,
For they have to ride those lonesome lines the long winter round;
They prove loyal to a comrade, no matter what's to do;
And when in love with a fair one they seldom prove untrue.

But springtime comes at last and finds them glad and gay;
They ride out to the round-up about the first of May;
About the first of August they start up the trail,
They have to stay with the cattle, no matter rain or hail.

But when they get to the shipping point, then they receive their tens,
Straightway to the barroom and gently blow them in;
It's the height of their ambition, so I've been truly told,
To ride good horses and saddles and spend the silver and gold.

Those last two things I've mentioned, it is their heart's desire,
And when they leave the shipping point, their eyes are like balls of
    fire.
It's of those fighting cattle, they seem to have no fear,
A-riding bucking broncos oft is their heart's desire.

They will ride into the branding pen, a rope within their hands,
They will catch them by each forefoot and bring them to the sands;
It's altogether in practice with a little bit of sleight,
A-roping Texas cattle, it is their heart's delight.

But now comes the rising generation to take the cowboy's place,
Likewise the corn-fed granger, with his bold and cheeky face;
It's on those plains of Texas a lone buffalo hunter does stand
To tell the fate of the cowboy that rode at his right hand.

THE BUFFALO HUNTERS

Come all you pretty girls, to you these lines I'll write,
We are going to the range in which we take delight;
We are going on the range as we poor hunters do,
And the tender-footed fellows can stay at home with you.

It's all of the day long as we go tramping round
In search of the buffalo that we may shoot him down;
Our guns upon our shoulders, our belts of forty rounds,
We send them up Salt River to some happy hunting grounds.

Our game, it is the antelope, the buffalo, wolf, and deer,
Who roam the wide prairies without a single fear;
We rob him of his robe and think it is no harm,
To buy us food and clothing to keep our bodies warm.

The buffalo, he is the noblest of the band,
He sometimes rejects in throwing up his hand.
His shaggy mane thrown forward, his head raised to the sky,
He seems to say, "We're coming, boys; so, hunter, mind your eye."

Our fires are made of mesquite roots, our beds are on the ground;
Our houses made of buffalo hides, we make them tall and round;
Our furniture is the camp kettle, the coffee pot, and pan,
Our chuck it is both bread and meat, mingled well with sand.

Our neighbors are the Cheyennes, the 'Rapahoes, and Sioux,
Their mode of navigation is a buffalo-hide canoe.
And when they come upon you they take you unaware,
And such a peculiar way they have of raising hunters' hair.

SIOUX INDIANS*

Reflectively ($\flat$ = 120)

I'll sing you a song, though it may be a sad one, Of
tri - als and trou - bles and where first be - gun. I
left my dear kin - dred, my friends, and my home, And we
crossed the wide des - erts and moun - tains to roam.

* Sent by J. W. Light, Waco, Texas (a student in Baylor University).

I'll sing you a song, though it may be a sad one,
Of trials and troubles and where first begun.
I left my dear kindred, my friends, and my home,
And we crossed the wide deserts and mountains to roam.

I crossed the Missouri and joined a large train
Which bore us o'er mountain and valley and plain;
And often of evenings out hunting we'd go
To shoot the fleet antelope and the wild buffalo.

Without any money provisions to buy
We'd sneak around the hills shooting elk on the sly;
We'd shoot the fat deer and take him to town
To buy flour to bake bread, and tea, a few pound.

We heard of Sioux Indians, all out on the plains,
A-killing poor drivers and burning their trains—
A-killing poor drivers with arrows and bow,
When captured by Indians no me cy they'd show.

We traveled three weeks till we came to the Platte,
And pitched out our tents at the head of a flat;
We spread down our blankets on the green grassy ground,
While our horses and oxen were a-grazing around.

While taking refreshments we heard a low yell,
The whoop of Sioux Indians coming up from the dell;
We sprang to our rifles with a flash in each eye.
"Boys," says our brave leader, "we'll fight till we die."

We gathered our horses, got ready to fight,
As the band of Sioux Indians just came in sight.
They came down upon us with a whoop and a yell,
At the crack of our rifles six of them fell.

They made a bold dash and came near to our train
And the arrows fell round us like hail and like rain;
But with our long rifles we fed them cold lead,
Till many a brave warrior around us lay dead.

With our small band there were just twenty-four,
And the Sioux Indians there were five hundred or more;
We fought them with courage; we spoke not a word,
Till the end of the battle was all that was heard.

We shot their bold chief at the head of his band;
He died like a warrior with a gun in his hand.
When they saw their bold chief lying dead in his gore,
They whooped and they yelled, and we saw them no more.

We hitched up our horses and started our train;
Three more bloody battles this trip on the plain;
And in our last battle three of our brave boys fell,
And we left them to rest in a green shady dell.

We traveled by day, guarded camp during night,
Till Oregon's mountains looked high in their might.
Now at Pocahontas beside a clear stream
Our journey is ended in the land of our dream.

CALIFORNIA JOE*

Well, mates, I don't like stories;
Or am I going to act
A part around the campfire
That ain't a truthful fact?

* Written by Captain Jack Crawford, Indian scout and hunter.

So fill your pipes and listen,
I'll tell you—let me see—
I think it was in Fifty
From that to Sixty-three.

You've all heard tell of Bridger;
I used to run with Jim,
And many a hard day's scouting
I've done 'longside of him.
Well, once near old Fort Reno,
A trapper used to dwell;
We called him old Pap Reynolds,
The scouts all knew him well.

One night in the spring of Fifty
We camped on Powder River,
And killed a calf of buffalo
And cooked a slice of liver.
While eating, quite contented,
I heard three shots or four;
Put out the fire and listened—
We heard a dozen more.

We knew that old man Reynolds
Had moved his traps up here;
So picking up our rifles
And fixing on our gear
We moved as quick as lightning—
To save was our desire.
Too late; the painted heathens
Had set the house on fire.

We hitched our horses quickly
And waded up the stream;

While down close beside the waters
I heard a muffled scream.
And there among the bushes
A little girl did lie.
I picked her up and whispered,
"I'll save you or I'll die."

Lord, what a ride! Old Bridger,
He covered my retreat;
Sometimes that child would whisper
In voice low and sweet,
"Poor Papa, God will take him
To Mamma up above;
There is no one left to love me,
There is no one left to love."

The little one was thirteen
And I was twenty-two;
I says, "I'll be your father
And love you just as true,"
She nestled to my bosom,
Her hazel eyes so bright,
Looked up and made me happy,—
Though close pursued that night.

One month had passed and Maggie—
We called her Hazel Eye—
In truth was going to leave me,
Was going to say good-by.
Her uncle, Mad Jack Reynolds,
Reported long since dead,
Had come to claim my angel,
His brother's child, he said.

[348]

What could I say? We parted,
Mad Jack was growing old;
I handed him a bank note
And all I had in gold.
They rode away at sunrise,
I went a mile or two,
And parting says, "We will meet again, Mag;
May God watch over you."

* * * * *

By a laughing, dancing brook
A little cabin stood,
And weary with a long day's scout,
I spied it in the wood.
The pretty valley stretched beyond,
The mountains towered above,
And near its willow banks I heard
The cooing of a dove

'Twas one grand panorama;
The brook was plainly seen,
Like a long thread of silver
In a cloth of lovely green;
The laughter of the water,
The cooing of the dove,
Was like some painted picture,
Some well told tale of love.

While drinking in the grandeur
And resting in the saddle,
I heard a gentle ripple
Like the dipping of a paddle,

[349]

And turning to the eddy,
A strange sight met my view—
A maiden with her rifle
In a little bark canoe.

She stood up in the center,
With her rifle to her eye;
I thought for just a second
My time had come to die.
I doffed my hat and told her,
If it was just the same,
To drop her little shooter,
For I was not her game.

She dropped the deadly weapon
And leaped from the canoe.
Says she: "I beg your pardon;
I thought you was a Sioux.
Your long hair and your buckskin
Looked warriorlike and rough;
My bead was spoiled by sunshine,
Or I'd have killed you sure enough."

"Perhaps it would've been better
If you'd dropped me then," says I;
"For surely such an angel
Could bear me to the sky."
She blushingly dropped her eyelids,
Her cheeks were crimson-red;
One half-shy glance she gave me
And then hung down her head.

I took her little hand in mine;
She wondered what it meant,

[350]

And yet she drew it not away,
But rather seemed content.
We sat upon the mossy bank,
Her eyes began to fill;
The brook was rippling at our feet,
The dove was cooing still.

I smoothed her golden tresses
Her eyes looked up in mine;
She seemed in doubt, then whispered,
" 'Tis such a long, long time.
Strong arms were thrown around me—
'I'll save you or I'll die.' "
I clasped her to my bosom,
My long-lost Hazel Eye.

The rapture of that moment
Was almost heaven to me;
I kissed her 'mid her tear-drops,
Her merriment and glee.
Her heart near mine was beating
When sobbingly she said,
"My dear, my brave preserver,
They told me you was dead.

"But oh, those parting words, Joe,
Have never left my mind,
You said, 'We'll meet again, Mag,'
Then rode off like the wind.
And oh, how I have prayed, Joe,
For you who saved my life,
That God would send an angel
To guide you through all strife!

[351]

"The one who claimed me from you,
My uncle, good and true,
Is sick in yonder cabin;
Has talked so much of you.
'If Joe was living, darling,'
He said to me last night,
'He would care for Maggie,
When God puts out my light.'"

We found the old man sleeping.
"Hush, Maggie, let him rest."
The sun was slowly setting
In the far-off glowing west.
And though we talked in whispers
He opened wide his eyes:
"A dream, a dream," he murmured,
"Alas, a dream of lies."

She drifted like a shadow
To where the old man lay.
"You had a dream, dear Uncle,
Another dream today?"
"Oh, yes, I saw an angel
As pure as mountain snow,
And near her at my bedside
Stood California Joe."

"I'm sure I'm not an angel,
Dear Uncle, that you know;
These arms are brawny, my hands, too,
My face is not like snow.
Now listen while I tell you,
For I have news to cheer;

[352]

Hazel Eye is happy,
For Joe is truly here."

It was but a few days after
The old man said to me,
"Joe, boy, she is an angel,
And good as angels be.
For three long months she hunted,
And trapped and nussed me too;
God bless you, boy, I believe it,
She's safe along with you."

* * * * *

The sun was slowly sinking,
When Maggie, my wife, and I
Came riding through the valley,
The tear-drops in her eye.
"One year ago today, Joe,
I saw the mossy grave;
We laid him 'neath the daisies,
My uncle, good and brave."

And comrades, every springtime
Is sure to find me there;
As something in the valley
Seemed always fresh and fair.
Our love is always kindled
While sitting by the stream,
Where two hearts were united
In love's sweet, happy dream.

[353]

THE OLD SCOUT'S LAMENT

Come all of you, my brother scouts,
And join me in my song;
Come, let us sing together
Though the shadows fall so long,

Of all the old frontiersmen
That used to scour the plain,
There are but very few of them
That with us yet remain.

Day after day they're dropping off,
They're going one by one;
Our clan is fast decreasing,
Our race is almost run.

There were many of our number
That never wore the blue,
But faithfully—they did their part,
As brave men, tried and true.

They never joined the army,
But had other work to do
In piloting the coming folks,
To help them safely through.

But, brothers, we are falling,
Our race is almost run;
The days of elk and buffalo
And beaver traps are gone.

Oh, the days of elk and buffalo!
It fills my heart with pain

[354]

To know these days are past and gone
To never come again.

We fought the redskin rascals
Over valley, hill, and plain;
We fought them in the mountain top,
And fought them down again.

These fighting days are over;
The Indian yell resounds
No more along the border;
Peace sends far sweeter sounds.

But we found great joy, old comrades,
To hear, and make it die;
We won bright homes for gentle ones,
And now, our West, good-by.

A MAN NAMED HODS*

Come all you old cow-punchers, a story I will tell,
And if you'll all be quiet, I sure will sing it well;
And if you boys don't like it, you sure can go to hell.

Back in the day when I was young, I knew a man named Hods;
He wasn't fit fer nothin' 'cep' turnin' up the clods.

But he came West in Fifty-three, behind a pair of mules,
And 'twas hard to tell between the three which was the biggest fools.

Up on the plains old Hod he got, and there his trouble began.
Oh, he sure did get in trouble—and old Hodsie wasn't no man.

* From J. B. Jones, Agricultural and Mechanical College of Texas.

He met a bunch of Indian bucks led by Geronimo,
And what them Indians did to him, well, shorely I don't know.

But they lifted off old Hodsie's skelp and left him out to die,
And if it hadn't been for me, he'd been in the sweet by-and-by.

But I packed him back to Santa Fe, and there I found his mules,
For them dad-blamed two critters had got the Indians fooled.

I don't know how they done it, but they shore did get away,
And them two mules is livin' up to this very day.

Old Hodsie's feet got toughened up, he got to be a sport,
He opened up a gamblin' house and a place of low resort;

He got the prettiest dancing girls that ever could be found—
Them girls' feet was like rubber balls and they never stayed on the
ground.

And then thar came Billy the Kid, he envied Hodsie's wealth,
He told old Hods to leave the town, 'twould be better for his health;

Old Hodsie took the hint and got, but he carried all his wealth.
And he went back to Noo York State with lots of dinero,
And now they say he's senator, but of that I shore don't know.

PATTONIO, THE PRIDE OF THE PLAIN*

Moderately fast (♩. = 63)

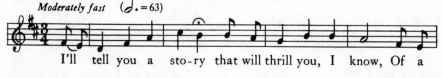

I'll tell you a sto-ry that will thrill you, I know, Of a

horse that I once owned in New Mex - i - co. You will

* From the singing of the Gant family, Austin, Texas, and of Eddie Murphy, Crowley,
Louisiana.

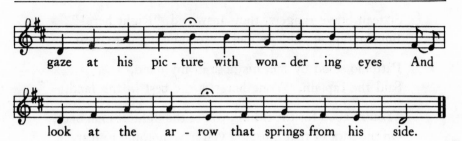

gaze at his pic-ture with won-der-ing eyes And

look at the ar-row that springs from his side.

I'll tell you a story that will thrill you, I know,
Of a horse that I once owned in New Mexico.

You will gaze at his picture with wondering eyes
And look at the arrow that springs from his side.

He was swift as an antelope and black as a crow
With a star on his forehead as white as the snow.

His arched neck was hidden by his swift-flowing mane,
And I called him Pattonio, the pride of the plain.

His hair, like a lady's, was glossy and fine,
He was restless and proud, but he was gentle and kind.

The country was new and the settlers was skeerce,
And the Indians on the warpath was savage and fierce.

Sixteen brave rangers were sent out from the post,
They never returned, and we knew they were lost.

Those scouts were sent out every day from the post,
They never came back, and we knew they were lost.

So the captain, he spoke, says, "Some one must go
Down on the dark borders of old Mexico."

Sixteen brave rangers, they answered, "Right here!"
But the captain, he saw me, I was standing quite near.

Pattonio stood by me, his nose in my hand,
Said the captain, "Your horse is the best in the land.

"You're good for the riding, you're the lightest man here,
On the back of that mustang you have nothing to fear."

Then, proud of my pony, I answered, "You know
Pattonio and I are both willing to go."

"For speed and endurance, I'll trust in the black."
They all shook my hands, and I mounted his back,

Rode down the black pathway, turned his head to the right;
The black struck a trot, and he kept it all night.

It was early next morning we were still on the go
Down to the black borders of old Mexico,

When right in behind me I heard a sharp yell
And I knew that the redskins were giving me hell.

I spoke to Pattonio, drew up on the reins,
I spoke to Pattonio, the pride of the plains.

Pattonio, he answered with a nod of his head,
And his black body lengthened and faster he sped.

Then I reached the fort and tried to dismount,
But an arrow held me fast, and so I could not.

You may gaze at the arrow, hangs on the wall,
It was driven through stirrup, foot, saddle, and all.

I've rode many horses all over the range,
But none like Pattonio, the pride of the plains.

TEXAS RANGERS*

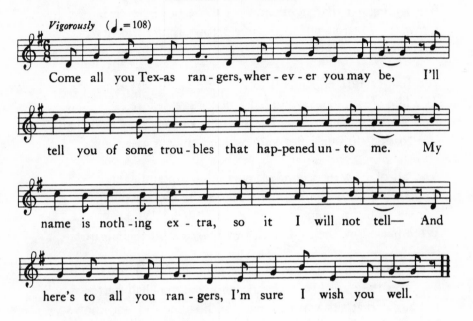

Come all you Tex-as ran-gers, wher-ev-er you may be, I'll tell you of some trou-bles that hap-pened un-to me. My name is noth-ing ex-tra, so it I will not tell— And here's to all you ran-gers, I'm sure I wish you well.

Come all you Texas rangers, wherever you may be,
I'll tell you of some troubles that happened unto me.
My name is nothing extra, so it I will not tell—
And here's to all you rangers, I'm sure I wish you well.

It was at the age of sixteen that I joined the jolly band,
We marched from San Antonio down to the Rio Grande.
Our captain he informed us, perhaps he thought it right,
"Before we reach the station, boys, you'll surely have to fight."

And when the bugle sounded our captain gave command.
"To arms, to arms," he shouted, "and by your horses stand."
I saw the smoke ascending, it seemed to reach the sky;
The first thought that struck me, my time had come to die.

* Cf. "The Ex-Ranger's Song," Shoemaker's *Mountain Minstrelsy of Pennsylvania*, p. 91.

I saw the Indians coming, I heard them give the yell;
My feelings at that moment, no tongue can ever tell.
I saw the glittering lances, their arrows round me flew,
And all my strength it left me, and all my courage too.

We fought full nine hours before the strife was o'er,
The like of dead and wounded I never saw before.
And when the sun was rising and the Indians they had fled,
We loaded up our rifles and counted up our dead.

And all of us were wounded, our noble captain slain,
And the sun was shining sadly across the bloody plain.
Sixteen as brave rangers as ever roamed the West
Were buried by their comrades with arrows in their breast.

'Twas then I thought of Mother, who to me in tears did say,
"To you they are all strangers, with me you had better stay."
I thought that she was childish, the best she did not know;
My mind was fixed on ranging, and I was bound to go.

Perhaps you have a mother, likewise a sister too,
And maybe so a sweetheart to weep and mourn for you;
If that be your situation, although you'd like to roam,
I'd advise you by experience, you had better stay at home.

I have seen the fruits of rambling, I know its hardships well;
I have crossed the Rocky Mountains, rode down the streets of hell;
I have been in the great Southwest where the wild Apaches roam,
And I tell you from experience you had better stay at home.

I am a harmless ranger, as I have said before,
My mother and my sister are on this earth no more;
The reason why I ramble, now you can plainly see,
I have no wife or sweetheart to weep and mourn for me.

And now my song is ended; I guess I have sung enough;
The life of a ranger I am sure is very tough.
And here's to all you ladies, I am sure I wish you well.
I am bound to go a-ranging; so, ladies, fare you well.

[*Version 2*]

Come all you Tex - as ran - gers, wher -
It was at the age of six - teen that I

ev - er you may be, I'll tell you of some trou-bles that
joined the jol - ly band, We marched from San An - to - nio down

hap-pened un - to me. My name is noth-ing ex - tra, so
to the Ri - o Grande. Our cap-tain he in - formed us, per -

it I will not tell— And here's to all you
haps he thought it right, Be - fore we reach the

ran - gers, I am sure I wish you well.
sta - tion, boys, you'll sure - ly have to fight."

DOWN SOUTH ON THE RIO GRANDE

From way down south on the Rio Grande,
Roll on steers for the Post Oak sand—
Way down South in Dixie, oh, boys, ho.

You'd laugh fur to see that fellow astraddle
Of a mustang mare on a rawhide saddle—
Way down South in Dixie, oh, boys, ho.

Rich as a king, and he wouldn't be bigger
Fur a pitchin' hoss and a lame old nigger—
Way down South in Dixie, oh, boys, ho.

Ol' Abe kep' gettin' bigger an' bigger,
Till he bust hisself 'bout a lame old nigger—
Way down South in Dixie, oh, boys, ho.

Old Jeff swears he'll sew him together
With powder and shot instead of leather—
Way down South in Dixie, oh, boys, ho.

Kin cuss an' fight an' hold or free 'em,
But I know them mavericks when I see 'em—
Way down South in Dixie, oh, boys, ho.

MUSTANG GRAY

Mabry (Mustang) Gray was one of the wildest, most scoundrelly
and bloodthirsty of the "Texians" who fought for Texas' Independ-
ence and who took a particular pleasure in shooting all the defenseless
Mexicans they encountered. His name and reputation have been more
realistically treated in a romance by one Honorable Jeremiah Clemens,

[362]

1858; but, for a full and judicious account of this early and ferocious specimen of cowboy, see J. Frank Dobie's article in *Publications of the Texas Folk-Lore Society*, Vol. X, p. 109.

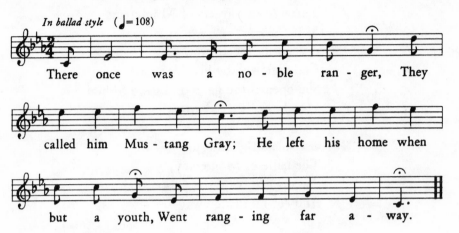

In ballad style (♩=108)

There once was a no-ble ran-ger, They called him Mus-tang Gray; He left his home when but a youth, Went rang-ing far a-way.

There once was a noble ranger,
They called him Mustang Gray;
He left his home when but a youth,
Went ranging far away.

But he'll go no more a-ranging,
The savage to affright;
He has heard his last war-whoop,
And fought his last fight.

He ne'er would sleep within a tent,
No comforts would he know;
But like a brave old Tex-i-an,
A-ranging he would go.

When Texas was invaded
By a mighty tyrant foe,
He mounted his noble war-horse
And a-ranging he did go.

[363]

Once he was taken prisoner,
Bound in chains upon the way,
He wore the yoke of bondage
Through the streets of Monterrey.

A señorita loved him,
And followed by his side;
She opened the gates and gave to him
Her father's steed to ride.

God bless the señorita,
The belle of Monterrey,
She opened wide the prison door
And let him ride away.

And when this veteran's life was spent,
It was his last command
To bury him on Texas soil
On the banks of the Rio Grande;

And there the lonely traveler,
When passing by his grave,
Will shed a farewell tear
O'er the bravest of the brave.

And he'll go no more a-ranging,
The savage to affright;
He has heard his last war-whoop,
And fought his last fight.

WAY DOWN IN MEXICO*

O boys, we're goin' for to fight,
Yo-ho, yo-ho!
We'll take the greasers now in hand
And drive 'em in the Rio Grande,
Way down in Mexico.

We'll hang old Santa Anna soon,
Yo-ho, yo-ho!
And all the greaser soldiers, too,
To the chune of "Yankee Doodle Doo,"
Way down in Mexico.

We'll scatter 'em like flocks of sheep,
Yo-ho, yo-ho!
We'll mow 'em down with rifle ball
And plant our flag right on their wall,
Way down in Mexico.

Old Rough and Ready,† he's a trump,
Yo-ho, yo-ho!
He'll wipe old Santa Anna out
And put the greasers all to rout,
Way down in Mexico.

Then we'll march back by-and-by,
Yo-ho, yo-ho!
And kiss the gals we left to home
And never more we'll go and roam,
Way down in Mexico.

* Sent by Mrs. Lawrence, Dayton, Texas, through J. B. Jones, Houston, Texas.
† General Taylor.

THE DYING RANGER

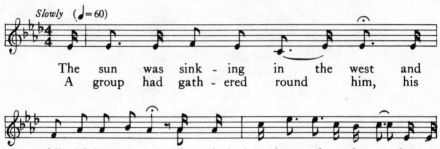

The sun was sink - ing in the west and
A group had gath - ered round him, his

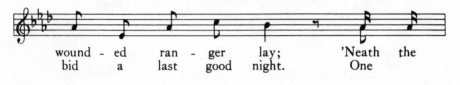

fell with lin-g'ring ray Through the branch-es of a for-est where a
com-rades in the fight, A tear rolled down each man-ly cheek as he

wound - ed ran - ger lay; 'Neath the
bid a last good night. One

shade of a pal-met-to and the sun-set sil-v'ry sky, Far a -
tried and true com-pan-ion was kneel-ing by his side To

way from his home in Tex-as, they laid him down to die.
stop his life-blood flow-ing, but, a-las, in vain he tried.

The sun was sinking in the west and fell with lingering ray
Through the branches of a forest where a wounded ranger lay;
'Neath the shade of a palmetto and the sunset silvery sky,
Far away from his home in Texas they laid him down to die.

A group had gathered round him, his comrades in the fight,
A tear rolled down each manly cheek as he bid a last good night.

One tried and true companion was kneeling by his side,
To stop his life-blood flowing; but, alas, in vain he tried.

When to stop the life-blood flowing he found 'twas all in vain,
The tears rolled down each man's cheek like light showers of rain.
Up spoke the noble ranger, "Boys, weep no more for me,
I am crossing the deep waters to a country that is free.

"Draw closer to me, comrades, and listen to what I say:
I am going to tell a story while my spirit hastens away,
Way back in northwest Texas, that good old Lone Star State,
There is one that for my coming with a weary heart will wait.

"A fair young girl, my sister, my only joy, my pride,
She was my friend from boyhood, I had no one left beside.
I have loved her as a brother, and with a father's care
I have strove from grief and sorrow her gentle heart to spare.

"My mother, she lies sleeping beneath the churchyard sod,
And many a day has passed away since her spirit fled to God.
My father, he lies sleeping beneath the deep blue sea;
I have no other kindred, there are none but Nell and me.

"But our country was invaded and they called for volunteers;
She threw her arms around me, then burst into tears,
Saying: 'Go, my darling brother, drive those traitors from our shore.
My heart may need your presence, but our country needs you more.'

"It is true I love my country, for her I gave my all.
If it hadn't been for my sister, I would be content to fall.
I am dying, comrades, dying, she will never see me more,
But in vain she'll wait my coming by our little cabin door.

"Comrades, gather closer and listen to my dying prayer.
Who will be to her as a brother, and shield her with a brother's care?"

Up spake the noble rangers, they answered one and all,
"We will be to her as brothers till the last one does fall."

One glad smile of pleasure o'er the ranger's face was spread;
One dark, convulsive shadow, and the ranger boy was dead.
Far from his darling sister we laid him down to rest
With his saddle for a pillow and his rifle across his breast.

MUSTER OUT THE RANGERS

Yes, muster them out, the valiant band
That guards our western home.
What matters to you in your eastern land
If the raiders here should come?
No danger that you shall awake at night
To the howls of a savage band;
So muster them out, though the morning light
Find havoc on every hand.

Some dear one is sick and the horses all gone,
So we can't for a doctor send;
The outlaws were in, in the light of the morn,
And no Rangers here to defend.
For they've mustered them out, the brave true band,
Untiring by night and day.
The fearless scouts of this border land
Made the taxes high, they say.

Have fewer men in the capitol walls,
Fewer tongues in the war of words,
But add to the Rangers, the living wall
That keeps back the bandit hordes.
Have fewer dinners, less turtle soup,
If the taxes are too high.

There are many other and better ways
To lower them if they try.

Don't waste so much of your money
Printing speeches people don't read.
If you'd only take off what's used for that
'Twould lower the tax indeed.
Don't use so much sugar and lemons;
Cold water is just as good
For a constant drink in the summer time
And better for the blood.

But leave us the Rangers to guard us still,
Nor think that they cost too dear;
For their faithful watch over vale and hill
Gives our loved ones naught to fear.

THE DISHEARTENED RANGER*

Come listen to a ranger, you kind-hearted stranger,
This song, though a sad one, you're welcome to hear;
We've kept the Comanches away from your ranches,
And followed them far o'er the Texas frontier.

Refrain:
So look to your ranches and mind the Comanches
For sure they will scalp you in less than a year.

We're weary of scouting, of traveling, and routing
The bloodthirsty villains o'er prairie and wood;
No rest for the sinner, no breakfast or dinner,
But he lies in a supperless bed in the mud.

* J. Evetts Haley in *Charles Goodnight* (p. 97) quotes a different and less singable version of this complaint which he says was composed by two rangers, Tom Pollard and Alec McClosky.

No corn nor potatoes, no bread nor tomatoes,
But jerked beef as dry as the sole of your shoe;
All day without drinking, all night without winking,
I'll tell you, kind stranger, this never will do.

Those great alligators, the state legislators,*
Are puffing and blowing two-thirds of their time;
But windy orations about rangers and rations
Never put in our pockets one-tenth of a dime.

They do not regard us, they will not reward us,
Though hungry and haggard with holes in our coats;
But the election is coming and they will be drumming
And praising our valor to purchase our votes.

Without glory or payment, nor victuals nor raiment,
No longer we'll fight on the Texas frontier.
So guard your own ranches, and mind the Comanches
Or surely they'll scalp you in less than a year.

Though sore it may grieve you, the rangers must leave you
Exposed to the arrows and knife of the foe;
So herd your own cattle and fight your own battle,
For home to the States I'm determined to go—

Where churches have steeples and laws are more equal,
Where houses have people and ladies are kind;
Where work is regarded and worth is rewarded;
Where pumpkins are plenty and pockets are lined.

Your wives and your daughters we have guarded from
    slaughter,
Through conflicts and struggles I shudder to tell;
No more we'll defend them, to God we'll commend them.
To the frontier of Texas we bid a farewell.

* King Sloan sends in a first line of this stanza: "The State Legislator, like great Alexander";
and his final line of the stanza runs: "Put in their pockets one half of each dime."

HERE'S TO THE RANGER!

He leaves unplowed his furrow,
He leaves his books unread
For a life of tented freedom
By lure of danger led.
He's first in the hour of peril,
He's gayest in the dance,
Like the guardsman of old England
Or the beau sabreur of France.

He stands our faithful bulwark
Against our savage foe;
Through lonely woodland places
Our children come and go;
Our flocks and herds untended
O'er hill and valley roam,
The ranger in the saddle
Means peace for us at home.

Behold our smiling farmsteads
Where waves the golden grain!
Beneath yon tree, earth's bosom
Was dark with crimson stain.
That bluff the death-shot echoed
Of husband, father, slain!
God grant such sight of horror
We never see again!

The gay and hardy ranger,
His blanket on the ground,
Lies by the blazing campfire
While song and tale go round;

[371]

And if one voice is silent,
One fails to hear the jest,
They know his thoughts are absent
With her who loves him best.

Our state, her sons confess it,
That queenly, star-crowned brow,
Has darkened with the shadow
Of lawlessness ere now;
And men of evil passions
On her reproach have laid,
But that the ready ranger
Rode promptly to her aid.

He may not win the laurel
Nor trumpet tongue of fame;
But beauty smiles upon him,
And ranchmen bless his name.
Then here's to the Texas ranger,
Past, present, and to come!
Our safety from the savage,
The guardian of our home.

THE DREARY BLACK HILLS

With an easy swing (♩. = 63)

Kind friends, you must pit - y my hor - ri - ble tale, I'm an
The round-house in Chey-enne is filled ev - 'ry night With

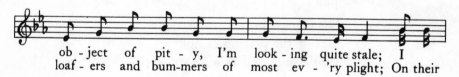

ob - ject of pit - y, I'm look - ing quite stale; I
loaf - ers and bum-mers of most ev - 'ry plight; On their

gave up my trade sell - ing Right's Pat-ent Pills, To
backs is no clothes, in their pock-ets no bills, Each

go hunt-ing gold in the drear-y Black Hills.
day they keep start-ing for the drear-y Black Hills.

REFRAIN

Don't go a-way, stay at home if you can; Stay a-

way from that cit-y, they call it Chey-enne; For

big Wal-li-pe or Co-man-che Bills, They will

lift up your hair on the drear-y Black Hills.

Kind friends, you must pity my horrible tale,
I'm an object of pity, I'm looking quite stale;
I gave up my trade selling Right's Patent Pills
To go hunting gold in the dreary Black Hills.

Refrain:

Don't go away, stay at home if you can;
Stay away from that city, they call it Cheyenne;

For big Wallipe or Comanche Bills,
They will lift up your hair on the dreary Black Hills.

The roundhouse in Cheyenne is filled ev'ry night
With loafers and bummers of most ev'ry plight;
On their backs is no clothes, in their pockets no bills,
Each day they keep starting for the dreary Black Hills.

One morning so early, one morning in May,
I met Kit Carson a-goin' away;
He was goin' away with Buffalo Bill,
He was goin' a-mining in the dreary Black Hills.*

I got to Cheyenne, no gold could I find,
I thought of the lunch route I'd left far behind;
Through rain, hail, and snow, frozen plumb to the gills—
They call me the orphan of the dreary Black Hills.

Kind friend, to conclude, my advice I'll unfold,
Don't go to the Black Hills a-hunting for gold;
Railroad speculators their pockets you'll fill
By taking a trip to those dreary Black Hills.

Oh, I wish the man that started this sell
Was a captive, and Crazy Horse had him in Hell;
There's no use in grieving or swearing like pitch,
But the man who would stay here is a son-of-a-bitch.

Don't go away, stay home if you can;
Stay away from that city, they call it Cheyenne,
For old Sitting Bull or Comanche Bills,
They will take off your scalp on the dreary Black Hills.

* The last two lines of this stanza are sometimes illogically sung:

No money in his pockets, his bills he couldn't pay;
They've got him in the lockup and he can't get away.

THE BLOODY INJIANS

I'd rather hear a rattler rattle,
I'd rather buck stampeding cattle,
I'd rather go to a greaser battle,
Than—
Than to—
Than to fight—
Than to fight the bloody In-ji-ans.

I'd rather eat a pan of dope,
I'd rather ride without a rope,
I'd rather from this country lope,
Than—
Than to—
Than to fight—
Than to fight the bloody In-ji-ans.

JOE BOWERS

As sung by the bullwhackers and mule-drivers, following the gold rush to California. The song was popular among the Southern soldiers, also, during the Civil War.

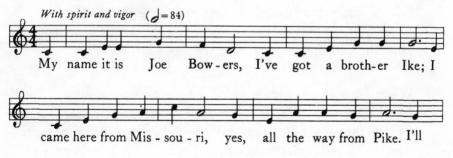

With spirit and vigor (♩ = 84)

My name it is Joe Bow-ers, I've got a broth-er Ike; I came here from Mis - sou - ri, yes, all the way from Pike. I'll

[375]

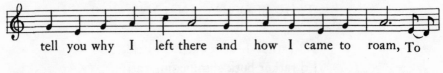

tell you why I left there and how I came to roam, To

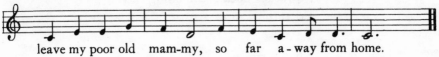

leave my poor old mam-my, so far a-way from home.

My name it is Joe Bowers, I've got a brother Ike;
I came here from Missouri, yes, all the way from Pike;
I'll tell you why I left there and how I came to roam,
To leave my poor old mammy, so far away from home.

I used to love a gal there, her name was Sallie Black,
I asked her for to marry me, she said it was a whack;
She says to me, "Joe Bowers, before you hitch for life,
You ought to have a little home to keep your little wife."

Says I, "My dearest Sallie, O Sallie, for your sake,
I'll go to California and try to raise a stake."
Says she to me: "Joe Bowers, you are the chap to win.
Give me a kiss to seal the bargain"—and I throwed a dozen in.

I'll never forget my feelings when I bid adieu to all.
Sal, she cotched me round the neck and I began to bawl.
When I begun they all commenced, you never heard the like,
How they all took on and cried the day I left old Pike.

When I got to this here country, I hadn't nary a red,
I had such wolfish feelings I wished myself most dead.
But the thoughts of my dear Sallie soon made these feelings git;
And whispered hopes to Bowers—Lord, I wish I had 'em yit.

[376]

At last I went to mining, put in my biggest licks,
Came down upon the boulders just like a thousand bricks.
I worked both late and early in rain and sun and snow,
But I was working for my Sallie; it was all the same to Joe.

I made a very lucky strike, as the gold itself did tell,
For I was working for my Sallie, the girl I loved so well.
I saved it for my Sallie that I might pour it at her feet;
That she might hug and kiss me and call me something sweet.

But one day I got a letter from my dear, kind brother Ike;
It came from old Missouri, yes, all the way from Pike;
It told me the gol-darndest news that ever you did hear,
My heart it is a-bustin', so please excuse this tear.

I'll tell you what it was, boys—you'll bust your sides, I know;
For when I read that letter you ought to seen poor Joe.
My knees gave way beneath me, and I pulled out half my hair;
And if you ever tell this now, you bet you'll hear me swear.

It said my Sallie was fickle, her love for me had fled,
That she had married a butcher, whose hair was awful red;
It told me more than that, it's enough to make me swear—
It said that Sallie had a baby and the baby had red hair.

Now I've told you all that I can tell about this sad affair,
'Bout Sallie marrying a butcher and the baby had red hair.
But whether it was a boy or girl the letter never said;
It only said its cussed hair was inclined to be red.

THE DAYS OF FORTY–NINE*

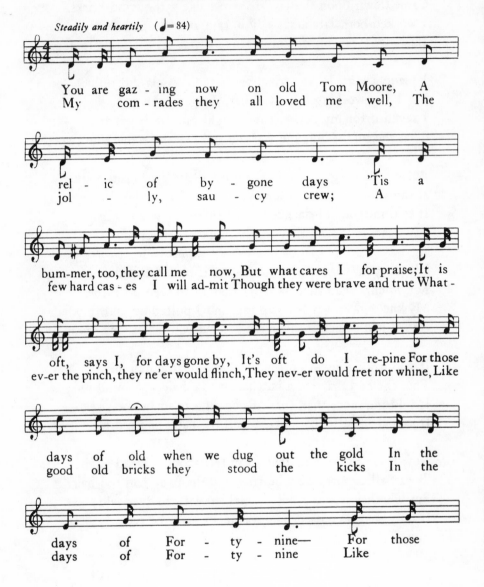

Steadily and heartily (♩ = 84)

You are gaz - ing now on old Tom Moore, A
My com - rades they all loved me well, The

rel - ic of by - gone days 'Tis a
jol - ly, sau - cy crew; A

bum-mer, too, they call me now, But what cares I for praise; It is
few hard cas - es I will ad-mit Though they were brave and true What-

oft, says I, for days gone by, It's oft do I re-pine For those
ev-er the pinch, they ne'er would flinch, They nev-er would fret nor whine, Like

days of old when we dug out the gold In the
good old bricks they stood the kicks In the

days of For - ty - nine— For those
days of For - ty - nine Like

* From Florence N. Gleason of Bakersfield, Calif.

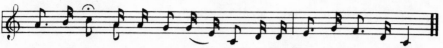

days   of   old when we dug out the gold In the days of For - ty-nine.
good old bricks they   stood the   kicks In the days of For - ty-nine.

You are gazing now on old Tom Moore,
A relic of bygone days;
'Tis a bummer, too, they call me now,
But what cares I for praise?
It's oft, says I, for the days gone by,
It's oft do I repine
For those days of old when we dug out the gold
In the days of Forty-nine,
For those days of old when we dug out the gold
In the days of Forty-nine.

My comrades they all loved me well,
The jolly, saucy crew,
A few hard cases I will admit,
Though they were brave and true;
Whatever the pinch, they ne'er would flinch,
They never would fret nor whine—
Like good old bricks they stood the kicks
In the days of Forty-nine.
Like good old bricks they stood the kicks
In the days of Forty-nine.

There's old "Lame Jess," that hard old cuss,
Who never would repent;
He never missed a single meal,
Nor never paid a cent.
But old "Lame Jess," like all the rest,
At death he did resign,
And his bloom went up the flume,
In the days of Forty-nine.

[379]

And his bloom went up the flume,
In the days of Forty-nine.

There is Ragshad Jim, the roaring man,
Who could outroar a buffalo, you bet,
He roared all day and he roared all night,
And I spec' he's roaring yet.
One night Jim fell in a prospect hole—
It was a roaring bad design—
And in that hole Jim roared out his soul
In the days of Forty-nine.
And in that hole Jim roared out his soul
In the days of Forty-nine.

There's Poker Bill, one of the boys,
Who was always in for a game,
Whether he lost or whether he won,
To him it was always the same.
He would ante you a slug, or rush the buck,
He'd go you a hatful blind—
In the game of death Bill lost his breath
In the days of Forty-nine.
In the game of death Bill lost his breath
In the days of Forty-nine.

There was old New York Jake, the butcher boy,
Who was fond of getting tight;
And every time he got on a spree
He was spoiling for a fight.
One night Jim rampaged against a knife
In the hands of old Bob Sine,
And over Jake they held a wake
In the days of Forty-nine.

And over Jake they held a wake
In the days of Forty-nine.

There was Monte Pete—I'll ne'er forget
The luck he always had;
He would deal you both day and night
Or as long as he had a scad.
It was a pistol shot that lay Pete out,
It was his last resign.
And Pete caught it dead shore in the door*
In the days of Forty-nine.
And Pete caught it dead shore in the door
In the days of Forty-nine.

Of all the comrades that I've had
There's none that's left to boast,
And I am left alone in my misery
Like some poor wandering ghost;
And as I pass from town to town
Folks call me the rambling sign—
There goes Tom Moore, a bummer shore,
Of the days of Forty-nine.
There goes Tom Moore, a bummer shore,
Of the days of Forty-nine.

THE FOOLS OF FORTY-NINE

When gold was found in Forty-nine the people thought 'twas gas,
And some were fools enough to think the lumps were only brass.
But soon they all were satisfied and started off to mine;
They bought their ships, came round the Horn, in the days of Forty-
nine.

* "In the door" is a term used in Monte. The first card that comes is the card in the door, the dealer's per cent.

Refrain:

Then they thought of what they'd been told
When they started after gold—
That they never in the world would make a pile.

The people all were crazy then, they didn't know what to do;
They sold their farms for just enough to pay their passage through;
They bid their friends a long farewell, said, "Dear wife, don't you cry,
I'll send you home the yellow lumps a piano for to buy."

The poor, the old, and the rotten scows were advertised to sail
From New Orleans with passengers, but they must pump and bail.
The ships were crowded more than full, and some hung on behind,
And others dived off from the wharf and swam till they were blind.

With rusty pork and stinking beef and rotten, wormy bread!
The captains, too, that never were up as high as the mainmast head!
The steerage passengers would rave and swear that they'd paid their
        passage,
And wanted something more to eat beside bologna sausage.

They then began to cross the plain with oxen, hollowing "Haw."
And steamers then began to run as far as Panama.
And there for months the people stayed, that started after gold,
And some returned disgusted with the lies that had been told.

The people died on every route, they sickened and died like sheep;
And those at sea before they died were launched into the deep;
And those that died while crossing the plains fared not so well as that,
For a hole was dug and they thrown in along the miserable Platte.

The ships at last began to arrive and the people began to inquire,
"They say that flour is a dollar a pound—do you think it will be any
        higher?"
And to carry their blankets and sleep outdoors, it seemed so very droll!
Both tired and mad, without a cent, they damned the lousy hole.

THE HAPPY MINER

I'm a happy miner, I love to sing and dance.
I wonder what my love would say if she could see my pants
With canvas patches on my knees and one upon the stern.
I'll wear them when I'm digging here and home when I return.

Refrain:
    So I get in a jovial way, I spend my money free.
    And I've got plenty! Will you drink lager beer with me?

She writes about her poodle dog, but never thinks to say:
"Oh, do come home, my honey dear, I'm pining all away."
I'll write her half a letter, then give the ink a tip.
If that don't bring her to her milk I'll coolly let her rip.

They wish to know if I can cook and what I have to eat,
And tell me should I take a cold be sure and soak my feet.
But when they talk of cooking I'm mighty hard to beat,
I've made ten thousand loaves of bread the devil couldn't eat.

I like a lazy partner so I can take my ease,
Lay down and talk of golden home, as happy as you please;
Without a thing to eat or drink, away from care and grief—
I'm fat and sassy, ragged, too, and tough as Spanish beef.

The dark-eyed señoritas are very fond of me,
You ought to see us throw ourselves when we get on a spree;
We are as saucy as a clipper ship dashing round the Horn;
Head and tail up, like a steer rushing through the corn.

I've never changed my fancy shirt, the one I wore away,
Until it got so rotten I finally had to say:

[383]

"Farewell, old standing collar, in all thy pride of starch.
I've worn thee from December till the seventeenth day of March."

No matter whether rich or poor, I'm happy as a clam.
I wish my friends at home could look and see me as I am.
With woolen shirt and rubber boots, in mud up to my knees,
And lice as large as chili beans fighting with the fleas.

I'll mine for half an ounce a day, perhaps a little less;
But when it comes to China pay I cannot stand the press.
Like thousands there, I'll make a pile, if I make one at all,
About the time the allied forces take Sebastopol.

THE ROAD TO COOK'S PEAK*

If you'll listen awhile I'll sing you a song,
And as it is short it won't take me long.
There are some things of which I will speak
Concerning the stage on the road to Cook's Peak—
On the road to Cook's Peak—
On the road to Cook's Peak—
Concerning the stage on the road to Cook's Peak.

It was in the morning at eight-forty-five,
I was hooking up all ready to drive
Out where the miners for minerals seek,
With two little mules on the road to Cook's Peak—
On the road to Cook's Peak—
On the road to Cook's Peak—
With two little mules on the road to Cook's Peak.

* Near Deming, N. M.

[384]

With my two little mules I jog along
And try to cheer them with ditty and song;
O'er the wide prairie where coyotes sneak,
While driving the stage on the road to Cook's Peak—
On the road to Cook's Peak—
On the road to Cook's Peak—
While driving the stage on the road to Cook's Peak—

Sometimes I have to haul heavy freight,
Then it is I get home very late.
In rain or shine, six days in the week,
'Tis the same little mules on the road to Cook's Peak.
On the road to Cook's Peak—
On the road to Cook's Peak—
'Tis the same little mules on the road to Cook's Peak.

And when with the driving of stage I am through
I will to my two little mules bid adieu.
And hope that those creatures, so gentle and meek,
Will have a good friend on the road to Cook's Peak—
On the road to Cook's Peak—
On the road to Cook's Peak—
Will have a good friend on the road to Cook's Peak.

Now all kind friends that travel about,
Come take a trip on the Wallis stage route.
With a plenty of grit, they never get weak,
Those two little mules on the road to Cook's Peak—
On the road to Cook's Peak—
On the road to Cook's Peak—
Those two little mules on the road to Cook's Peak.

IN THE SUMMER OF SIXTY*

In the summer of Sixty, as you very well know,
The excitement at Pike's Peak was then all the go;
Many went there with fortunes and spent what they had
And came back flat busted and looking quite sad.

'Twas then I heard farming was a very fine branch,
So I spent most of my money in buying a ranch,
And when I got to it with sorrow and shame,
I found a big miner had jumped my fine claim.

So I bought a revolver and swore I'd lay low
The very next fellow that treated me so;
I then went to Denver and cut quite a dash
And took extra pains to show off my cash.

With a fine span of horses, my wife by my side,
I drove through the streets with my hat on one side;
As we were a-goin' past old "Denver Hall,"
Sweet music came out that did charm us all;

Says I, "Let's go in and see what's the muss,
For I feel right now like having a fuss."
There were tables strung out over the hall,
Some was a-whirling a wheel with a ball;

Some playing cards and some shaking dice
And lots of half-dollars that looked very nice.
I finally strayed to a table at last
Where all the poor suckers did seem to stick fast.

* From p. 189 (No. 89), Louise Pound's *American Ballads and Folk Songs* (New York: Scribner). Miss Pound notes that the text was obtained from Frances Francis of Cheyenne, Wyoming, in 1911.

And there stood a man with cards in his hand,
And these were the words which he did command,
"Now, gents, the winning card is the ace.
I guess you will know it if I show you its face."

One corner turned down, it's plain to be seen,
I looked at the feller and thought he was green.
One corner turned down, 'twas so plain to be seen
I looked at the feller and thought he was green.

So I bet all my money, and, lo and behold!
'Twas a trey spot of clubs, and he took all my gold,
Then I went home and crawled into bed
And divil a word to my wife ever said.

'Twas early next morning I felt for my purse
Biting my lips to keep down a curse;
Yes, 'twas early next morning as the sun did rise
You might have seen with your two blessed eyes,

In an ox wagon, 'twas me and my wife,
Goin' down the Platte River for death or for life.

A RIPPING TRIP*

You go aboard a leaky boat and sail for San Francisco,
You've got to pump to keep her afloat, you've got that, by jingo!
The engine soon begins to squeak, but nary a thing to oil her;
Impossible to stop the leak—rip, goes the boiler.

The captain on the promenade looking very savage;
Steward and the cabin maid fightin' 'bout the cabbage;
All about the cabin floor passengers lie seasick;
Steamer bound to go ashore—rip, goes the physic.

* To tune of *Pop Goes the Weasel*.

[387]

Pork and beans they can't afford, the second cabin passengers;
The cook has tumbled overboard with fifty pounds of sassengers;
The engineer, a little tight, bragging on the Mail Line,
Finally gets into a fight—rip, goes the engine.

SWEET BETSY FROM PIKE

"A California Immigrant Song of the Fifties"

Did you ever hear tell of sweet Betsy from Pike, Who
crossed the wide prairies with her lover Ike, With
two yoke of cattle and one spotted hog, A
tall Shanghai rooster and an old yaller dog. Sing
too-ral-li-oo-ral-li-oo-ral-li-ay, Sing
too-ral-li-oo-ral-li-oo-ral-li-ay.

Did you ever hear tell of sweet Betsy from Pike,
Who crossed the wide prairies with her lover Ike,
With two yoke of cattle and one spotted hog,
A tall Shanghai rooster and an old yaller dog?

Refrain:
    Sing-too-ral-li-oo-ral-li-oo-ral-li-ay,
    Sing-too-ral-li-oo-ral-li-oo-ral-li-ay.

One evening quite early they camped on the Platte,
'Twas near by the road on a green shady flat;
Where Betsy, quite tired, lay down to repose,
While with wonder Ike gazed on his Pike County rose.

They swam the wide rivers and crossed the tall peaks,
And camped on the prairie for weeks upon weeks.
Starvation and cholera and hard work and slaughter,
They reached California spite of hell and high water.

Out on the prairie one bright starry night
They broke the whisky and Betsy got tight;
She sang and she shouted and danced o'er the plain,
And made a great show for the whole wagon train.

The Injuns came down in a wild yelling horde,
And Betsy was skeered they would scalp her adored;
Behind the front wagon wheel Betsy did crawl,
And there fought the Injuns with musket and ball.

They soon reached the desert, where Betsy gave out,
And down in the sand she lay rolling about;
While Ike in great terror looked on in surprise,
Saying "Betsy, get up, you'll get sand in your eyes."

The alkali desert was burning and bare,
And Isaac shrank from the death that lurked there:
"Dear old Pike County, I'll go back to you."
Says Betsy, "You'll go by yourself if you do."

Saying, Good-by, Pike County,
Farewell for a while;
I'd go back tonight
If it was but a mile.

Sweet Betsy got up in a great deal of pain
And declared she'd go back to Pike County again;
Then Ike heaved a sigh and they fondly embraced,
And she traveled along with his arm 'round her waist.

The wagon tipped over with a terrible crash,
And out on the prairie rolled all sorts of trash;
A few little baby clothes done up with care
Looked rather suspicious—though 'twas all on the square.

The Shanghai ran off and the cattle all died,
The last piece of bacon that morning was fried;
Poor Ike got discouraged, and Betsy got mad,
The dog wagged his tail and looked wonderfully sad.

One morning they climbed up a very high hill,
And with wonder looked down into old Placerville;
Ike shouted and said, as he cast his eyes down,
"Sweet Betsy, my darling, we've got to Hangtown."

Long Ike and sweet Betsy attended a dance,
Where Ike wore a pair of his Pike County pants;
Sweet Betsy was covered with ribbons and rings.
Quoth Ike, "You're an angel, but where are your wings?"

A miner said, "Betsy, will you dance with me?"
"I will that, old hoss, if you don't make too free;
But don't dance me hard. Do you want to know why?
Doggone you, I'm chock-full of strong alkali."

Long Ike and sweet Betsy got married of course,
But Ike getting jealous obtained a divorce;
And Betsy, well satisfied, said with a shout,
"Good-by, you big lummax, I'm glad you backed out."

    Saying, Good-by, dear Isaac.
    Farewell for a while,
    But come back in time
    To replenish my pile.

BILL PETERS, THE STAGE DRIVER*

    Bill Peters was a hustler
    From Independence town;
    He warn't a college scholar
    Nor man of great renown,
    But Bill had a way o' doing things
    And doin' 'em up brown.

    Bill driv the stage from Independence
    Up to the Smoky Hill;
    And everybody knowed him thar
    As Independence Bill—
    Thar warn't no feller on the route
    That driv with half the skill.

* Sent through J. B. Jones of Houston, Texas, by Dolph Jones, Fort Worth, Texas, who found it in Colorado.

Bill driv four pair of horses,
Same as you'd drive a team,
And you'd think you was a-travelin'
On a railroad driv by steam;
And he'd git thar on time, you bet,
Or Bill ud bust a seam.

He carried mail and passengers,
And he started on the dot,
And them teams o' hisn, so they say,
Was never known to trot;
But they went it in a gallop
And kept their axles hot.

When Bill's stage ud bust a tire,
Or something ud break down,
He'd hustle round and patch her up
And start off with a bound;
And the wheels o' that old shack o' his
Scarce ever touched the ground.

And Bill didn't 'low no foolin',
And when Injuns hove in sight
And bullets rattled at the stage,
He druv with all his might;
He'd holler, "Fellers, give 'em hell—
I ain't got time to fight."

Then the way them wheels ud rattle,
And the way the dust ud fly,
You'd think a million cattle,
Had stampeded and gone by;
But the mail ud get thar just the same,
If the horses had to die.

[392]

He driv that stage for many a year
Along the Smoky Hill,
And a pile o' wild Comanches
Did Bill Peters have to kill—
And I reckon if he'd had good luck
He'd been a-drivin' still.

But he chanced one day to run agin
A bullet made o' lead,
Which was harder than he bargained for,
And now poor Bill is dead;
And when they brung his body home
A barrel of tears was shed.

THE CALIFORNIA STAGE COMPANY

There's no respect for youth or age
On board the California stage,
But pull and haul about the seats
As bedbugs do about the sheets.

Refrain:
> They started as a thieving line
> In eighteen hundred and forty-nine;
> All opposition they defy,
> So the people must root hog or die.

You're crowded in with Chinamen,
As fattening hogs are in a pen;
And what will more a man provoke
Is musty plug tobacco smoke.

[393]

The ladies are compelled to sit
With dresses in tobacco spit;
The gentlemen don't seem to care,
But talk on politics and swear.

The dust is deep in summer time,
The mountains very hard to climb,
And drivers often stop and yell,
"Get out, all hands, and push uphill."

The drivers, when they feel inclined,
Will have you walking on behind,
And on your shoulders lug a pole
To help them out some muddy hole.

They promise when your fare you pay,
"You'll have to walk but half the way";
Then add aside, with cunning laugh,
"You'll have to push the other half."

They have and will monopolize
The business till the people rise,
And send them kiting down below
To start to live with Bates and Rowe.

FREIGHTING FROM WILCOX TO GLOBE*

Come all you jolly freighters that has freighted on the road,
That has hauled a load of freight from Wilcox to Globe;
We freighted on this road for sixteen years or more
A-hauling freight for Livermore—no wonder that I'm poor.

* From Mrs. M. B. Wight, Fort Thomas, Ariz.

And it's home, dearest home; and it's home you ought to be,
Over on the Gila in the white man's country,
Where the poplar and the ash and mesquite will ever be
Growing green down on the Gila; there's a home for you and
    me.

'Twas in the spring of Seventy-three I started with my team,
Led by false illusion and those foolish, golden dreams;
The first night out from Wilcox my best wheel horse was stole,
And it makes me curse a little to come out in the hole.

This then only left me three—Kit, Mollie and old Mike;
Mike being the best one of the three, I put him out on spike;
I then took the mountain road, so the people would not smile,
And it took fourteen days to travel thirteen mile.

But I got there all the same with my little three-up spike;
It taken all my money, then, to buy a mate for Mike.
You all know how it is when once you get behind,
You never get even again till you damn steal them blind.

I was an honest man when I first took to the road,
I would not swear an oath, nor would I tap a load;
But now you ought to see my mules when I begin to cuss,
They flop their ears and wiggle their tails and pull the load or bust.

Now I can tap a whisky barrel with nothing but a stick;
No one can detect me, I've got it down so slick;
Just fill it up with water—sure, there's no harm in that.

Now my clothes are not the finest, nor are they genteel;
But they will have to do me till I can make another steal.
My boots are number elevens, for I swiped them from a chow,
And my coat cost dos reals, from a little Apache squaw.

Now I have freighted in the sand, I have freighted in the rain,
I have bogged my wagons down and dug them out again;
I have worked both late and early till I was almost dead,
And I have spent some nights sleeping in an Arizona bed.

Now barbed wire and bacon is all that they will pay,
But you have to show your copper checks to get your grain and hay;
If you ask them for five dollars, old Meyers will scratch his pate,
And the clerks in their white, stiff collars say, "Get down and pull
your freight."

But I want to die and go to hell, get there before Livermore and
Meyers
And get a job of hauling coke to keep up the devil's fires;
If I get the job of singeing them, I'll see they don't get free;
I'll treat them like a yaller dog, as they have treated me.

And it's home, dearest home; and it's home you ought to be,
Over on the Gila, in the white man's country,
Where the poplar and the ash and mesquite will ever be
Growing green down on the Gila; there's a home for you and
me.

THE BULLWHACKER*

I'm a lonely bullwhacker
On the Red Cloud Line,
I can lick any son of a gun
That will yoke an ox of mine.
And if I can catch him,
You bet I will or try,
I'd lam him with an ox-bow—
Root hog or die.

* As sung by the Forty-niners and other profane ox-drivers.

It's out on the road
With a very heavy load,
With a very awkward team
And a very muddy road,
You may whip and you may holler,
But if you cuss it's on the sly;
Then whack the cattle on, boys—
Root hog or die.

It's out on the road
These sights are to be seen,
The antelope and buffalo,
The prairie all so green—
The antelope and buffalo,
The rabbit jumps so high;
It's whack the cattle on, boys—
Root hog or die.

It's every day at twelve
There's something for to do;
And if there's nothing else,
There's a pony for to shoe;
I'll throw him down,
And still I'll make him lie;
Little pig, big pig,
Root hog or die.

Now perhaps you'd like to know
What we have to eat—
A little piece of bread
And a little dirty meat,

[397]

A little black coffee,
And whisky on the sly;
It's whack the cattle on, boys—
Root hog or die.

There's hard old times on Bitter Creek
That never can be beat,
It was root hog or die
Under every wagon sheet;
We cleaned up all the Indians,
Drank all the alkali,
And it's whack the cattle on, boys—
Root hog or die.

There was good old times in Salt Lake
That never can pass by,
It was there I first spied
My China girl called Wi.
She could smile, she could chuckle,
She could roll her hog eye;
Then it's whack the cattle on, boys—
Root hog or die.

Oh, I'm going home
Bullwhacking for to spurn,
I ain't got a nickel,
And I don't give a durn.
'Tis when I meet a pretty girl,
You bet I will or try,
I'll make her my little wife—
Root hog or die.

BRIGHAM YOUNG

[*Version 1**]

I'll sing you a song that has often been sung
About an old Mormon they called Brigham Young.
Of wives he had many who were strong in the lungs,
Which Brigham found out by the length of their tongues.
Ri tu ral, lol, lu ral.

Oh, sad was the life of a Mormon to lead,
Yet Brigham adhered all his life to his creed.
He said 'twas such fun, and true, without doubt,
To see the young wives knock the old ones about.
Ri tu ral, lol, lu ral.

One day as old Brigham sat down to his dinner
He saw a young wife was not getting thinner;
When the elders cried out, one after the other,
By the holy, she wants to go home to her mother.
Ri tu ral, lol, lu ral.

Old Brigham replied, which can't be denied,
He couldn't afford to lose such a bride.
"Then do not be jealous but banish your fears;
For the tree is well known by the fruit that it bears."
Ri tu ral, lol, lu ral.

"That I love one and all, you very well know,
Then do not provoke me or my anger will show.
What must be our fate if found here in a row,
If Uncle Sam comes with his row-de-dow-dow."
Ri tu ral, lol, lu ral.

* From Put's *Golden West Songster* (1857). Tune: "Villikers and His Dinah."

"Then cease all your quarrels and do not despair.
To meet Uncle Sam, I will quickly prepare.
Hark! I hear 'Yankee Doodle' played over the hills!
Ah! here's the enemy with their powder and pills!"
Ri tu ral, lol, lu ral.

[*Version 2**]

Now Brigham Young is a Mormon bold,
And a leader of the roaring rams,
And shepherd of a lot of fine tub sheep
And a lot of pretty little lambs.
Oh, he lives with his five and forty wives,
In the city of the Great Salt Lake,
Where they breed and swarm like hens on a farm
And cackle like ducks to a drake.

Chorus:

    Oh, Brigham, Brigham Young,
    It's a miracle how you survive,
    With your roaring rams and your pretty little lambs
    And your five and forty wives.

Number forty-five is about sixteen,
Number one is sixty and three;
And they make such a riot, how he keeps them quiet
Is a downright mystery to me.
For they clatter and they chaw and they jaw, jaw, jaw,
And each has a different desire.
It would aid the renown of the best shop in town
To supply them with half they desire.

* From Put's *Golden West Songster.*

Now, Brigham Young was a stout man once,
And now he is thin and old;
And I am sorry to state he is bald on the pate,
Which once had a covering of gold.
For his oldest wives won't have white wool,
And his young ones won't have red,
So, with tearing it out, and taking turn about,
They have torn all the hair off his head.

Now, the oldest wives sing songs all day,
And the young ones all sing songs;
And amongst such a crowd he has it pretty loud—
They're as noisy as Chinese gongs.
And when they advance for a Mormon dance
He is filled with the direst alarms;
For they are sure to end the night in a tabernacle fight
To see who has the fairest charms.

Now, if any man here envies Brigham Young
Let him go to the Great Salt Lake;
And if he has the leisure to enjoy his pleasure,
He'll find it a great mistake.
One wife at a time, so says my rhyme,
Is enough—there's no denial.
So, before you strive to be lord of forty-five,
Take two for a month on trial.

THE MORMON BISHOP'S LAMENT

I am a Mormon bishop and I will tell you what I know.
I joined the confraternity some forty years ago.
I then had youth upon my brow and eloquence my tongue,
But I had the sad misfortune then to meet with Brigham Young.

He said, "Young man, come join our band and bid hard work farewell,
You are too smart to waste your time in toil by hill and dell;
There is a ripening harvest and our hooks shall find the fool,
And in the distant nations we shall train them in our school."

I listened to his preaching and I learned all the rôle,
And the truth of Mormon doctrines burned deep within my soul.
I married sixteen women and I spread my new belief,
I was sent to preach the gospel to the pauper and the thief.

'Twas in the glorious days when Brigham was our only Lord and King,
And his wild cry of defiance from the Wasatch tops did ring.
'Twas when that bold Bill Hickman and that Porter Rockwell led,
And in the blood atonements the pits received the dead.

They took in Dr. Robertson and left him in his gore,
And the Aiken brothers sleep in peace on Nephi's distant shore.
We marched to Mountain Meadows, and on that glorious field
With rifle and with hatchet we made man and woman yield.

'Twas there we were victorious with our legions fierce and brave.
We left the butchered victims on the ground without a grave.
We slew the load of emigrants on Sublette's lonely road
And plundered many a trader of his then most precious load.

Alas for all the powers that were in the bygone time.
What we did as deeds of glory are condemned as bloody crime.
No more the blood atonements keep the doubting one in fear,
While the faithful were rewarded with a wedding once a year.

As the nation's chieftain president says our days of rule are o'er
And his marshals with their warrants are on watch at every door,

Old John he now goes skulking on the byroads of our land,
Or unknown he keeps in hiding with the faithful of our band.

Old Brigham now is stretched beneath the cold and silent clay,
And the chieftains now are fallen that were mighty in their day;
Of the six and twenty women that I wedded long ago
There are two now left to cheer me in these awful hours of woe.
The rest are scattered where the Gentile's flag's unfurled
And twoscore of my daughters are now numbered with the world.

Oh, my poor old bones are aching, and my head is turning gray;
Oh, the scenes were black and awful that I've witnessed in my day.
Let my spirit seek the mansion where old Brigham's gone to dwell,
For there's no place for Mormons but the lowest pits of hell.

A MORMON IMMIGRANT SONG*

I used to live on Cottonwood and owned a little farm,
I was called upon a mission that gave me much alarm;
The reason that they called me, I'm sure I do not know;
But to hoe the cane and cotton, straightway I must go.

I yoked up Jim and Baldy, all ready for the start;
To leave my farm and garden, it almost broke my heart;
But at last we got started, I cast a look behind,
For the sand and rocks of Dixie were running through my mind.

Now, when we got to Black Ridge, my wagon it broke down,
And I, being no carpenter and forty miles from town—
I cut a clumsy cedar and rigged an awkward slide,
But the wagon ran so heavy poor Betsy couldn't ride.

* Said to have been written in 1861 by George A. Hicks, who died at Spanish Fork, Utah, in 1926.

While Betsy was out walking I told her to take care,
When all of a sudden she struck a prickly pear,
Then she began to hollow as loud as she could bawl—
If I were back in Cottonwood I wouldn't go at all.

Now, when we got to Sand Ridge, we couldn't go at all,
Old Jim and old Baldy began to puff and loll;
I cussed and swore a little, for I couldn't make the route,
For the team and I and Betsy were all of us played out.

At length we got to Washington; I thought we'd stay awhile
To see if the flowers would make their virgin smile;
But I was much mistaken, for when we went away
The red hills of September were just the same in May.

It is so very dreary, there's nothing here to cheer,
But old pathetic sermons we very often hear;
They preach them by the dozens and prove them by the book,
But I'd sooner have a roasting-ear and stay at home and cook.

I am so awful weary I'm sure I'm almost dead;
'Tis six long weeks last Sunday since I have tasted bread;
Of turnip-tops and lucerne greens I've had enough to eat,
But I'd like to change my diet to buckwheat cakes and meat.

I had to sell my wagon for sorghum seed and bread;
Old Jim and old Baldy have long since been dead.
There's no one left but me and Bet to hoe the cotton tree—
God pity any Mormon that attempts to follow me!

THE LITTLE OLD SOD SHANTY*

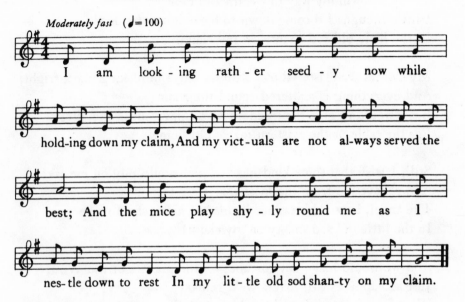

I am looking rather seedy now while holding down my claim,
And my victuals are not always served the best;
And the mice play shyly round me as I nestle down to rest
In my little old sod shanty on my claim.

The hinges are of leather and the windows have no glass,
While the board roof lets the howling blizzards in,
And I hear the hungry coyote as he slinks up through the grass
Round the little old sod shanty on my claim.

Yet, I rather like the novelty of living in this way,
Though my bill of fare is always rather tame;
But I'm as happy as a clam on the land of Uncle Sam
In the little old sod shanty on my claim.

* Sing to the tune of "The Little Log Cabin in the Lane." Composed by Lindsey Baker, of Kermit, W. Va., in the fall of 1888, after his brother returned home from two or three years in a little sod shanty on the plains of Kansas.

But when I left my Eastern home, a bachelor so gay,
To try and win my way to wealth and fame,
I little thought I'd come down to burning twisted hay
In the little old sod shanty on my claim.

My clothes are plastered o'er with dough, I'm looking like a fright,
And everything is scattered round the room;
But I wouldn't give the freedom that I have out in the West
For the table of the Eastern man's old home.

Still, I wish that some kind-hearted girl would pity on me take
And relieve me from the mess that I am in;
The angel, how I'd bless her if this her home she'd make
In the little old sod shanty on my claim!

And we would make our fortunes on the prairies of the West,
Just as happy as two lovers we'd remain;
We'd forget the trials and troubles we endured at the first
In the little old sod shanty on my claim.

And if fate should bless us with now and then an heir
To cheer our hearts with honest pride of fame,
Oh, then we'd be contented for the toil that we had spent
In the little old sod shanty on our claim.

When time enough had lapsed and all those little brats
To noble man and womanhood had grown,
It wouldn't seem half so lonely as round us we should look
And we'd see the old sod shanty on our claim.

GREER COUNTY*

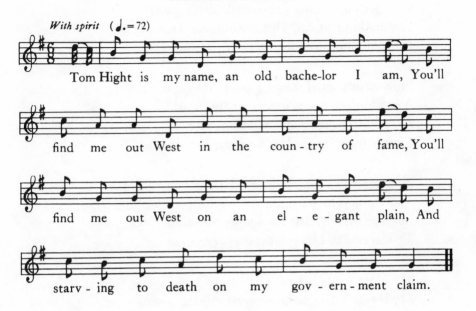

Tom Hight is my name, an old bachelor I am,
You'll find me out West in the country of fame,
You'll find me out West on an elegant plain,
And starving to death on my government claim.

Hurrah for Greer County! the land of the free,
The land of the bedbug, grasshopper and flea;
I'll sing of its praises and tell of its fame,
While starving to death on my government claim.

My house is built of natural sod,
Its walls are erected according to hod;
Its roof has no pitch but is level and plain,
I always get wet if it happens to rain.

* From Tom Hight's scrapbook, Oklahoma City, Okla., 1909. The "Tom Hight" of the song
is the universal claim holder of early Oklahoma days.

[407]

How happy am I on my government claim!
I've nothing to lose, and nothing to gain;
I've nothing to eat, I've nothing to wear—
From nothing to nothing is the hardest fare.

How happy am I when I crawl into bed!
A rattlesnake hisses a tune at my head,
A gay little centipede, all without fear,
Crawls over my pillow and into my ear.

Now all you claim holders, I hope you will stay
And chew your hardtack till you're toothless and gray;
But for myself, I'll no longer remain
To starve like a dog on my government claim.

My clothes are all ragged as my language is rough,
My bread is corndodgers, both solid and tough;
But yet I am happy, and live at my ease
On sorghum molasses, bacon, and cheese.

Good-by to Greer County where blizzards arise,
Where the sun never sinks and a flea never dies,
And the wind never ceases but always remains
Till it starves us all out on our government claims.

Farewell to Greer County, farewell to the West,
I'll travel back East to the girl I love best,
I'll travel back to Texas and marry me a wife,
And quit corn bread for the rest of my life.

LIFE IN A HALF–BREED SHACK

'Tis life in a half-breed shack,
The rain comes pouring down;
"Drip" drops the mud through the roof,
And the wind comes through the wall.
A tenderfoot cursed his luck
And feebly cried out "Yah!"

Refrain:

Yah! Yah! I want to go home to my ma!
Yah! Yah! This bloomin' country's a fraud!
Yah! Yah! I want to go home to my ma!

He tried to kindle a fire
When it's forty-five below;
He aims to chop at a log
And amputates his toe;
He hobbles back to the shack
And feebly cries out "Yah!"

He gets on a bucking cayuse
And thinks to flourish around,
But the buzzard-head takes to bucking
And lays him flat out on the ground.
As he picks himself up with a curse,
He feebly cries out "Yah!"

He buys all the town lots he can get
In the wrong end of Calgary,
And he waits and he waits for the boom
Until he's dead broke like me.
He couldn't get any tick
So he feebly cries out "Yah!"

He couldn't do any work
And he wouldn't know how if he could;
So the police run him for a vag
And set him to bucking wood.
As he sits in the guardroom cell,
He feebly cries out "Yah!"

Come all ye tenderfeet
And listen to what I say,
If you can't get a government job
You had better remain where you be.
Then you won't curse your luck
And cry out feebly "Yah!"

DAKOTA LAND*

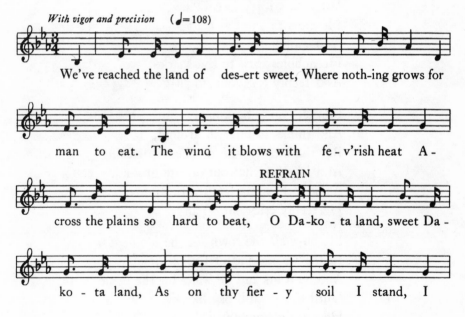

With vigor and precision (♩=108)

We've reached the land of des-ert sweet, Where noth-ing grows for man to eat. The wind it blows with fe - v'rish heat A - cross the plains so hard to beat,

REFRAIN

O Da-ko - ta land, sweet Da - ko - ta land, As on thy fier - y soil I stand, I

* From p. 280, *The American Songbag*. Carl Sandburg found this song in the Edwin Ford Piper Collection of Pioneer Songs at the University of Iowa. Tune: "Beulah Land," a gospel hymn.

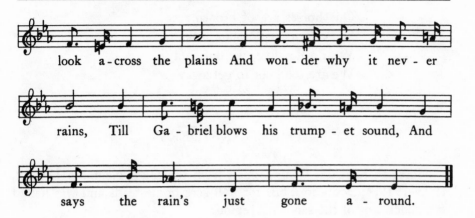

look a-cross the plains And won-der why it nev - er

rains, Till Ga - briel blows his trump - et sound, And

says the rain's just gone a - round.

We've reached the land of desert sweet,
Where nothing grows for man to eat.
The wind it blows with feverish heat
Across the plains so hard to beat.

    O Dakota land, sweet Dakota land,
    As on thy fiery soil I stand,
    I look across the plains
    And wonder why it never rains,
    Till Gabriel blows his trumpet sound
    And says the rain's just gone around.

We've reached the land of hills and stones
Where all is strewn with buffalo bones.
O buffalo bones, bleached buffalo bones,
I seem to hear your sighs and moans.

We have no wheat, we have no oats,
We have no corn to feed our shoats;
Our chickens are so very poor
They beg for crumbs outside the door.

[411]

Our horses are of bronco race;
Starvation stares them in the face.
We do not live, we only stay;
We are too poor to get away.

THE KINKAIDERS*

Moses P. Kinkaid, Congressman from the Sixth Nebraska District, 1903–1919, introduced a bill for 640-acre homesteads and was hailed as a benefactor of the sand-hill region.

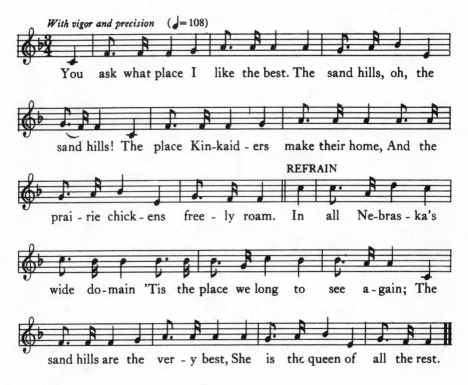

With vigor and precision (♩ = 108)

You ask what place I like the best. The sand hills, oh, the sand hills! The place Kin-kaid-ers make their home, And the prai-rie chick-ens free-ly roam.

REFRAIN

In all Ne-bras-ka's wide do-main 'Tis the place we long to see a-gain; The sand hills are the ver-y best, She is the queen of all the rest.

* From Carl Sandburg's *American Songbag*. He found the song in the Edwin Ford Piper Collection of Pioneer Songs at the University of Iowa.

You ask what place I like the best.
The sand hills, oh, the sand hills!
The place Kinkaiders make their home,
And the prairie chickens freely roam.

In all Nebraska's wide domain
'Tis the place we long to see again;
The sand hills are the very best,
She is the queen of all the rest.

The corn we raise is our delight,
The melons, too, are out of sight,
Potatoes grown are extra fine
And can't be beat in any clime.

The peaceful cows in pastures dream
And furnish us with golden cream,
So I shall keep my Kinkaid home
And never far away shall roam.

Then let us all with hearts sincere
Thank him for what has brought us here,
And for the homestead law he made,
This noble Moses P. Kinkaid.

WEST TEXAS*

Where you can go farther and see less,
Where there are more creeks and less water,
Where there are more cows and less milk,

* Sent by Prof. Newton Gaines, Texas Christian University, Fort Worth, Texas, 1922. He says that the poem was written by a fourteen-year-old high-school girl, Leona Mae Austin, who had lived in Childress, Texas, for several years. Mr. Gaines remarks: "Leona Mae Austin evidently went through the drought of 1916-18, and her words probably repeat the complaints that she heard from the lips of her elders."

Where there is more climate and less rain,
Where there is more horizon and fewer trees.
Than any other place in the Union.

Beautiful West Texas, what do you think,
Plenty of grapes and nothing to drink;
Plenty of creeks and no water on hand,
No oats for your horses but plenty of land.
Plenty of ponies, none fit to ride;
Plenty of poverty, and some little pride.

Plenty of hides and no leather tanned,
Though the scabby mesquite encumbers the land;
Plenty of cattle, no butter or milk,
No dress for the garden, but plenty of silk.
Plenty of rain when it comes down at all,
Enough and to spare, would it come at your call.

Plenty of bacon, year before last,
Will be plenty again when comes a good mast;
Hide-bottom chairs—not plenty, and all so low
When a fellow eats, he has to hang on his elbow.
Plenty to eat such as corn bread and bacon,
Which reminds of the home long since forsaken.

Plenty of wind, no drawback on that,
When *talking* of stock, is plenty of that;
Plenty of rocks, their cisterns to wall,
They never find time to do it at all.
O Land of Great Promise—not fulfilled,
What a great country this might be, if the people willed!
With corn bread and bacon men have enough,
And the women get happy over some snuff.

[414]

WESTWARD HO

I love not Colorado
Where the faro table grows,
And down the desperado
The rippling bourbon flows;

Nor seek I fair Montana
Of bowie-lunging fame;
The pistol ring of fair Wyoming
I leave to nobler game.

Sweet poker-haunted Kansas
In vain allures the eye;
The Nevada rough has charms enough,
Yet its blandishments I fly.

Shall Arizona woo me
Where the meek Apache bides?
Or New Mexico where natives grow
With arrow-proof insides?

Nay, 'tis where the grizzlies wander
And the lonely diggers roam,
And the grim Chinese from the squatter flees
That I'll make my humble home.

I'll chase the wild tarantula,
And the fierce coyote I'll dare;
And the locust grim—I'll battle him
In his native wildwood lair.

[415]

Or I'll seek the gulch deserted
And dream of the wild red man,
And I'll build a cot on a corner lot
And get rich as soon as I can.

THE FAR, FAR WEST*

Give me a home in the far, far West;
That's the place I love the best;
Put a Thirty-Thirty under my leg,
And a Colt's Forty-five so I won't be afraid.

Put me out whare they is nothing but cows,
And a few wild horses on the range do browse;
Whare lightning flash and thunder pops,
Whare horses pitch that you cain't stop.

Give me a home in the far, far West;
All other places I do detest.
Put me down close to the Mexican line,
Whare I can cross over most any time.

Put the ranch house down by some sycamore trees,
So I can lay in the shade and take my ease;
Whare panthers scream and grizzlies roam,
That sounds to me like home sweet home.

But when life is over and my race is run,
When death shadows gather and my time has come,
When I've rode my last horse and have turned my last steer,
When my soul has winged its way to that celestial sphere,
When my grave has been dug and I've been laid to rest,
Please let it be in the far, far West.

From J. E. McCauley, Seymour, Texas, 1924.

[416]

THE COWBOY'S LAMENT

Slowly, with pathos (♩ = 100)

As I walked out in the streets of La -
"Oh, beat the drum slow - ly and play the fife

re - do, As I walked out in La -
low - ly, Play the dead march as you

re - do one day, I spied a poor
car - ry me a - long; Take me to the green

cow - boy wrapped up in white lin - en, Wrapped
val - ley, there lay the sod o'er me, For

up in white lin - en as cold as the clay.
I'm a young cow - boy and I know I've done wrong.

I want no fenced-in graveyard
With snorin' souls about—
Just cache me in the desert
When my light goes out.

[417]

As I walked out in the streets of Laredo,*
As I walked out in Laredo one day,
I spied a poor cowboy wrapped up in white linen,
Wrapped up in white linen as cold as the clay.

"Oh, beat the drum slowly and play the fife lowly,
Play the dead march as you carry me along;
Take me to the green valley, there lay the sod o'er me,
For I'm a young cowboy and I know I've done wrong.

"I see by your outfit that you are a cowboy"—
These words he did say as I boldly stepped by.
"Come sit down beside me and hear my sad story;
I am shot in the breast and I know I must die.

"Let sixteen gamblers come handle my coffin,
Let sixteen cowboys come sing me a song.
Take me to the graveyard and lay the sod o'er me,
For I'm a poor cowboy and I know I've done wrong.

"My friends and relations they live in the Nation,
They know not where their boy has gone.
He first came to Texas and hired to a ranchman,
Oh, I'm a young cowboy and I know I've done wrong.

* The beginning stanza of one version:

> As I passed by Tom Sherman's barroom,
> Tom Sherman's barroom quite early one morn,
> I spied a young cowboy all dressed in his buckskins,
> All dressed in his buckskins and fit for the grave.

Other versions begin:

> As I rode up to the fragrant barroom,
> As I rode up to the barroom one day, etc.

"It was once in the saddle I used to go dashing,*
It was once in the saddle I used to go gay;
First to the dram-house and then to the card-house;
Got shot in the breast and I am dying today.

"Get six jolly cowboys to carry my coffin;†
Get six pretty maidens to bear up my pall.
Put bunches of roses all over my coffin,
Put roses to deaden the sods as they fall.

"Then swing your rope slowly and rattle your spurs lowly,
And give a wild whoop as you carry me along;
And in the grave throw me and roll the sod o'er me
For I'm a young cowboy and I know I've done wrong.

"Oh, bury beside me my knife and six-shooter,‡
My spurs on my heel, my rifle by my side,
And over my coffin put a bottle of brandy
That the cowboys may drink as they carry me along.

"Go bring me a cup, a cup of cold water,
To cool my parched lips," the cowboy then said;
Before I returned his soul had departed,
And gone to the round-up—the cowboy was dead.

* Another version runs:

> It was once in the saddle I used to look handsome,
> It was once in the saddle I used to go gay,
> First took to drinking and then took to gambling,
> Got shot in the breast and I'm dying today.

† Two parallel stanzas:

> Get six jolly fellows to carry my coffin,
> And six pretty maidens to bear up my pall,
> And give to each of them bunches of roses
> That they may not smell me as they bear me along.

> Over my coffin put handfuls of lavender,
> Handfuls of lavender on every side;
> Bunches of roses all over my coffin,
> Saying, "There goes a cowboy cut down in his pride."

‡ A variant stanza from the late lamented ballad collector, Professor Shearin.

We beat the drum slowly and played the fife lowly,
And bitterly wept as we bore him along;
For we all loved our comrade, so brave, young, and handsome,
We all loved our comrade although he'd done wrong.

Where men lived raw, in the desert's maw,
And hell was nothing to shun;
Where they buried 'em neat, without preacher or sheet,
And writ on their foreheads, crude but sweet,
"This Jasper was slow with a gun."

Iron Head's Version*

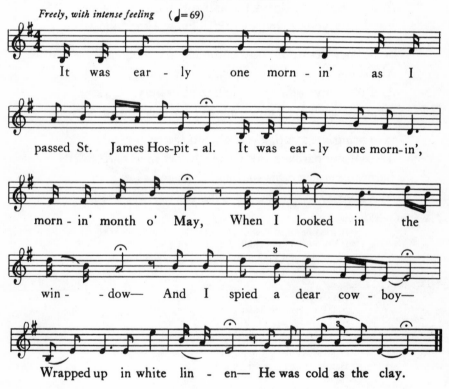

It was ear-ly one morn-in' as I passed St. James Hos-pit-al. It was ear-ly one morn-in', morn-in' month o' May, When I looked in the win-dow— And I spied a dear cow-boy— Wrapped up in white lin-en— He was cold as the clay.

* As he sang it in the Texas Penitentiary.

It was early one mornin' as I passed St. James Hospital,
It was early one mornin', mornin' month o' May,
When I looked in the window and I spied a dear cowboy—
Wrapped up in white linen, he was cold as the clay.

Says, "Come, dear mother, mother, an' seat yourself nigh me,
Come, dear father, too, and sing me a song,
For my knee-bones are achin' an' my poor heart am breakin',
Well, I know I'm a po' cowboy, father, an' I know I done wrong.

"Six young gamblers, papa, to balance my coffin,
Sixteen young whore gals for to sing me a song,
Tell them to bring 'long a bunch of them sweet-smellin' roses,
So they can't smell we while they drive me 'long.

"Well, in my saddle, father, I used to go dashing,
Father, in my young days when I used to look gay,
Down roun' some church-house, carryin' those handsome young
    ladies—
Well, the women oughta carry me, follow me to my grave."

[*Version 3*]

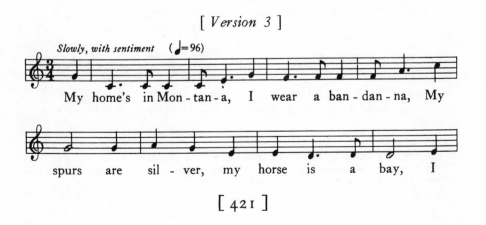

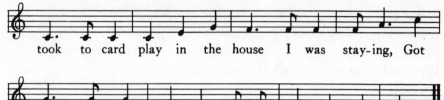

took to card play in the house I was stay-ing, Got

shot through the bow - els, And you see where I lay.

My home's in Montana, I wear a bandanna,*
My spurs are silver, my horse is a bay,
I took to card play in the house I was staying,
Got shot through the bowels, and you see where I lay.

SAM HALL†

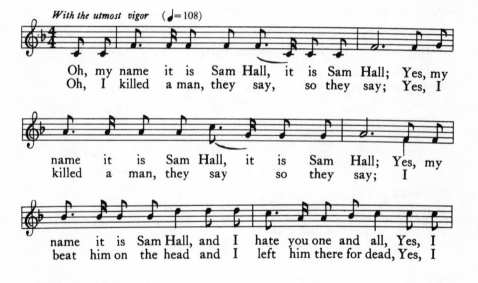

With the utmost vigor (♩ = 108)

Oh, my name it is Sam Hall, it is Sam Hall; Yes, my
Oh, I killed a man, they say, so they say; Yes, I

name it is Sam Hall, it is Sam Hall; Yes, my
killed a man, they say so they say; I

name it is Sam Hall, and I hate you one and all, Yes, I
beat him on the head and I left him there for dead, Yes, I

---

* From *Singing Cowboy,* by Margaret Larkin (New York: Knopf).
† From *American Ballads and Folk Songs,* collected and compiled by John A. Lomax and Alan Lomax (New York: Macmillan, 1934).

slower

hate   you   one   and   all,   God   damn   your   eyes.
left   him   there for   dead, God   damn   his   eyes.

Oh, my name it is Sam Hall, it is Sam Hall;
Yes, my name it is Sam Hall, it is Sam Hall;
Yes, my name it is Sam Hall, and I hate you one and all,
Yes, I hate you one and all, God damn your eyes.

Oh, I killed a man, they say, so they say;
Yes, I killed a man, they say, so they say;
I beat him on the head, and I left him there for dead,
Yes, I left him there for dead, God damn his eyes.

Oh, the parson he did come, he did come;
Yes, the parson he did come, he did come;
And he looked so bloody glum, as he talked of Kingdom Come—
He can kiss my ruddy bum, God damn his eyes.

And the sheriff he came too, he came too;
Yes, the sheriff he came too, he came too;
Yes, the sheriff he came too, with his men all dressed in blue—
Lord, they were a bloody crew, God damn their eyes.

Now up the rope I go, up I go;
Yes, up the rope I go, up I go;
And those bastards down below, they'll say, "Sam, we told you so,"
They'll say, "Sam, we told you so," God damn their eyes.

I saw my Nellie dressed in blue, dressed in blue;
I saw my Nellie in the crowd, all dressed in blue.
Says my Nellie, dressed in blue, "Your trifling days are through—
Now I know that you'll be true, God damn your eyes."

[423]

And now in heaven I dwell, in heaven I dwell;
Yes, now in heaven I dwell, in heaven I dwell;
Yes, now in heaven I dwell—Holy Christ; it is a sell—
All the whores are down in hell, God damn their eyes.

A HOME ON THE RANGE*

Oscar J. Fox, San Antonio, Texas, published an arrangement of this song after it had remained unnoticed for many years in *Cowboy Songs*. For a time "Home on the Range" was the most popular song on the air. A suit for a half-million dollars was brought on copyright—probably the largest sum ever asked for one song. A Negro saloon keeper in San Antonio gave me the music to "Home on the Range" as herein reprinted. The words are also identical with the version of *Cowboy Songs*, 1910. They were assembled from several sources and have since often been pirated.

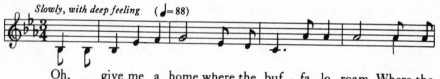

Oh,   give me a home where the buf - fa - lo roam, Where the
Where the air is so pure and the Zeph-yrs so free, The

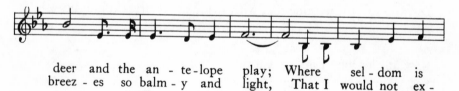

deer and the an - te-lope play; Where sel - dom is
breez - es so balm - y and light, That I would not ex -

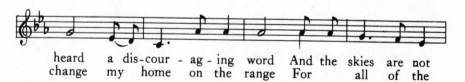

heard a dis-cour - ag - ing word And the skies are not
change my home on the range For all of the

* The second version (pp. 427-428), a variant of this one, should be sung in an entirely different spirit.

REFRAIN

cloud-y all day. Home, home on the range, Where the
cit - ies so bright.

deer and the an - te - lope play; Where sel - dom is heard a dis -

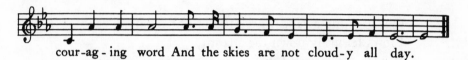

cour-ag - ing word And the skies are not cloud-y all day.

Oh, give me a home where the buffalo roam,
Where the deer and the antelope play,
Where seldom is heard a discouraging word
And the skies are not cloudy all day.

Home, home on the range,
Where the deer and the antelope play;
Where seldom is heard a discouraging word
And the skies are not cloudy all day.

Where the air is so pure, the zephyrs so free,
The breezes so balmy and light,
That I would not exchange my home on the range
For all the cities so bright.

The red man was pressed from this part of the West,
He's likely no more to return
To the banks of Red River where seldom if ever
Their flickering campfires burn.

[425]

How often at night when the heavens are bright
With the light of the glittering stars,
Have I stood here amazed and asked as I gazed
If their glory exceeds that of ours.

Oh, I love these wild flowers in this dear land of ours;
The curlew I love to hear scream;
And I love the white rocks and the antelope flocks
That graze on the mountain-tops green.

Oh, give me a land where the bright diamond sand
Flows leisurely down the stream;
Where the graceful white swan goes gliding along
Like a maid in a heavenly dream.

Then I would not exchange my home on the range,
Where the deer and the antelope play;
Where seldom is heard a discouraging word
And the skies are not cloudy all day.

    Home, home on the range,
    Where the deer and the antelope play;
    Where seldom is heard a discouraging word
    And the skies are not cloudy all day.

[*Version 2*]

With a rollicking lilt (♩.= 66)

Oh, give me a home where the buf - fa - lo roam, Where the
Oh, give me a jail where I can get bail If

deer and the an - te - lope play, Where sel - dom is heard a dis -
un - der the shin - ing sun; I'll wake with the dawn, I'll

cour - ag - ing word And the skies are not cloud - y all
chase the wild fawn, I'll ride with my sad - dle and

REFRAIN

day. A home, a home, where the buf - fa - lo roam, Where the
gun.

deer and the an - te - lope play; Where sel - dom is heard a dis -

cour - ag - ing word And the skies are not cloud - y all day.

[427]

Oh, give me a home where the buffalo roam,
Where the deer and the antelope play,
Where seldom is heard a discouraging word,
And the skies are not cloudy all day.

Refrain:
A home, a home, where the buffalo roam,
Where the deer and the antelope play;
Where seldom is heard a discouraging word,
And the skies are not cloudy all day.

Oh, give me a jail where I can get bail,
If under the shining sun;
I'll wake with the dawn, I'll chase the wild fawn,
I'll ride with my saddle and gun.

INDEX

Index

Index